Arithmetic

CONCEPTS AND SKILLS

Murray Gechtman ∗ *James Hardesty*

LOS ANGELES PIERCE COLLEGE

The Macmillan Company, New York / Collier-Macmillan Limited, London

PREFACE

An arithmetic text at the college level should be more than a recipe and drill book. We have written this text for adults who are deficient in arithmetic. Consequently, we have tried to stress the understanding of concepts along with the development of basic skills.

The first three chapters are devoted to establishing, through the primitive notion of sets, the ideas of number, one-to-one correspondence, order, binary operations and their inverse operations, and numeration. In short, the system of whole numbers is established as an ordered set in which the operations of addition and multiplication and their inverse operations enjoy certain properties.

Chapters Four through Seven extend the whole-number system, first to the system of integers, then to the system of rational numbers, and finally to the real-number system. We believe that this systematic approach will give the student a sense of an evolving mathematical structure.

A discussion of the basic arithmetic operations in bases other than ten is introduced in Chapter Eight. We feel the student attains a clearer understanding of the basic arithmetic operations and, in general, of the whole number system after he performs computations in numeration systems with bases other than ten. However, it seems that these computations are meaningful only after the student understands and can perform the computations in base-ten notation.

Chapter Nine deals with measurement and computation with denominate numbers. In this chapter we have also included area and volume computations and an informal discussion of a square-root algorithm. This latter discussion establishes a pattern that the student may use to find square roots.

The text contains over 2500 problems. Each exercise set is designed to provide ample drill material as well as a large variety of challenging problems. The worded problems have a wide application to real-life situations.

We have attempted to introduce algebraic notation wherever we felt it was appropriate, but only after the student is led to a symbolic statement by a series of examples or a plausibility argument. We feel that by exposing the student to symbolic statements, he will learn to appreciate and, indeed, seek out patterns.

Finally, we wish to thank all those who encouraged us to begin and helped us to complete this manuscript.

M. G.

J. H.

CONTENTS

chapter three
WHOLE NUMBERS

chapter four
INTEGERS

chapter five
PRIME NUMBERS

chapter nine
THE ARITHMETIC OF MEASUREMENT

chapter one

NUMBER

1.0 Introduction

The study of arithmetic should not be merely a process whereby the student learns a collection of rules that enables him to properly add, subtract, multiply, and divide numbers. Such a study is almost always boring and seldom productive. We would rather ask first: What is a number? How does one count? What exactly does it mean to add or multiply two numbers? We shall find that rules for computation come naturally out of our attempts to answer the above questions.

We begin our study in this chapter with the basic idea of sets. The concept of a natural number will then be formed in terms of sets and the notion of a one-to-one correspondence between sets. Next we discuss the symbolic way to represent natural numbers and how you can determine if one number is greater than another. Finally, we introduce the notion of an open sentence and its solution set. Here again you will find sets playing a large role in clarifying an important concept.

1.1 Sets

One of the most basic ideas in all mathematics is the notion of a set. A *set* is a well-defined collection of things. The members of your family

1

form a set. The students enrolled in your school form a set. A herd of cattle is a set.

A set can be named in several ways. One way to name a set is to list the names of its members and enclose the list in braces. For example, the vowels in the English alphabet form a set. To name this set we write

$$\{a, e, i, o, u\}$$

We read this as "The set whose members are *a, e, i, o, and u.*" The states in the United States whose names begin with the letter C form a set. The name of this set is

$$\{\text{California, Colorado, Connecticut}\}$$

This is read "The set whose members are California, Colorado, and Connecticut." This set might also be written

$$\{\text{Colorado, California, Connecticut}\}$$

or

$$\{\text{Connecticut, Colorado, California}\}$$

since the order of listing is immaterial.

A second way to name a set is to state a property of each of the members of the set and enclose this phrase in braces. For instance, the set $\{a, e, i, o, u\}$ can be written

$$\{\text{vowels in the English alphabet}\}$$

and the set {California, Colorado, Connecticut} can be written

$$\{\text{states in the United States whose names begin with C}\}$$

In our discussion of sets we shall wish to refer to the "things" that belong to a particular set. We call these things the *members* or *elements* of the set. The states of California, Colorado, and Connecticut are the members of {California, Colorado, Connecticut}. John is a member of {Mary, Ellen, John, James}. To symbolize set membership we use the symbol "∈," which is read "is a member of" or "belongs to" or "is in." Hence "John ∈ {Mary, Ellen, John, James}" and "Colorado ∈ {California,

Colorado, Connecticut}" are true statements. Also "3 ∈ {1, 2, 3, 4, 5}"
and "*u* ∈ {*a, e, i, o, u*}" are true statements.

To indicate that something does not belong to a particular set we write
"∉," which is read "is not a member of." That is, "7 ∉ {1, 2, 3, 4, 5}"
and "Frank ∉ {Mary, Ellen, John, James}" are true statements.

If two sets contain the same members, we say the sets are *equal*. Since
sets are frequently denoted by capital letters, the sentence "$A = B$" means
set A and set B are equal sets; that is, the members of set A are precisely
the same things as the members of set B. We say that A and B are names
for the same set.

Suppose $A = \{a, b, c, d, e\}$ and $B = \{b, d, a, c, e\}$. Then $A = B$. Also
$b \in A$, $a \in B$, $f \notin A$, $h \notin B$.

If each element of a set A is also an element of a set B we say "A is a
subset of B" and write "$A \subseteq B$."

Examples:

1. If $A = \{$California, Colorado$\}$
   and $B = \{$Colorado, Connecticut, California$\}$
   then $A \subseteq B$ is true.
2. If $A = \{1, 2, 3, 4, 5\}$
   and $B = \{1, 2, 4, 5, 6, 7\}$
   then $A \nsubseteq B$ is true, since $3 \in A$ but $3 \notin B$.
3. If $A = \{$senior mathematics majors at Pomona College$\}$
   and $B = \{$senior men mathematics majors at Pomona College$\}$
   then $B \subseteq A$ is true but $A \subseteq B$ may or may not be true.

If A is a subset of B and B is not a subset of A, we say "A is a *proper
subset* of B" and write "$A \subset B$." That is, each element in set A is an element in set B but there is at least one element in set B that is not in set A.

Examples:

1. If $A = \{$California, Colorado$\}$
   and $B = \{$Colorado, Connecticut, California$\}$
   then $A \subset B$ is true.
2. If $A = \{1, 2, 3, 4, 5, 6, 7, 8, 9, 10\}$
   and $B = \{2, 4, 6, 8, 10\}$
   then $B \subset A$ is true.
3. If $A = \{a, e, i, o, u\}$
   and $B = \{$vowels in the English alphabet$\}$

then $A \subset B$ is false even though $A \subseteq B$ is true. In this case we write "$A \not\subset B$," which means "A is not a proper subset of B."

The set that has no members is called the *empty set* or *null set*. The symbol used to name this set is "$\emptyset$." Each of the sets

$$A = \{\text{four-headed mathematicians}\}$$
$$B = \{\text{2-foot-tall professional basketball players}\}$$

is an empty set. In fact, $A = B$, because the elements of A and B are the same (they have no elements). This discussion leads us to the conclusion that the empty set is unique; that is, there is exactly one empty set.

Another important property of the empty set is that it is a subset of every set. We say, for example, that $\emptyset$ is a subset of set A above. If this were not true, we should be able to find an element of $\emptyset$ that is not an element of A. (Why?) We cannot do this because $\emptyset$ has no elements.

Example: Let $A = \{1, 2, 3\}$. Name all the subsets of A.

Solution: $\emptyset$, $\{1\}$, $\{2\}$, $\{3\}$, $\{1, 2\}$, $\{1, 3\}$, $\{2, 3\}$, $\{1, 2, 3\}$

Before going further, we wish to stress the distinction between an element of a set and a set containing only one element. b is an element of the set $\{b\}$. However, b does not equal $\{b\}$, nor is b a subset of $\{b\}$.

Example: List the elements and the subsets of the set $\{b\}$.

Solution: b is the only element in $\{b\}$. The subsets of $\{b\}$ are $\emptyset$ and $\{b\}$.

It is possible to list the names of all the members in each set discussed above. There are, however, sets that do not have this property. The set of points on a line segment is a set whose members cannot be listed. The set of flight paths a plane can take in traveling from New York to Los Angeles is another set whose members cannot all be listed. A third set of this type is the set of numbers that we use for counting. Sets such as these are called *infinite sets*. If all the members of a set can be listed, it is a *finite set*. If a set is not finite, then it is an infinite set.

Exercises 1.1

Write a list name for each of the following sets.

Examples:

(a) The set of lakes in the Great Lakes.

Solution: {Huron, Superior, Michigan, Erie, Ontario}

(b) The set of consonants in the English alphabet.

Solution: $\{b, c, d, f, g, h, j, k, l, m, n, p, q, r, s, t, v, w, x, y, z\}$

1. The set of months in the year.
2. The set of continents on Earth.
3. The set of types of coins minted by the United States Treasury Department.
4. The set of persons in your family.
5. The set of states in the United States whose names begin with I.
6. The set of human beings who are more than 10 feet tall.
7. The set of oceans on Earth.
8. The set of countries that border the continental United States.
9. The set of automobiles in your garage.
10. The set of courses in which you are currently enrolled.

Write a name for each of the following sets by stating a defining property for the set and enclosing it in braces.

Examples:

(a) {Sunday, Monday, Tuesday, Wednesday, Thursday, Friday, Saturday}.

Solution: {days of the week}.

(b) {April, June, September, November}.

Solution: {months of the year having exactly 30 days}.

11. {Johnson, Kennedy, Eisenhower, Truman}
12. {New York, Chicago, Los Angeles}
13. {Brooklyn, Queens, Manhattan, Bronx, Richmond}
14. {2, 4, 6, 8, 10}
15. {General Motors, Ford, Chrysler}
16. {France, The Netherlands, Belgium, Luxembourg, West Germany, Italy}

17. {red, blue, yellow}
18. {United States, Canada, Mexico}
19. {Atlantic, Pacific, Indian, Arctic}
20. {April, May, June}

True or false?

Examples:

(a) $b \in \{a, b, c, d\}$.

Solution: True, since b *is* one of the elements of $\{a, b, c, d\}$.

(b) $\{a, b\}$ = {first two letters of the English alphabet}.

Solution: True, since the members of these two sets are identical.

21. San Francisco $\in$ {cities on the West Coast of the U.S.}
22. Brazil $\notin$ {countries in South America}
23. $\{g, d, k\} \in$ {letters in the first half of the English alphabet}
24. $g \in \{e, f, g, h\}$
25. $s = \{s\}$
26. $\{g, b, y, t, e, p\} = \{y, t, p, g, e, b\}$
27. $\{1, 4, 9, 8, 7, 3\} = \{9, 4, 3, 1, 8\}$
28. {months of the year} $\neq$ {days of the year}
29. Wednesday $\in$ {months of the year}
30. $9 \in \{3, 6, 9\}$ and $7 \notin \{3, 6, 9\}$
31. $3 \in \{1, 2, 3\}$ or $11 \in \{1, 5, 7, 9\}$

Tell whether each of the following sets is finite or infinite.

Examples:

(a) $\{3, 6, 9, 12, 15, \ldots\}$.

Solution: Infinite set. The three dots ". . ." indicate that the sequence continues on "in the same manner."

(b) $\{4, 14, 24, \ldots, 94\}$.

Solution: Finite set. The three dots here indicate that the sequence continues in the same manner until the number 94 is reached.

32. {letters in the English alphabet}

33. {words in the English language}
34. {numbers used for counting}
35. {points on a 1-inch line segment}
36. {points on a 1,000,000-mile line segment}
37. {points on a circle}
38. {people on Earth}
39. {2, 3, 5, 7, 11, 13, . . . , 37}
40. {5, 10, 15, 20, . . . , 6,000,000,000,000}
41. {5, 10, 15, 20, . . .}
42. {1, 2, 3, 5, 8, 13, 21, 34, . . .}
43. {2, 4, 6, 8, 10, 12, . . . , 999,999,999,998}

In each of problems 44 through 54, write a true statement using A, B, and one of the symbols, $\subset$, $\not\subset$, $=$.

Example: $A = $ {vowels in the English alphabet},
　　　　　$B = $ {letters in the English alphabet}.

Solution: $A \subset B$.

44. $A = $ {c, d}
    $B = $ {consonants in the English alphabet}
45. $A = $ {1, 2, 3, 4, 5}
    $B = $ {1, 3, 5, 7, 9}
46. $A = $ {2, 4, 6, 8}
    $B = $ {1, 2, 3, 4, 5, 6, 7, 8, 9}
47. $A = \varnothing$
    $B = $ {1, 2, 3}
48. $A = $ {states in the United States}
    $B = $ {state capitols in the United States}
49. $A = $ {Costa Rica, Jamaica, Panama, Brazil, Chile}
    $B = $ {countries in South America}
50. $A = $ {successful Project Mercury spaceshots}
    $B = $ {Project Mercury spaceshots}
51. $A = $ {stars in our solar system}
    $B = $ {Sun, Moon, Jupiter}
52. $A = $ {six-legged mathematics students}
    $B = $ {students in your mathematics class}
53. $A = $ {Misses America since 1960}
    $B = $ {winners of the Miss America Beauty Pageant since 1960}
54. $A = $ {1, 3, 5, 7, . . .}
    $B = $ {2, 4, 6, 8, . . .}

55. List all the subsets of set $A = \{a\}$. How many are there?

56. List all the subsets of set A in problem 44. How many are there?

57. List all the subsets of set B in problem 47. How many are there?

58. From your results in problems 55 through 57, can you predict the number of subsets of a set containing six elements? Ten elements?

Let A be any set. Which of the following statements are true and which are false?

　　　59. $A \subset A$ 　　　**60.** $A \subseteq A$ 　　　**61.** $\emptyset \subseteq A$ 　　　**62.** $\emptyset \subset A$

Let $A = \{1, 2, 3, 4\}$. Identify each of the following statements as true or false and tell why.

　　　63. $\{1, 2\} \subseteq \{1, 2, 3, 4\}$ 　　　　　**64.** $\{1, 2\} \in \{1, 2, 3, 4\}$

　　　65. $2 \subseteq \{1, 2, 3, 4\}$ 　　　　　　**66.** $2 \in \{1, 2, 3, 4\}$

　　　67. $1 \subset \{1, 2\} \subset \{1, 2, 3, 4\}$ 　　　**68.** $\emptyset \subset 3$

1.2 Natural Numbers

Consider the sets

$$A = \{\text{Sam, Pete, Henry, Jack}\}$$
$$B = \{w, x, y, z\}$$

It is possible to pair the members of set A with the members of set B in such a way that each member of one set is paired with one and only one member of the other set and there are no members of either set left unpaired. One such pairing is

　　　　　Sam　　　Pete　　　Henry　　　Jack
　　　　　　↕　　　　　↕　　　　　↕　　　　　↕
　　　　　　w　　　　x　　　　　y　　　　　z

Such a pairing is called a *one-to-one correspondence*. If a one-to-one correspondence can be established between two sets, then we say that the sets are *equivalent*. Sets A and B are equivalent sets.

Example: Let

$$C = \{h, i, s\}$$
$$D = \{h, e, r, s\}$$
$$E = \{t, h, e, i, r, s\}$$

Note that C and D are not equivalent, D and E are not equivalent, and C and E are not equivalent.   However, D is equivalent to each of the sets A and B named above.

If you examine the sets {Sam}, {t}, {Boston}, {Mercury}, you can see that they are equivalent sets.   You might also note that each of them is equivalent to {1}.   We say that each set that is equivalent to {1} has the property of *oneness*, or *cardinality* 1.

Similarly, each of the sets {Fresno, Gary}, {f, g}, {Jupiter, Saturn} is equivalent to {1, 2}.   We say that each set equivalent to {1, 2} has the property of *twoness*, or cardinality 2.   Thus the cardinal number *one* can be thought of as the property shared by all sets having a single element. Similarly, the cardinal number *two* is the common property of all sets containing a pair of elements.   Continuing in this manner, we obtain the cardinal numbers 3, 4, 5, 6, 7, 8, 9, 10, 11, 12, etc.   The set of numbers

$$N = \{1, 2, 3, 4, 5, 6, 7, \ldots\}$$

obtained in this way is called the *set of natural numbers.*

In Section 1.1 we introduced the empty set, $\varnothing$, which has no members. This set is not equivalent to any of the sets, {1}, {1, 2}, {1, 2, 3}, etc.   We assign "0" as the cardinality of the empty set.   If we form a set made up of the natural numbers together with the number 0, we obtain the *set of whole numbers.*

$$W = \{0, 1, 2, 3, 4, 5, 6, 7, \ldots\}$$

The symbols we write when we talk about a number are called *numerals.* A numeral is a name for a number just as "Abraham Lincoln" is the name of a former President of the United States.   Sometimes we shall wish to distinguish a number from its name.   When we do so, the number is to be thought of as an idea, whereas the numeral is simply a name for that idea.   Each number has many names, but each numeral is a name for only one number.   For example, each numeral in Figure 1.1 names the cardinal number of the set {a, e, i, o, u} and only that number.

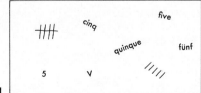

FIGURE 1.1

Exercises 1.2

Which of the following pairs of sets can be placed in a one-to-one correspondence?

Examples:

(a) The set of fingers on your hands and the set of natural numbers
1 through 10.

Solution: These two sets may be placed in a one-to-one correspondence
by pairing each finger with one and only one of the natural numbers 1
through 10 in such a way that each number is paired with exactly one finger.
One such correspondence is shown in Figure 1.2.

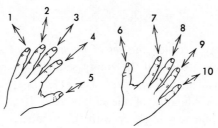

FIGURE 1.2

(b) {a, b, c, d, e} and {3, 6, 9, 12, 15, 18}.

Solution: Here we might begin by matching according to the following
scheme:

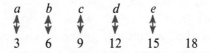

But 18 in the second set is not paired with any member of the first set. We
might try some other pairing schemes, but each time we shall have one
member of the second set that cannot be paired with a member of the first
set. Hence these two sets cannot be placed in a one-to-one correspondence.

1. {states in the United States}
   {natural numbers from 1 through 50}
2. {your acquaintances}
   {your friends}

3. {your favorite foods}
    {cities in the United States}
4. {fingers on one hand}
    {member countries of the United Nations Security Council}
5. {positions on a baseball team}
    {whole numbers, numerals for which may be written with one symbol}
6. {shoes in your closet}
    {outfits in your wardrobe}
7. {positions on a football team}
    {whole numbers between 43 and 55}
8. {seats on an airliner}
    {passengers on that airliner}
9. {eyes on a human being}
    {ears on a human being}
10. {natural numbers}
    {even natural numbers}
11. Which of the pairs of sets in problems 1 through 10 are equivalent sets?

True or false?

12. {apples, pears, peaches, bananas} is equivalent to
    {steaks, chops, roasts, patties}.
13. {natural numbers 13 through 42} is equivalent to
    {natural numbers 27 through 56}.
14. {whole numbers 63 through 146} is equivalent to
    {years between the signing of the Declaration of Independence and the War Between the States}.
15. 1498 ∈ {natural numbers}.
16. 5,000,000 is a whole number.
17. {whole numbers} = {natural numbers}.
18. {whole numbers} is equivalent to {natural numbers}.
19. {0} ∈ {whole numbers}.
20. 0 ∈ {whole numbers}.
21. The elements of the set of natural numbers are numerals.
22. Each whole number is a natural number.
23. Each natural number is a whole number.
24. The set of whole numbers is an example of a finite set.
25. The set {2, 4, 6, 8, . . .} is equivalent to the set of natural numbers.
26. The set of natural numbers is equivalent to {1, 3, 5, 7, . . .}.
27. Find the cardinal number of each set in problems 1 through 20 of Exercises 1.1.

28. State the distinction between a number and a numeral.

1.3 Numeration

A common method for keeping a count is illustrated in Figure 1.3.

 FIGURE 1.3

Twenty-three things have been counted, in groups of five, and the number twenty-three is represented by the numeral ⫽⫽⫽ ⫽⫽⫽ ⫽⫽⫽ ⫽⫽⫽ ⫽⫽⫽ ///. Five is a special number called the *base* in this counting or number-naming scheme. For example, the number six is represented by ⫽⫽⫽/ , a single group of five segments together with a single segment. The numeral for twelve is ⫽⫽⫽⫽⫽⫽//, two groups of five segments together with two segments. It is not too difficult to follow the above pattern to write the numeral for any natural number. Why then do we not write ⫽⫽⫽ ⫽⫽⫽ ⫽⫽⫽ ⫽⫽⫽ /// instead of 23? The answer is that the number-naming scheme illustrated in Figure 1.3 (let us refer to it as the *stick system of numeration*) is inefficient when compared to the decimal numeration system (number-naming scheme) that is in almost universal use today.

This latter system uses ten as the base number. We call ten tens "one hundred," ten hundreds "one thousand," and so on. The set of numerals

$$\{0, 1, 2, 3, 4, 5, 6, 7, 8, 9\}$$

whose elements are called *digits*, name the number zero and the first nine natural numbers. The number ten is named by the base-ten numeral 10, read "one ten, zero ones." 57, read "five tens, seven ones," is the base-ten numeral for the number fifty-seven.

The essential feature that makes the base-ten, or decimal,* numeration system a marvelously efficient system is its use of the *place-value principle* in naming numbers. 15 and 51 are base-ten numerals that use the same digits, yet they name the numbers fifteen and fifty-one, respectively. In each of these numerals, 1 and 5 have the digit values one and five, respectively. However in 15, 1 has place value ten, whereas in 51, 1 has place value one. You can contrast the use of 5 in each numeral in the same manner.

*Decimal comes from the Latin "decem," meaning ten.

By using the set of digits and the place-value principle, we can write a base-ten numeral for each natural number. All the possible arrangements of two digits are used to name the natural numbers ten through ninety-nine. If we attempted to name one hundred using two digits and the place-value principle we would succeed only in repeating one of the numbers already named. Thus a three-digit arrangement is used to name one hundred. 99 is read "nine tens, nine ones." 100 is read "ten tens, zero ones" or "one hundred, zero tens, zero ones." 647 is read "six hundreds, four tens, seven ones." Following this pattern we see that it is possible to name all the natural numbers through nine hundred ninety-nine, and that it is not possible to name ten hundreds using some arrangement of three digits. The first four-digit numeral, 1000, then is a name for ten hundreds or one thousand. Similarly, we obtain "10,000" for ten thousands and "100,000" for 10 ten thousands or one hundred thousands. Figure 1.4 illustrates the place-value principle in base ten for numerals 0 through 9,999,999,999, the latter being read "nine billion, nine hundred ninety-nine million, nine hundred ninety-nine thousand, nine hundred ninety-nine." Imagine trying to write this numeral in the stick numeration system.

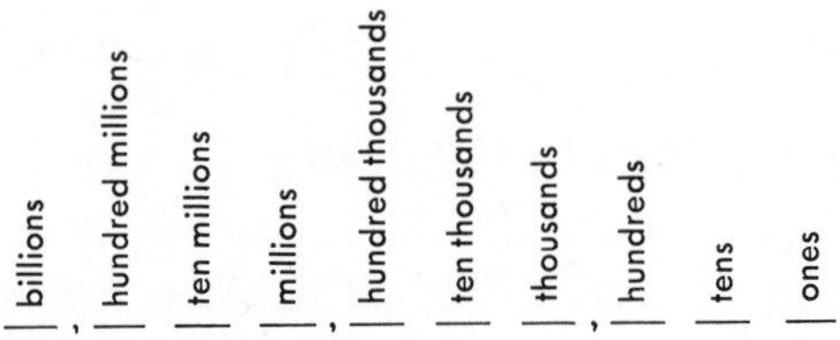

FIGURE 1.4

Exercises 1.3

Write a base-ten numeral for each of the following numbers.

1. Fifty-seven
2. Two hundred eighty-three
3. Five thousand eight hundred ninety-six
4. Six hundred forty-eight thousand
5. Thirty-two million two
6. Four hundred thousand four hundred four
7. Ninety thousand ninety-nine
8. Seventy million seven thousand seventy
9. Fifty-three billion twenty million three hundred eight
10. Twenty million twenty thousand two hundred

Write the word name for each of the following base-ten numerals.

11. 333   **12.** 604   **13.** 55,704   **14.** 404,009
15. 70,008,090   **16.** 5,480,067   **17.** 50,008   **18.** 760,067

19. How many numerals can be written using each of the digits 1 and 2 at most once in any numeral? Use no other digits.

20. How many numerals can be written using each of the digits 3, 5, and 8 at most once in any numeral? Use no other digits.

21. In what way is the stick numeration system more efficient than our base-ten place-value system?

22. Provide an argument to show that by using only the ten digits and the base-ten place-value system and any combination of one or two digits it is only possible to name the numbers from zero through ninety-nine.

23. Zero is not used in the stick numeration system. Why is it necessary in our base-ten place-value numeration system?

24. Our number-naming scheme uses ten as its base. Might it be possible to develop a place-value numeration system using some other number as base? Try to develop a place-value numeration system using five as the base. What are the digits in this system?

1.4 Graphing the Whole Numbers

A convenient way to visualize the set of whole numbers is to imagine a set of equally spaced points along a ray (see Figure 1.5). We can establish

FIGURE 1.5

a one-to-one correspondence with this set and the set of whole numbers by, beginning at the left, matching the first point with 0, the second point with 1, the third point with 2, etc. Picturing this correspondence on the ray, we obtain Figure 1.6, which we call a *number line*. Each point is called

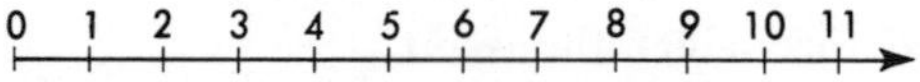

$$\begin{array}{ccccccccccccc} 0 & 1 & 2 & 3 & 4 & 5 & 6 & 7 & 8 & 9 & 10 & 11 \end{array}$$

FIGURE 1.6

the *graph* of the number to which it corresponds and each number is called the *coordinate* of the point to which it corresponds. Hence the seventh point from the left is the graph of the whole number 6 and 6 is the coordinate of the seventh point from the left.

Frequently we shall wish to graph only certain whole numbers or certain subsets of the set of whole numbers. For instance, suppose we are asked to graph {2, 3, 5, 7}. To do this, we first draw a picture of the number line. Then we make a heavy dot (in this text we shall use colored dots) at each point that is the graph of an element of the given set. This has been done in Figure 1.7.

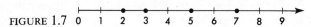

FIGURE 1.7 0   1   2   3   4   5   6   7   8   9

Exercises 1.4

Graph each of the following sets of numbers.

Examples:

(a) {2, 4, 6, 8}.

Solution: 0   1   2   3   4   5   6   7   8   9   10

(b) {1050, 1100, 1175, 1300, 1325}.

Solution: 1050   1100   1175   1300 1325

Note that it is not always necessary or convenient to show the point corresponding to zero on your picture.

1. {3, 6, 9, 12, 15, 18}   **2.** {2, 3, 5, 7, 11, 13, 17, 19}
3. {1, 2, 3, 5, 8, 13, 21, 34, 55}   **4.** {21, 23, 25, 27, 29}
5. {66, 68, 70, . . . , 82}   **6.** {3, 6, 9, . . . , 30}
7. {4, 8, 12, . . . , 28}   **8.** {5, 10, 15, . . . , 30}

Example: {numbers belonging to the set in problem 6 *and* to the set in problem 7}.

Solution: 10   12   14   16   18   20   22   24   26

Example: {numbers belonging to the set in problem 6 *or* to the set in problem 7}.

Solution: 0   2   4   6   8   10   12   14   16   18   20   22   24   26   28   30

9. {numbers belonging to the set in problem 6 *and* to the set in problem 8}

10. {numbers belonging to the set in problem 6 *or* to the set in problem 8}
11. {numbers belonging to the set in problem 7 *and* to the set in problem 8}
12. {numbers belonging to the set in problem 7 *or* to the set in problem 8}
13. {numbers belonging to the set in problem 6 *and* to the set in problem 7 *and* to the set in problem 8}

In each of the following problems, write a name for the set of whole numbers whose graph is shown.

Examples:

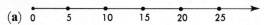

(a) 0   5   10   15   20   25

Solution: {5, 10, 15, 20, 25}.

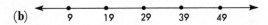

(b)   9   19   29   39   49

Solution: {9, 19, 29, 39, 49}.

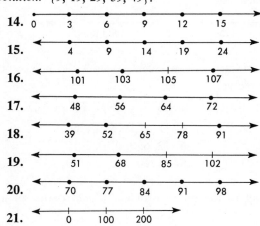

14. 0   3   6   9   12   15

15.   4   9   14   19   24

16.   101   103   105   107

17.   48   56   64   72

18.   39   52   65   78   91

19.   51   68   85   102

20.   70   77   84   91   98

21.   0   100   200

1.5 The Order Relation

We have noted that two sets may or may not be equivalent. When they are not, it is possible to find a proper subset of one of the sets that is equivalent to the second set. In such a case we say that the number associated with the first set is *greater than* the number associated with the second set. As an example, consider the sets

$$A = \{a, b, c, d, e, f, g\}$$
$$B = \{w, x, y, z\}$$

$\{a, b, c, d\} \subset A$ and $\{a, b, c, d\}$ is equivalent to B. Consequently, we say that the cardinal number of set A, 7, is greater than the cardinal number of set B, 4. That is, 7 is greater than 4.

The symbol for "is greater than" is ">." Instead of writing "7 is greater than 4" we write "$7 > 4$." Similarly, "$8 > 3$" means "8 is greater than 3." For each two points on the number line, the coordinate of the point on the right is greater than the coordinate of the point on the left. Thus the graph of 8 is to the right of the graph of 3 on the number line.

The sentence "4 is less than 7" means the same thing as the sentence "7 is greater than 4." The symbol for "is less than" is "<." So "$9 <$ 17" means "9 is less than 17," and, on the graph of the number line, the graph of 9 is to the left of the graph of 17. In general, for each two whole numbers a and b, $a < b$ means $b > a$.

From the above discussion we see that the relation "is greater than" *orders* the whole numbers. When an ordered set of whole numbers is listed, b appears after a in the list "if and only if"* $b > a$. When the natural numbers are so ordered, they are called the *counting numbers*.

Each of the symbols, $>$, $<$, $=$, can be given an opposite meaning by writing a "/" through the symbol. Thus "$4 \not> 6$" means "4 is not greater than 6" and "$100 \not< 8$" means "100 is not less than 8."

Exercises 1.5

True or false?

1. $9 > 11$ **2.** $78 = 87$ **3.** $63 > 36$

4. $29 < 92$ **5.** $88 \neq 88$ **6.** $567 \neq 657$

7. $486 \not< 479$ **8.** $123{,}456{,}789 < 123{,}465{,}798$

9. For each whole number a, $a > 0$.

10. For each natural number b, $b > 0$.

11. For each natural number c, $c \not< 1$.

12. There is a largest whole number.

13. There is a smallest whole number.

14. Each natural number is greater than some whole number.

*The phrase "if and only if" is used to express two distinct sentences. Used above it means "If $b > a$, then b appears after a in the list," as well as "If b appears after a in the list, then $b > a$." This phrase will be used a number of times in the text.

15. Each whole number is greater than some natural number.

16. $0 \neq 1$

For each of the following problems, rearrange the elements of the set from largest to smallest.

Example: $\{53, 64, 37, 49, 57, 61, 59, 43\}$.

Solution: $\{64, 61, 59, 57, 53, 49, 43, 37\}$.

17. $\{1374, 1437, 1347, 1473, 1734, 1743\}$

18. $\{678, 876, 768, 867, 687\}$

19. $\{1,000,000,001, 200,000,002, 30,000,003, 4,000,004, 500,005\}$

For each of the following pairs of sets, indicate a correspondence or pairing of the elements of the sets. Then decide whether the cardinality of one set is greater than that of the other, or whether the sets are equivalent.

20. $\{3, 7, 11, \ldots, 31\}$ **21.** $\{3, 8, 13, \ldots, 48\}$
     $\{a, b, c, \ldots, k\}$ $\{z, y, x, \ldots, m\}$

22. $\{a, b, c, \ldots, p\}$ **23.** $\{7, 16, 25, \ldots, 70\}$
     $\{z, y, x, \ldots, h\}$ $\{2, 4, 6, \ldots, 20\}$

24. $\{1, 11, 111, \ldots, 1,111,111\}$ **25.** $\{1, 4, 9, 16, \ldots, 225\}$
     $\{2, 22, 222, \ldots, 2,222,222\}$ $\{43, 44, 45, \ldots, 57\}$

Use the appropriate symbol, $>$, $<$, or $=$, to replace each question mark.

         26. 4 ? 5   **27.** 8 ? 7   **28.** 15 ? 12   **29.** 3 ? 3

30. Cardinality of $\{a, b, c\}$? cardinality of $\{p, q\}$.

31. Cardinality of $\{$natural numbers less than 6$\}$? cardinality of $\{$vowels in the alphabet$\}$.

1.6 Open Sentences and Variables

Pick a natural number. If I then say to you, "Your number is greater than 8," you can examine your chosen number and tell me whether or not I am correct. If you have not chosen a number, you will not be able to decide whether my sentence is true or false. In fact, it is neither. It is an *open sentence*. To make it true or false it is necessary to replace the phrase "your number" by the name of some number. The phrase "your number" is a *placeholder* or *variable* in this sentence. It can be replaced by any name of a natural number to yield a statement which is either true or false. The set of all possible replacements of the variable is called the *domain of the variable*.

Example: Identify the placeholder or variable in the sentence "He is a general in the United States Army." What is an appropriate domain of the variable?

Solution: The variable is the word "he." An appropriate domain of the variable is {men in the United States Army}. There are other sets that could also serve as a domain.

Each element of the domain of the variable is called a *value* of the variable.

Example: Let the domain of the variable t be the set of whole numbers. Name three values of t.

Solution: 0, 65, and 45,794 are three values of the variable t. Any other whole number is also a value of t.

The set of values of the variable that yield true statements is called the *solution set* of the open sentence. The solution set of the sentence "Your number is greater than 8" is the set of numbers {9, 10, 11, 12, . . .}. Each number in this set is a natural number, so each number in this set is in the domain of the variable. Also each number in this set converts the open sentence into a true statement.

Example: What is the solution set of the sentence "$m < 16$" if the domain of the variable m is the set of whole numbers greater than 10?

Solution: The solution set is {11, 12, 13, 14, 15}. Each number in the solution set converts "$m < 16$" into a true statement and is also in the domain of the variable. Note that although 6 converts "$m < 16$" into a true statement, 6 is not in the domain of the variable and, consequently, not in the solution set.

In place of using phrases like "your number" for variables, we usually use letters of the English alphabet. Thus in place of writing "Your number is greater than 8" we might write "n is greater than 8." Here the variable n plays the same role as the variable "your number." Further abbreviation is possible by remembering that the phrase "is greater than" can be replaced by "$>$." This final abbreviation is "$n > 8$." The solution set of "$n > 8$" is the set of natural numbers n such that $n > 8$. The phrase "the set of natural numbers n such that $n > 8$" can be abbreviated and written in *set-builder notation* as

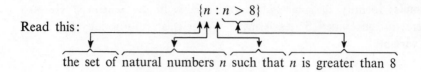

Read this:

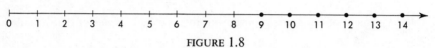

the set of natural numbers n such that n is greater than 8

Note that $\{n : n > 8\} = \{9, 10, 11, 12, 13, \ldots\}$. The graph of the solution set of $n > 8$ is shown in Figure 1.8.

FIGURE 1.8

As another illustration consider the open sentence "$n < 6$." If we wish to find its solution set, we need more information. For instance, we cannot yet be sure whether its solution set is $\{1, 2, 3, 4, 5\}$ or $\{0, 1, 2, 3, 4, 5\}$ or perhaps even something else. To decide, we need to know the domain of the variable n. If the values of n are only natural numbers, then the set $\{1, 2, 3, 4, 5\}$ is the correct solution set. It is important, then, that the domain of the variable be specified. If it is not specified as part of the statement of the problem, then it is necessary to include a comment as to what domain you choose in order to obtain a solution set.

If a variable or placeholder has only one possible value, that is, if its domain contains only one member, we call it a *constant*.

Examples: (a) 5, 468, 1007, and 66,666,666 are constants.

(b) If $t \in \{64\}$, then the only possible replacement for t is 64 and we say that t is a constant.

(c) If $g \in \{103\}$, then g has only one possible replacement and g is a constant.

Suppose m is a variable whose domain is the set of whole numbers. Then the open sentence "$m < 3$ *or* $m = 3$" has as its solution set $\{0, 1, 2, 3\}$, since 0, 1, and 2 each convert "$m < 3$" into a true statement while 3 converts "$m = 3$" into a true statement. The *or* sentence above becomes true when either one part *or* the other part is true. A common abbreviation for "is less than or equal to" is "$\leq$". Hence the sentence "$m < 3$ or $m = 3$" could be abbreviated "$m \leq 3$," read "m is less than or equal to 3." Similarly "$m \geq 8$" means "m is greater than or equal to 8" and "6 $\nleq m$" means "6 is *not* less than or equal to m."

Exercises 1.6

Which of the following sentences are open sentences, that is, sentences that are neither true nor false?

1. George Washington was a President of the United States.
2. He is a classmate of mine.
3. That one is mine.
4. Maryland is more populous than Delaware.
5. $7 \in \{1, 3, 5, 7, 9\}$
6. $x \in \{t, u, v, w, x, y, z\}$.
7. $b \in \{$vowels in the English alphabet$\}$.
8. m is a natural number.
9. 10,101 is a natural number.

10. 6 is greater than m.	**11.** $5 < 3$.	**12.** $k < m$.
13. $5 \ngtr 3$.	**14.** $f \geq 7$.	**15.** $86 \leq n$.
16. $33 \leq 33$.	**17.** $m \ngeq m$.	**18.** $m \geq 0$.
19. $m \leq 0$.	**20.** $m \nless 0$.	

21–40. For each of problems 1 through 20 above: If it is an open sentence, state a possible domain of the variable(s); if it is not an open sentence, tell whether it is true or false.

For each of the following problems, let the domain of each variable be the set of whole numbers, W. Use set-builder notation (page 20) to describe the set. List the elements of the solution set of each open sentence and graph the solution set.

Example: $6 \geq k$.

Solution: The solution set is $\{k : 6 \geq k\} = \{0, 1, 2, 3, 4, 5, 6\}$. The graph of this set is

41. $7 < m$	**42.** $5 \geq h$	**43.** $t \nless 8$
44. $y \ngtr 11$	**45.** $z \nleq 100$	

Example: $t \geq 5$ and $t < 9$.

Solution: The solution set is $\{t : t \geq 5 \text{ and } t < 9\} = \{5, 6, 7, 8\}$. The graph is

46. $h > 3$ and $h \leq 8$ **47.** $m > 4$ and $m < 13$
48. $m < 4$ and $m \geq 13$ **49.** $k < 6$ and $3 \geq k$
50. $17 < b$ and $b < 23$ **51.** $56 \leq z$ and $z \leq 64$
52. $458 \leq y$ and $y < 472$ **53.** $57 \leq d$ and $d \leq 48$
54. $1001 \geq r$ and $r \geq 989$ **55.** $0 < n$ and $n < 1$

1.7 Summary

What is a number? It is an idea. The number one is the property of oneness shared by all sets containing a single element. The number two is the property of twoness shared by all sets containing a pair of elements. Therefore to express the idea of number, we began this chapter with a discussion of sets, set membership, and subsets. We were then able to compare two sets by comparing their elements. If they had the same elements, they were equal sets. If they had different elements but it was possible to find a one-to-one correspondence between the elements, the sets were said to be equivalent. That is, they had the same cardinality. They then shared the property of oneness, or twoness, or threeness, etc.

Thus we were able to describe the natural numbers. Our next problem was to find symbols to represent numbers. Hence we discussed numerals and the base-ten numeration system. Then we sought some relationships between the natural numbers. We saw that two natural numbers were equal provided they each were the cardinality of two equivalent sets. They were unequal and one was greater than the other if they were cardinalities of sets that were not equivalent. Consequently, we introduced an order into the set of natural numbers with the relation "greater than." This order was conveniently illustrated on a number line by the process of graphing.

Finally, since we shall be seeking answers to questions about addition, subtraction, multiplication, and division in the form of open sentences, we discussed the concept of an open sentence. An open sentence is neither true nor false until the variable in the sentence is replaced by an element in its domain.

Exercises 1.7—Review

Complete each sentence:

1. The set $A = \{1, 2, 3\}$ and the set $B = \{a, b, c\}$ are _____.

2. The set A is a proper subset of the set B if each element in A is also
_____ and there is at least one element in _____
that is not in _____.

3. The set that contains no elements is called the _____.

4. If two sets are equivalent, you can find a(n) _____ between
their elements.

5. A numeral is a(n) _____ for a number.

6. We call a system for representing numbers by numerals a(n) _____.

7. The symbol $<$ means _____.

8. The symbol $\not\subset$ means _____.

9. A domain for the variable "he" in the sentence "He is in my mathematics class" is _____.

10. _____ is the symbol for "is a member of."

Let $A = \{a, c, b, d, e\}$. Indicate whether each of the following sentences
is true or false.

11. $d \in A$ 12. $\{a, b\} \in A$ 13. $\{b, e\} \subset A$

14. $\varnothing \not\subset A$ 15. $\{a, b, c, d\} \subset \{a, b, c, d\}$

16. Give two different names for the empty set.

Indicate which of the following pairs of sets are equivalent.

17. {members of your family}
{your brothers and sisters}

18. {legs of a dog}
{limbs of a man}

19. {natural numbers less than 10}
{natural numbers between 11 and 20 inclusive}

20. What can you say about the cardinalities of two equivalent sets?

21. What are the digits in the base-ten numeration system?

Write a base-ten numeral for:

22. Seventy-seven thousand eight hundred twenty-four

23. Eight million two hundred fifty-eight thousand three

24. What feature of our numeration system allows us to write any natural
number with only the ten symbols 0, 1, 2, 3, 4, 5, 6, 7, 8, 9?

Graph each of the following sets.

25. $\{3, 7, 12\}$ 26. $\{48, 54, 60\}$ 27. $\{1008, 1009, 1010, 1011\}$

28. {natural numbers greater than 9 and less than 15}

29. $\{n \in N: 4 \leq n \text{ and } n < 12\}$

30. Let $A = \{a, b, c, d, e, f, g\}$ and $B = \{r, s, t\}$. How is the idea of one-to-one correspondence used to show that 7 is greater than 3?

Make each of the following sentences true by replacing the asterisk, *, by one of the symbols $\leqslant$ or $\not\leqslant$.

31. 3 * 2   **32.** 18 * 11   **33.** 41 * 45

Use set-builder notation to describe each of the following sets.

34. {natural numbers greater than 5}
35. {whole numbers less than 20}
36. {natural numbers greater than 5 and less than 20}

Find an appropriate domain for the variable in each of the following sentences.

37. She is a student at UCLA.
38. He plays for the Dodgers.
39. The door was open.
40. It was a coin.

chapter two

SETS

2.0 Introduction

Now that we have discussed the idea of number, it would seem natural to discuss next a way to combine numbers. Before doing so, however, we shall ask: What does it mean to add two numbers? and What exactly is addition and multiplication? These questions will be answered in Chapter Three using set concepts discussed in this chapter. By introducing the set operations "union," "intersection," and "Cartesian product" first, we may use them in Chapter Three to define the addition and multiplication operations.

Thus this chapter is concerned with certain set operations and their properties which are then used in Chapter Three, where we begin our discussion of addition and multiplication.

2.1 Venn Diagrams and the Universal Set

To visualize relationships between sets, it is useful to draw diagrams to represent the sets and the associated relationships. Figure 2.1 is called a *Venn diagram*. The regions within the boundaries represent sets and their respective elements. In Figure 2.1 we see that sets *A* and *B* are subsets of the set *U* and have no elements in common. Sets that have no elements in common are called *disjoint sets*.

25

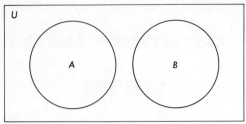

FIGURE 2.1

   In discussing and comparing sets it is useful to consider an all-inclusive set that contains at least the elements of the sets under consideration. Such a set is called a *universal set*. The set U of Figure 2.1 is a universal set. We shall generally denote the universal set by the letter U.

Example: Draw a Venn diagram for the sets S, M, and F, where

$$S = \{\text{students in your math class}\}$$
$$M = \{\text{male students in your math class}\}$$
$$F = \{\text{female students in your math class}\}$$

Name an appropriate universal set for this problem.

Solution: Since each of the sets M and F are subsets of the set S, S is an appropriate universal set. The Venn diagram for this problem is shown in Figure 2.2. Note also that sets M and F are disjoint sets, since they have no common elements.

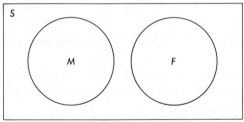

FIGURE 2.2

Example: Mary, age 13, Peter, age 8, and Philip, age 15, are the children in the John Smith family. Draw a Venn diagram to illustrate the relationships between the following sets:

$$F = \{\text{persons in the John Smith family}\}$$
$$G = \{\text{boys in the John Smith family}\}$$
$$H = \{\text{children in the John Smith family older than 10}\}$$

What is an appropriate universal set? Are sets G and H disjoint sets?

Solution: Since each of the sets *G* and *H* are subsets of the set *F*, an appropriate universal set is *F*. The Venn diagram is shown in Figure 2.3. The sets *G* and *H* each contain the element, Philip; hence *G* and *H* are not disjoint sets.

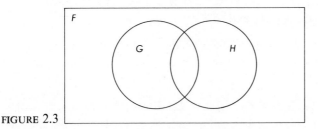

FIGURE 2.3

Exercises 2.1

For each of problems 1 through 10, examine the diagram of Figure 2.4 and tell whether the statement is true or false.

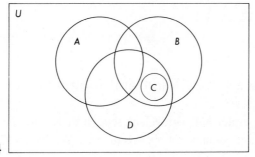

FIGURE 2.4

1. *B* is the universal set.   **2.** *C* and *A* are disjoint sets.
3. *A* and *D* are not disjoint sets.   **4.** *A* is a subset of *C*.
5. Each element of *B* is an element of *C*.
6. Each element of *C* is an element of *D*.

7. $C \nsubseteq A$ **8.** $C \subseteq D$ **9.** $D \subseteq U$ **10.** $C \subseteq B$

For each of problems 11 through 20, give an appropriate universal set for the pair of sets listed.

11. {2, 4, 6, 8, 10} and {1, 5, 9}
12. {1, 2, 3, . . . , 10} and {5, 10, 15, 20}
13. {persons born since 1940} and {persons less than 65 years old}
14. {white automobiles} and {blue sport coupes}

15. {United States, Canada, Mexico} and {Brazil, Peru}

16. {Atlantic, Indian} and {Arctic, Pacific}

17. {a, e, i, o, u} and {m, n, p, q}

18. {St. Louis, Pittsburgh, Boston} and {Houston, Dallas, Galveston}

19. {Norway, Denmark, Germany} and {Sweden, Finland}

20. {35, 0, 119, 52, 64} and ∅.

Draw a Venn diagram to illustrate the relationships among each of the following collections of sets. In each case, choose an appropriate universal set, U.

21. $N = \{1, 2, 3, 4, 5, \ldots\}$ **22.** $W = \{0, 1, 2, 3, 4, 5, \ldots\}$
$\quad\;\; E = \{2, 4, 6, 8, 10, \ldots\}$ $\quad\;\; F = \{5, 10, 15, 20, 25, \ldots\}$
$\quad\;\; O = \{1, 3, 5, 7, 9, \ldots\}$ $\quad\;\; S = \{6, 12, 18, 24, 30, \ldots\}$

23. $D = \{1, 2, 3, \ldots, 10\}$ **24.** $H = \{1, 2, 3, 4, \ldots, 100\}$
$\quad\;\; P = \{2, 3, 5, 7\}$ $\quad\;\; T = \{1, 2, 3, 4, \ldots, 1000\}$
$\quad\;\; T = \{3, 6, 9\}$ $\quad\;\; Q = \{4, 8, 12, 16, \ldots, 500\}$

25. $A = \{3, 6, 9, \ldots, 60\}$
$\quad\;\; B = \{4, 8, 12, \ldots, 60\}$
$\quad\;\; C = \{6, 12, 18, \ldots, 60\}$
$\quad\;\; D = \{18, 36, 54\}$

2.2 Set Operations—Union and Intersection

In discussing equal and equivalent sets, subsets and universal sets, we have been making comparisons between sets. We have asked of two sets

1. Are they the same set?

2. Do the sets have the same number of elements?

3. Are the elements of one set also the elements of the other set?

Now we wish to know if there is some rather "natural" way to combine the elements of two sets to form a third set.

Suppose $A = \{1, 2, 3, 4\}$ and $B = \{5, 6, 7, 8, 9\}$. Then the set

$$C = \{1, 2, 3, 4, 5, 6, 7, 8, 9\}$$

might be a natural combination of the elements of sets A and B. We say C is the *union* of set A and set B and write $A \cup B = C$ (read "A union B is equal to C"). This process of combination of the elements of two sets to form a third set is a *set operation*.

Examples:

1. A = {Mary, Risa, Jack}, B = {Joe, Mark}
   $A \cup B$ = {Mary, Risa, Jack, Joe, Mark}
2. C = {a, b, r, p}, D = {b, p, x, y}
   $C \cup D$ = {a, b, r, p, x, y}
3. E = {states bordering on Canada}
   F = {states bordering on Mexico}
   $E \cup F$ = {states bordering on Canada or Mexico (or both)}

In general, the *union* of two sets, A and B, is a third set, C, which contains every element that belongs either to A or to B or to both sets.   This
definition is illustrated in Figure 2.5, where the colored region represents

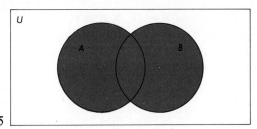

FIGURE 2.5

$A \cup B$.   We could also use set-builder notation to define the union of two
sets A and B. $A \cup B = \{x \in U: x \in A$ or $x \in B\}$.

Another natural way to combine the elements of two sets, A and B, is
to form a third set, C, which contains every element that is a member of
both set A *and* set B. C is called the *intersection* of sets A and B, written
$A \cap B = C$.

Examples:

1. A = {2, 4, 6, 8, 10}, B = {4, 8, 9}
   $A \cap B$ = {4, 8}
2. C = {a, b, r, p}, D = {b, p, x, y}
   $C \cap D$ = {b, p}
3. E = {20, 40, 60, 80}, F = {10, 30, 50, 70, 90}
   $E \cap F = \varnothing$ The sets E and F have no elements in common.   They
   are disjoint sets.

In general, the intersection of two sets A and B is a third set C, which
contains every element that is a member of both set A and set B.   The
definition of $A \cap B$ is illustrated in Figure 2.6 as the colored region.   Using
set-builder notation, $A \cap B = \{x \in u: x \in A$ and $x \in B\}$.

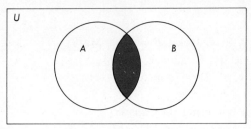

FIGURE 2.6

Exercises 2.2

In each of the following problems, find the union and intersection of the given pair of sets.

1. $A = \{a, e, i, o, u\}$ and $B = \{a, b, c, d, e\}$.
2. $C = \{\text{John, Mary, Alice, Henry}\}$ and $D = \{\text{Mary, Henry}\}$.
3. $E = \{2, 4, 6, 8, 10, 12\}$ and $F = \{4, 8, 12\}$.
4. $G = \{5, 15, 25, 35, 45, 75\}$ and $H = \{5, 10, 15, \ldots, 95\}$.
5. $K = \{3, 6, 9, 12, \ldots, 39\}$ and $L = \{4, 8, 12, \ldots, 40\}$.
6. $M = \{3, 6, 9, 12, \ldots, 99\}$ and $P = \{4, 8, 12, \ldots, 100\}$.
7. $Q = \{3, 6, 9, 12, \ldots, 60\}$ and $R = \{5, 10, 15, 20, \ldots, 60\}$.
8. Let $U = \{\text{rivers in the United States}\}$
  $A = \{\text{rivers east of the Rocky Mountains}\}$
  $B = \{\text{rivers that flow north to south}\}$.
Name the sets $A \cup B$ and $A \cap B$ by stating a defining property of the elements of these sets.
9. Let $U = \{\text{natural numbers 3 through 20}\}$
  $A = \{\text{natural numbers 5 through 11}\}$
  $B = \{\text{natural numbers 3 through 8}\}$.
  (a) Name the sets $A \cup B$ and $A \cap B$ by stating a defining property of the elements of these sets.
  (b) Name the sets $A \cup B$ and $B \cap A$ by listing their elements.
10. Let $U = \{n \in N\colon 7 < n \leq 13\}$; N is the set of natural numbers
  $A = \{n \in U\colon n > 10\}$
  $B = \{n \in U\colon n \leq 11\}$.
Follow the directions of problems 9(a) and 9(b) for these sets.
11. Let $U = \{p \in W\colon p < 25\}$; W is the set of whole numbers
  $A = \{p \in U\colon p > 8\}$
  $B = \{p \in U\colon p \leq 8\}$.
Follow the directions of problems 9(a) and 9(b) for these sets.
12. Suppose A and B are any two subsets of some universal set U. Which of the following statements are true?

(a) $A \cup A = A$ (b) $A \cup \varnothing = A$ (c) $A \cap A = \varnothing$
(d) $A \cap \varnothing = A$ (e) $A \cup \varnothing = \varnothing$ (f) $A \cup B \subseteq A$
(g) $A \cap B \subseteq A$ (h) $A \cap B \subseteq B$ (i) $A \cup B = U$
(j) If $A \cap B = \varnothing$, then A and B are disjoint sets.

13. Show the relationships between the sets in each of the following sentences by drawing Venn diagrams and naming appropriate universal sets.
    (a) The assembly hall was filled with either Democrats or Republicans.
    (b) The language department offers Spanish, French, and German. Students are expected to take at least one foreign language. A good number of the students take two foreign languages and some take all three foreign languages.
    (c) The students at the meeting fit into one of five categories—honor student-athlete, student government member, honor student, athlete, honor student-student government member.

Review your answers to problem 12. To state that a generalized statement is true means that it is true for each set A and for each set B. A generalization is considered false if there is at least one instance of it that is false. Such an instance is called a *counterexample*.

Example: Problem 12(c) is a false statement. If $A = \varnothing$, then the instance $\varnothing \cap \varnothing = \varnothing$ is true. But if $A = \{1, 2\}$, then the instance $\{1, 2\} \cap \{1, 2\} = \varnothing$ is false, since $\{1, 2\} \cap \{1, 2\} = \{1, 2\} \neq \varnothing$. This last instance is a counterexample for the generalization $A \cap A = \varnothing$.

14. (a) Provide a counterexample for each false statement in problem 12.
    (b) Each false statement in problem 12 can be converted into a true statement by changing only one symbol in the statement. For example, problem 12(c) becomes true when $\varnothing$ is replaced by A to yield $A \cap A = A$. [There are still other ways to convert the statement of problem 12(c) to a true statement. Can you find some?] Convert each false statement in problem 12 into a true statement by changing only one symbol in the statement. Do this in at least two ways.

2.3 Properties of Set Operations

The set operations union and intersection are called *binary* operations, since we operate on *two* subsets A and B of some universal set U to form a

third set C.   Our purpose in this section is to state and discuss some properties of the binary operations union and intersection.   With this in mind,
we shall assume, in what follows, that A, B, and C are subsets of some
universal set U.

Closure Property

$A \cup B$ and $A \cap B$ are subsets of U.

Example: Let $U = W$, the set of whole numbers.

$A = \{1, 5, 6, 11, 12\}, \quad B = \{2, 3, 4, 6, 10, 12, 15\}$

$A \cup B = \{1, 2, 3, 4, 5, 6, 10, 11, 12, 15\}$

$A \cap B = \{6, 12\}$

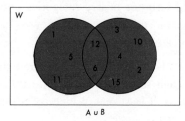
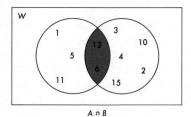

FIGURE 2.7

$A \cup B$ and $A \cap B$ are each subsets of W (see Figure 2.7).

The result of forming the union or intersection of any two sets A and B
does not depend on the order in which the sets are taken.   This property
of the operations is called the

Commutative Property

$A \cup B = B \cup A, \quad A \cap B = B \cap A.$

Example: Let $U = \{$even whole numbers$\}$,

$A = \{4, 8, 12, 16, 20, 24\}, B = \{6, 12, 18, 24\}.$

$A \cup B = \{4, 6, 8, 12, 16, 20, 24\} = B \cup A$

$A \cap B = \{12, 24\} = B \cap A$

Can we form the union of three sets, A, B, and C, "$A \cup B \cup C$"?
Since union is a binary operation, it cannot be performed on three sets.
We must first associate or pair two of the sets, form their union, then find

the union of this set with the remaining set. Thus "$A \cup B \cup C$" is meaningful if it is written "$(A \cup B) \cup C$" or "$A \cup (B \cup C)$." The property of set operations that guarantees that either way of pairing the sets will give the same result is known as the

Associative Property

$$(A \cup B) \cup C = A \cup (B \cup C), \quad (A \cap B) \cap C = A \cap (B \cap C).$$

Example: Let $U = W$,

$A = \{2, 4, 6\}, B = \{6, 8, 10\}, C = \{4, 6, 10, 14\}$.
$A \cup B = \{2, 4, 6, 8, 10, 14\}$
$(A \cup B) \cup C = \{2, 4, 6, 8, 10\} \cup \{4, 6, 10, 14\}$
$\qquad\qquad = \{2, 4, 6, 8, 10, 14\}$

Also

$B \cup C = \{4, 6, 8, 10, 14\}$
$A \cup (B \cup C) = \{2, 4, 6\} \cup \{4, 6, 8, 10, 14\}$.
$\qquad\qquad = \{2, 4, 6, 8, 10, 14\}$

Hence, for these three sets, $(A \cup B) \cup C = A \cup (B \cup C)$. A similar discussion leads to the result that $(A \cap B) \cap C = A \cap (B \cap C) = \{6\}$

In view of the associative property we can now say that "$A \cup B \cup C$" means "Associate two of the sets, A and B or B and C, form their union, and then form the union of this set with the remaining set."

Now consider $\{a, b, c, d, e\} \cup \varnothing$. This is the set $\{a, b, c, d, e\}$. In fact, for each set A we have the

Identity Property for union

$$A \cup \varnothing = A = \varnothing \cup A.$$

$\varnothing$ is called the *identity element* for the operation union.

(*Note:* Each of the previous examples was used only to illustrate, not to prove, the properties of the set operations. On the basis of our intuitive knowledge about sets, we shall assume the validity of these properties.)

Exercises 2.3

Show that $A \cup B = B \cup A$ and $A \cap B = B \cap A$ for each of the following pairs of sets A and B.

1. $A = \{a, e, i\}$ and $B = \{a, e, i, o, u\}$.
2. $A = \{2, 4, 6, 8\}$ and $B = \{6, 8, 10\}$.
3. $A = \{$even natural numbers$\}$ and $B = \{$odd natural numbers$\}$.
4. $A = \{x \in W: x < 10\}$ and
   $B = \{x \in W: 7 < x \le 14\}$. $W = \{$whole numbers$\}$.
5. $A = \{t \in N: 20 > t > 12\}$ and
   $B = \{k \in N: 1 > k\}$. $N = \{$natural numbers$\}$.
6. State appropriate universal sets for each of problems 1 through 5.

Show that $(A \cup B) \cup C = A \cup (B \cup C)$ and $(A \cap B) \cap C = A \cap (B \cap C)$ for each of the following collections of sets A, B, and C.

7. $A = \{n \in N: n \le 5\}$, $B = \{n \in N: 2 < n < 8\}$, $C = \{1, 3, 5, 7\}$
8. $A = \{$registered voters in Los Angeles$\}$
   $B = \{$registered Democrats in Los Angeles over 50 years old$\}$
   $C = \{$registered women voters in Los Angeles$\}$
9. $A = N$, $B = W$, $C = \{n \in N: n$ is an odd number$\}$
10. $A = \{$students at O.K. College$\}$
    $B = \{$seniors at O.K. College$\}$
    $C = \{$mathematics majors at O.K. College$\}$
11. State appropriate universal sets for each of problems 7 through 10.
12. Let $U = W$, $A = \{2, 4, 6, \ldots, 20\}$, $B = \{10, 11, 12, \ldots, 17\}$, and
    $C = \{1, 3, 5, \ldots, 19\}$.   Which of the following statements are true?
    (a) $A \cup B \subseteq U$ (b) $A \cup B \subseteq A$
    (c) $A \cup B \subseteq B$ (d) $A \cap B \subseteq U$
    (e) $A \cap B \subseteq B$ (f) $A \cap B = B$
    (g) $A \cap (B \cup C) = (A \cap B) \cup (A \cap C)$
    (h) $A \cup (B \cap C) = (A \cup B) \cap (A \cup C)$
    (i) $A \cup B = A$ (j) $A \cup (B \cup C) \subseteq U$
    (k) $A \cup (B \cup C) \subseteq B \cup C$ (l) $(A \cap B) \cap C \subseteq U$
    (m) $(A \cap B) \cap C \subseteq C$
13. Repeat problem 12 with $U = W$ and letting A, B, and C be any subsets of U.
14. What restriction must be placed on set B of problem 12(i) to make that generalization true?
15. Let A be any set.   Which of the following statements are true?
    (a) $A \cup A = A$ (b) $A \cap A = A$ (c) $A \cap \varnothing = A$
    (d) $A \cup \varnothing = \varnothing$ (e) $A \cup \varnothing = A$ (f) $A \cap \varnothing = \varnothing$
16. Let U be the following set of differently colored paints.
    $U = \{$white, black, blue, red, yellow$\}$
    Let M be the binary operation of mixing two colors to obtain a third color.

(a) Is M closed in U?

(b) Is M commutative?

(c) Is M associative?

(d) Does M have an identity element in U?

17. True or false? For each of the sets, A, B, and C, $(A \cup B) \cup C = A \cup (B \cup C) = (A \cup C) \cup B$. Explain your answer.

18. In what way can the expression "$A \cap B \cap C \cap D$" be made meaningful?

19. Use Venn diagrams to illustrate that, for each of the sets, A, B, and C, $B \cup A = A \cup B$ and $(A \cap B) \cap C = A \cap (B \cap C)$.

20. Use the definitions of union and of intersection to show that $A \cup B = B \cup A$ and $A \cap B = B \cap A$ for each of the sets A and B.

2.4 The Cartesian Product

Consider this problem. You have two chairs, call them r and s, and three differently colored paints, call them a, b, and c. How many different pairs of the type "(chair, paint)" can you have? After some thought you might conclude that, since there are two chairs and each chair can be painted in any one of the three colors, you can form six pairs

$$(r, a), (r, b), (r, c), (s, a), (s, b), (s, c)$$

This set of six pairs could also have been obtained directly if you simply tried to list every possible combination of r with the given colors and every combination of s with the given colors.

Consider the problem again, but stated differently. Given set $A = \{r, s\}$ and set $B = \{a, b, c\}$, form the set C of ordered pairs of the type (element in A, element in B). Stated in this way the problem becomes one of combining the sets A and B in a "certain way" to form a third set C,

$$C = \{(r, a), (r, b), (r, c), (s, a), (s, b), (s, c)\}$$

The set C is called the *Cartesian product* of A and B and is denoted "$A \times B$."

The Cartesian product, $A \times B$, of two sets A and B is the set of all ordered pairs (a, b) such that $a \in A$ and $b \in B$. Symbolically, $A \times B = \{(a, b): a \in A \text{ and } b \in B\}$.

(*Note:* The operation Cartesian product is a binary operation.)

Example: Suppose $U = W$, $A = \{1, 2\}$, and $B = \{1, 2, 3\}$.
Find $A \times B$ and $B \times A$.

Solution: $A \times B = \{(1, 1), (1, 2), (1, 3), (2, 1), (2, 2), (2, 3)\}$
$B \times A = \{(1, 1), (1, 2), (2, 1), (2, 2), (3, 1), (3, 2)\}$
A graphic representation of the Cartesian product sets $A \times B$
and $B \times A$ is shown in Figure 2.8. Note that the sets $A \times B$
and $B \times A$ are equivalent but not equal. (Why?)

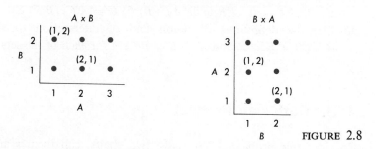

FIGURE 2.8

Example: Let $U = \{$Frank, Irv, Bill, Mary, Janet, Phyliss$\}$,
$F = \{$Frank, Irv, Bill$\}$, and $G = \{$Mary, Janet, Phyliss$\}$.
Find $F \times G$ and $G \times F$. Are the sets $F \times G$ and $G \times F$ equal?
Are they equivalent?

Solution: $F \times G = \{$(Frank, Mary), (Frank, Janet), (Frank, Phyliss),
(Irv, Mary), (Irv, Janet), (Irv, Phyliss),
(Bill, Mary), (Bill, Janet), (Bill, Phyliss)$\}$
$G \times F = \{$(Mary, Frank), (Mary, Irv), (Mary, Bill),
(Janet, Frank), (Janet, Irv), (Janet, Bill),
(Phyliss, Frank), (Phyliss, Irv), (Phyliss, Bill)$\}$
$F \times G \neq G \times F$, $F \times G$ is equivalent to $G \times F$.

Now we ask whether the operation Cartesian product has the same
properties as the binary operations union and intersection. The two previous examples show that the Cartesian product sets $A \times B$, $B \times A$, $F \times G$,
and $G \times F$ are not subsets of U. Consequently, forming the Cartesian
product of two subsets A and B of a universal set U is not a closed operation
in U. It is also apparent from these two examples that Cartesian product
is not a commutative operation.

As was the case for union and intersection, the expression "$A \times B \times C$"
is meaningless unless we first associate two of the sets A and B or B and C.
Thus if we interpret "$A \times B \times C$" as "$(A \times B) \times C$" or "$A \times (B \times C)$"

we can ask if Cartesian product is an associative operation. The following example shows that it is not.

Example: Let $U = W$, $A = \{1, 2\}$, $B = \{3, 4\}$, $C = \{5\}$. Then

$$(A \times B) \times C = \{(1, 3), (1, 4), (2, 3), (2, 4)\} \times \{5\}$$
$$= \{[(1, 3), 5], [(1, 4), 5], [(2, 3), 5], [(2, 4), 5]\}$$
$$A \times (B \times C) = \{1, 2\} \times \{(3, 5), (4, 5)\}$$
$$= \{[1, (3, 5)], [1, (4, 5)], [2, (3, 5)], [2, (4, 5)]\}$$

Thus $(A \times B) \times C \neq A \times (B \times C)$.

We leave it to you to refer to the definition of Cartesian product to convince yourself that the following statement is true. If U is some universal set and A is any nonempty subset of U, there is no subset B of U such that $A \times B = A$. In other words the operation Cartesian product does not have an identity property, since an identity element cannot be found.

Let us look again at the first two examples of this section. This time we concern ourselves with the number of elements in the sets A, B, F, G, and the corresponding Cartesian product sets. Let $n(A)$ mean the number of elements in the set A, or the cardinality of A. In the first example, then, $n(A) = 2$, $n(B) = 3$, and $n(A \times B) = n(B \times A) = 6$. In the second example, $n(F) = n(G) = 3$ and $n(F \times G) = n(G \times F) = 9$. Although we cannot say that Cartesian product is a commutative operation, we can state that, for each two sets A and B, the cardinality of $A \times B$ is equal to the cardinality of $B \times A$.

In the third example it was shown that $n(A \times [B \times C]) = n([A \times B] \times C) = 4$, and we can assert that although Cartesian product is not an associative operation in U, the cardinality of $(A \times B) \times C$ is equal to the cardinality of $A \times (B \times C)$.

Again we emphasize that the examples do not prove that, for subsets A, B, and C of some universal set U,

$$n(A \times B) = n(B \times A) \text{ and } n([A \times B] \times C) = n(A \times [B \times C])$$

They serve only to illustrate these properties.

Let us now consider one more

Example: Let $U = W$, $A = \{1, 2, 3\}$, $B = \{1\}$.

Then $A \times B = \{(1, 1), (2, 1), (3, 1)\}$,

$n(A) = 3$, $n(B) = 1$, and $n(A \times B) = 3$ (see Figure 2.9).

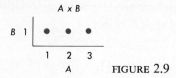

FIGURE 2.9

This last example suggests that even though Cartesian product is a binary operation that does not enjoy the identity property, the cardinality of $A \times B$ will always be equal to the cardinality of A if the cardinality of B is one. That is, for each two sets A and B, if $n(B) = 1$, then $n(A \times B) = n(A)$.

Now we ask for $n(A \times B)$ if $A \neq \emptyset$ and $B = \emptyset$. $A \times B$ is the set of all ordered pairs (a, b) such that a is a member of A and b is a member of B. But if B is the empty set, there is no member b in B to pair with each element a in A. Therefore $A \times B = \emptyset$ and the cardinality of this Cartesian product is zero.

Exercises 2.4

Figures 2.8 and 2.9 are called *arrays* or *graphs*. Draw an array to illustrate the Cartesian product $A \times B$ for each of the following pairs of sets.

1. $A = \{a, b, c\}$ $B = \{x, y\}$
2. $A = \{$black, red$\}$ $B = \{$black, white, yellow$\}$
3. What is $n(A \times B)$ in problem 1?
4. What is $n(B \times A)$ in problem 2?
5. What is $n(A \times B)$ if $A = \{$states in the United States$\}$ and $B = \{$Albany, Sacramento$\}$?
6. What is the cardinality of $A \times B$ if $A = \{$whole numbers$\}$ and $B = \{5, 10, 20\}$?

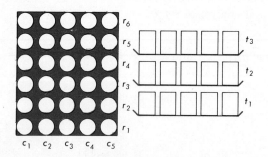

7. The figure represents the top and front views of a stack of trays filled with glasses. Suppose $A = \{r_1, r_2, r_3, r_4, r_5, r_6\}$, $B =$

$\{c_1, c_2, \ldots, c_6\}$, and $C = \{t_1, t_2, t_3\}$. Find $n[(A \times B) \times C]$, $n[A \times (B \times C)]$, $n[(A \times C) \times B]$, and $n[A \times (C \times B)]$.

Suppose A, B, and C are any subsets of some universal set U. Which of the following statements are true?

8. $A \times B = B \times A$.

9. $(A \times B) \times C = A \times (B \times C)$.

10. $(A \times B) \times C \neq A \times (B \times C)$.

11. $n(A \times B) = n(B \times A)$.

12. $n(A \times \emptyset) = 0$.

13. If $n(B) = 1$, then $n(A \times B) = 1$.

14. $n[A \times (B \times C)] \neq n[(A \times B) \times C]$.

15. $A \times B \neq B \times A$.

16. The binary operation Cartesian product is associative.

17. The binary operation Cartesian product is not commutative.

Complete the following statements.

18. The Cartesian product $A \times B$ is a set of _____.

19. $A \times B = B \times A$ if and only if _____.

20. The Cartesian product $A \times \emptyset$ is always _____.

21. The cardinality of the Cartesian product of the sets A and B, where $n(A)$ is infinite and $n(B)$ is finite, is always _____.

22. Let $A = \{n \in N : n \leq 10\}$ and $B = \{n \in N : n < 6\}$.

     (a) Find $A \times B$ and illustrate it with an array.

     (b) Let $R = \{(x, y) \in A \times B : y < x\}$. List the elements of R and indicate the elements of R on your array for $A \times B$.

23. Using the definitions of Cartesian product and union, supply an argument to show that, for each of the sets, A, B, and C, $A \times (B \cup C) = (A \times B) \cup (A \times C)$.

2.5 Summary

Sets can be combined by certain operations. Forming the union of two sets A and B often results in a larger set than either A or B, while forming the intersection of sets A and B frequently results in a set smaller than either A or B. Each operation is performed on two sets to obtain a third set. Hence they are binary operations.

Cartesian product is a third binary operation discussed in this chapter. The elements of the Cartesian product of A and B, unlike the elements of either the union or intersection of A and B, are not elements of A or of B. The elements are ordered pairs (a, b) where $a \in A$ and $b \in B$.

The operations union and intersection enjoy the properties of commutativity and associativity, which have to do with the order and manner in which sets can be combined. If two sets are combined under either operation, a third set of the same kind is formed and, by definition, each operation has the closure property. The operation union also enjoys an identity property, since it has an identity element, the empty set.

Cartesian product has none of the above properties. If, however, you concern yourself with the cardinalities of the sets A, B, and $A \times B$, you then find that:

1. $n(A \times B) = n(B \times A)$.
2. $n[(A \times B) \times C] = n[A \times (B \times C)]$.
3. if $n(B) = 1$, then $n(A \times B) = n(A)$.

Exercises 2.5—Review

Complete each sentence.

1. When discussing sets, we assume they are subsets of an all-inclusive set called the _____.
2. A diagram depicting the relationships between sets is called (a)n _____.
3. If two sets have no common elements, they are _____.
4. An operation that combines two sets to form a third set is called a(n) _____.
5. The set that is formed from the sets A and B and whose elements are either in A or in B or in both sets is called the _____ of A and B.
6. The elements of the set $A \times B$ are _____.
7. Since intersection is a commutative operation, we obtain the same result if we intersect A with B or if we intersect _____.
8. If A and B are subsets of the universal set U, the elements of $A \times B$ are _____ in U. Therefore we say that Cartesian product is not a _____ operation in U.
9. It is always true that $A \cap B$ is a _____ of either A or B.
10. It is possible to form the union of the sets A, B, and C by grouping them as $(A \cup B) \cup C$ or $A \cup (B \cup C)$. The _____ property of the operation union guarantees that the sets formed are equal.

11. Draw a Venn diagram to illustrate the relationships between the sets
    $U = \{$natural numbers$\}$
    $A = \{1, 2, 3, 4, 5, 6\}$
    $B = \{1, 3, 5, 7, 8, 9, 10, 11\}$
    $C = \{2, 3, 4, 7, 10, 11\}$
12. Are A and B of problem 11 disjoint sets? A and C? B and C?

Use problem 11 to

13. List the elements of $A \cap B$.
14. List the elements of $A \cup B$.
15. List the elements of $A \cap (B \cap C)$.
16. List the elements of $(A \cup B) \cup C$.

Find an appropriate universal set for each pair of sets.

17. $\{0, 2, 3\}$ and $\{100, 101, 108, 250\}$
18. $\{$dogs$\}$ and $\{$dachshunds$\}$
19. $\{$Mississippi River, Missouri River$\}$ and $\{$Lake Michigan, Lake Tahoe$\}$

Let $U = \{n \in N: 5 < n < 18\}$
    $A = \{n \in N: 6 < n < 12\}$
    $B = \{n \in N: 8 < n < 11 \text{ or } 13 < n < 17\}$
    $C = \{9, 10, 11, 12, 13, 14, 15\}$.

20. List the elements of $A \cap B$.
21. List the elements of $B \cup C$.
22. List the elements of $(A \cup B) \cup C$.
23. List the elements of $B \cap C$.
24. List the elements of $(A \cap B) \cap C$.
25. Draw a Venn diagram for each of the sets listed above.

Let U be some universal set and A, B, and C be subsets of U. Indicate whether each of the following general statements is true or false. If you declare a statement false, provide a counterexample to support your claim.

26. $A \cup B \cup C \subseteq U$ 27. $A \cup B \subseteq A$
28. $A \cap \varnothing = A$ 29. $A \cup \varnothing = A$
30. $B \cap B = \varnothing$ 31. $B \cap B = B$

With U, A, B, and C the same sets used in problems 20 through 25, show that:

32. $A \cup B = B \cup A$ 33. $A \cap B = B \cap A$
34. $(A \cup B) \cup C = A \cup (B \cup C)$

35. $(A \cap B) \cap C = A \cap (B \cap C)$
36. $(A \cap B) \cap C \subseteq C$ **37.** $C \subset A \cup (B \cup C)$
38. $A \cap (B \cup C) = (A \cap B) \cup (A \cap C)$
39. $A \cap (B \cap C) = (A \cup B) \cap (A \cup C)$

Let $A = \{a, b\}$, $B = \{r\}$, $C = \{w, x, y\}$. List the elements of:

40. $A \times B$ **41.** $B \times A$
42. $(A \times B) \times C$ **43.** $B \times C$
44. $A \times C$ **45.** $A \times (B \times C)$

Use the above sets to answer the following questions.

46. Determine the number of elements in each of the sets in problems 40 through 45.
47. Does $n(A \times B) = n(B \times A)$?
48. Does $n(A) \cdot n(B) = n(A \times B)$?
49. Does $n[(A \times B) \times C] = n[A \times (B \times C)]$?
50. Does $n[(A \times B) \times C] = n(A) \cdot n(C) + n(B) \cdot n(C)$?
51. Does $n[A \times (B \times C)] = n(A) \cdot n(B) + n(A) \cdot n(C)$?
52. Why does $n(B \times C) = n(C)$ and $n(A \times B) = n(A)$?

chapter three

WHOLE NUMBERS

3.0 Introduction

The text might have properly begun with the sentence "This is *how* we add." A set of rules would have followed and we would have been on our way. Such an approach leaves the student unaware of any sense of the historical development of arithmetic. Addition is one of the achievements of that development. It evolved from the more primitive notions of sets and counting and it is this development that we attempt to show in this chapter.

The operation of addition on two whole numbers arises naturally from a discussion of the union of two disjoint sets whose cardinalities are the numbers to be added. Hence we will find that the addition operation enjoys many of the properties of the set operation union. These properties will be used to construct an addition algorithm, which is a plan, or a set of rules, for performing the operation of addition.

The multiplication operation will be developed from the set operation Cartesian product, and an algorithm will be constructed from this operation.

Finally, we shall define the operations of subtraction and division as the "inverse," or "undoing," operations for addition and multiplication, respectively.

3.1 Addition

Consider the following.

Example: Let $A = \{$Bill, Mary, John$\}$ and $B = \{$Carl, Alice$\}$. Then $A \cup B = \{$Bill, Mary, John, Carl, Alice$\}$ and A and B are disjoint sets since $A \cap B = \varnothing$. Also $n(A) = 3$, $n(B) = 2$, and $n(A \cup B) = 5$.

If A and B are any two disjoint sets, we shall call the number associated with $A \cup B$ the *sum* of the numbers associated with sets A and B. The process or operation of finding a sum of two numbers is a binary operation called *addition*, and is denoted by the plus sign, "$+$". In the preceding example we say the sum of 3 and 2 is 5, written $3 + 2 = 5$. The numbers being added are called the *addends*.

Suppose now that we wish to add 26 and 10. Our definition tells us to find two disjoint sets A and B such that $n(A) = 26$ and $n(B) = 10$, then form the union of A and B. To obtain a simple name for $26 + 10$, we must then *count* the elements in $A \cup B$. Choosing $A = \{$letters in the English alphabet$\}$ and $B = \{0, 1, 2, \ldots, 9\}$, we find that $A \cap B = \varnothing$ and $A \cup B = \{a, b, c, \ldots, y, z, 0, 1, 2, \ldots, 9\}$. Hence $n(A) = 26$, $n(B) = 10$, and, by counting, $n(A \cup B) = 36$. Thus we have

$$n(A) + n(B) = n(A \cup B)$$

or, equivalently, $26 + 10 = 36$.

Finding the sum of two large numbers by using the definition of addition directly is a tedious process. We shall instead use the definition to describe, in Section 3.2, certain properties of addition and then use these properties to develop a simpler method for computing sums.

The number line provides us with an excellent visual interpretation of the addition process. Figure 3.1 illustrates that 5 is the measure of a segment obtained by combining two segments, one of measure 3 and one of measure 2, in a head-to-tail fashion. When this process is begun at the zero point, the coordinate of the head of the last segment is the desired sum.

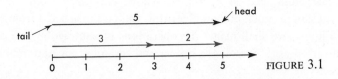

FIGURE 3.1

Exercises 3.1

For each pair of values of a and b given below, name two sets A and B such that $n(A) = a$, and $n(B) = b$. Then use these two sets to solve the sentence "$a + b = n(A \cup B)$."

1. $a = 3$, $b = 7$ **2.** $a = 5$, $b = 11$
3. $a = 0$, $b = 23$ **4.** $a = 18$, $b = 8$
5. $a = 6$, $b = 6$ **6.** $a = 9$, $b = 0$

Consider the following sets:

$A = \{$Alabama, Alaska, Arizona, Arkansas$\}$
$B = \{$Bismark, Boston$\}$
$C = \{1, 4, 7, 10, 13, 16, 19\}$
$D = \{r, s, t, u, v, w, x, y, z\}$
$E = \{4, 9, 14, 19, \ldots, 54\}$
$F = \{101, 103, 105, 107, \ldots, 145\}$

In each of the following problems, find the number associated with the indicated set.

7. $A \cup B$ **8.** $B \cup C$ **9.** $E \cup D$
10. $D \cup F$ **11.** $C \cup B$ **12.** $F \cup E$
13. $F \cup C$ **14.** $E \cup E$ **15.** $E \cup F$
16. $F \cup D$ **17.** $(A \cup B) \cup C$ **18.** $(D \cup E) \cup F$
19. $(C \cup D) \cup F$ **20.** $(B \cup F) \cup D$ **21.** $D \cup (E \cup F)$
22. $C \cup (D \cup F)$ **23.** $B \cup (F \cup D)$ **24.** $A \cup (D \cup F)$
25. $(A \cup D) \cup F$ **26.** $(F \cup D) \cup C$ **27.** $(E \cup D) \cup F$

For each of the following problems, compute the indicated sum. Then draw a number-line diagram to illustrate the corresponding addition fact.

28. $6 + 5$ **29.** $4 + 9$ **30.** $7 + 8$
31. $8 + 3$ **32.** $9 + 4$ **33.** $11 + 17$
34. $24 + 45$ **35.** $63 + 87$ **36.** $67 + 83$
37. $45 + 24$ **38.** $137 + 432$ **39.** $246 + 642$
40. $942 + 58$ **41.** $58 + 942$ **42.** $958 + 42$
43. $1 + (2 + 3)$ **44.** $(1 + 2) + 3$ **45.** $(3 + 6) + 9$
46. $9 + (6 + 3)$ **47.** $(7 + 8) + 9$ **48.** $7 + (8 + 9)$

In each of the following problems, replace the letter by a numeral for a whole number so that the resulting sentence is true·

49. $5 + 9 = n$ **50.** $7 + 6 = m$ **51.** $9 + 6 = k$
52. $5 + 5 = p$ **53.** $7 + 9 = q$ **54.** $7 + x = 19$
55. $8 + y = 24$ **56.** $r = 7 + 16$ **57.** $s + 8 = 8$
58. $16 + g = 16$ **59.** $17 = f + 17$ **60.** $9 + n = 6 + 9$
61. $m + 8 = 8 + m$ **62.** $19 = 8 + h$ **63.** $y + 18 = 18 + y$

3.2 Properties of Addition

Now let us use the definition of addition to obtain some of the properties of the addition of whole numbers. The definition of addition states that $a + b$ is $n(A \cup B)$, where $n(A) = a$ and $n(B) = b$ and $A \cap B = \varnothing$. But $n(A \cup B)$ is a whole number, as are a and b. Thus we have the

Closure Property

The sum of each pair of whole numbers is a whole number.

Suppose now that A and B are two sets such that $n(A) = a$ and $n(B) = b$. Since we know that $A \cup B = B \cup A$, it follows that

$$\begin{aligned}
a + b &= n(A) + n(B) \\
&= n(A \cup B) \\
&= n(B \cup A) \\
&= n(B) + n(A) \\
&= b + a
\end{aligned}$$

Hence for addition of whole numbers we have the

Commutative Property

For each of the whole numbers a and b, $a + b = b + a$. That is, the order in which two whole numbers are added does not affect their sum.

The commutative property of addition of whole numbers is easily illustrated using the number line (see Figure 3.2).

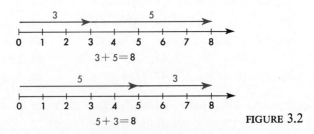

FIGURE 3.2

Addition, we noted, is a binary operation. How then do we add three numbers? What does "$a + b + c$" mean? Since we can only operate on two numbers at a time, "$a + b + c$" is meaningful as "$(a + b) + c$" or as "$a + (b + c)$." But does $(a + b) + c = a + (b + c)$? Let A, B, and C be three mutually disjoint sets, that is $A \cap B = \varnothing$, $A \cap C = \varnothing$, and $B \cap C = \varnothing$. Let $n(A) = a$, $n(B) = b$, and $n(C) = c$. Since, for each three sets, A, B, and C, $(A \cup B) \cup C = A \cup (B \cup C)$, we have

$$
\begin{aligned}
(a + b) + c &= [n(A) + n(B)] + n(C) \\
&= n(A \cup B) + n(C) \\
&= n[(A \cup B) \cup C] \\
&= n[A \cup (B \cup C)] \\
&= n(A) + n(B \cup C) \\
&= n(A) + [n(B) + n(C)] \\
&= a + (b + c)
\end{aligned}
$$

Consequently, we can state the

Associative Property

For each of the whole numbers, a, b, and c, $(a + b) + c = a + (b + c)$.

The number line is again useful in illustrating the associative property of addition of whole numbers (see Figure 3.3).

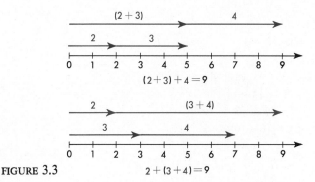

FIGURE 3.3

Next we ask if there is some number that can be added to any first number so that the sum is that first number. That is, is there a number b such that, for any number a, $a + b = a$? To answer this, suppose again that A is any set with $n(A) = a$. Since $n(\varnothing) = 0$ and $A \cup \varnothing = A$, we have

$$a + 0 = n(A \cup \varnothing)$$
$$= n(A)$$
$$= a$$

This fact is called the

Identity Property

For each whole number a, a + 0 = a.

The number 0 is called the *additive identity* element for the set of whole numbers.

Exercises 3.2

Each of the following sentences is an instance of one of the following properties of addition of whole numbers: the commutative property, the associative property, the identity property. For each sentence, identify the property and verify that the sentence is true.

1. $6 + 7 = 7 + 6$
2. $8 + 0 = 8$
3. $(7 + 8) + 9 = 7 + (8 + 9)$
4. $9 + 0 = 0 + 9$
5. $0 + 0 = 0$
6. $(5 + 0) + 7 = 5 + (0 + 7)$
7. $19 + 74 = 74 + 19$
8. $57 = 57 + 0$
9. $687 + 0 = 687$
10. $18 + (42 + 55) = (18 + 42) + 55$
11. $(14 + 3) + 0 = 14 + 3$
12. $(4 + 3) + 7 = 4 + (3 + 7)$
13. $6 + (4 + 8) = (6 + 4) + 8$
14. $(4 + 8) + 2 = 4 + (8 + 2)$
15. $(33 + 12) + (7 + 4) = (7 + 4) + (33 + 12)$

Which of the following sentences are true?

16. $0 + 8 = 8$ 17. $0 + 17 = 17$
18. $93 = 0 + 93$ 19. $543 = 0 + 543$

20. On the basis of problems 16 through 19, it seems reasonable that, for each whole number a, $0 + a = a$. Using the basic properties

discussed in this section, provide an argument to support this assertion.

21. Here is the start of a table of addition facts for the whole numbers zero through nine. For example, the entry in the fourth row and sixth column of the body of the table is the sum of 3 and 5 and corresponds to the addition fact "$3 + 5 = 8$." Copy and complete the table.

+	0	1	2	3	4	5	6	7	8	9
0		1								
1							7			
2				5						
3						8				
4									12	
5			7							
6										15
7	7									
8					12					
9								16		

22. Imagine a diagonal line being drawn from the upper left corner of the table to the lower right corner. What do you note about the corresponding entries on either side of this line ? What property of addition of whole numbers supports this observation ?

23. What property of addition is suggested by the first column and first row in the body of your addition table ?

Fill in the blank in each of the following sentences to make true statements. The domain of each variable is the set of whole numbers.

24. $3 + (\_\_ + 4) = (3 + k) + 4$
25. $\_\_ + r = r$
26. $p + 3 = \_\_ + p$
27. $k + (4 + 3) = 7 + \_\_$

Each of the following sentences is true because it is a consequence of one or more of the properties of addition of whole numbers. For each sentence, name the property or properties.

28. $687 = 0 + 687$

29. $(5 + 2) + (1 + 0) = (2 + 5) + 1$

30. $(8 + 4) + 2 = 4 + (8 + 2)$

31. $3 + (2 + 5) = (2 + 5) + 3$

32. $(8 + 6) + 10 = 8 + (10 + 6)$

33. $21 + (0 + 6) = 6 + 21$

34. $(14 + 7) + 9 = 14 + (7 + 9)$

35. $(14 + 7) + (6 + 23) = (14 + 6) + (7 + 23)$

36. We defined a binary operation on the set of whole numbers as a process whereby two whole numbers are combined in a certain way to form a third number. Two binary operations are given below. For each operation, determine, for the set of whole numbers, if it (i) is closed, (ii) is commutative, (iii) is associative, (iv) has an identity element in the set of whole numbers.

    (a) L is the binary operation that selects the larger of a pair of whole numbers. Examples: $4 \text{ L } 10 = 10$, $6 \text{ L } 2 = 6$, $7 \text{ L } 7 = 7$.

    (b) T is the binary operation that adds twice the second number to the first. Examples: $2 \text{ T } 3 = 8$, $3 \text{ T } 2 = 7$, $5 \text{ T } 4 = 13$.

For which of the following subsets of whole numbers is ordinary addition of whole numbers a closed operation?

37. $\{2, 4, 6, 8, \ldots\}$ **38.** $\{0, 1, 2, 3\}$

39. $\{5, 10, 15, 20, 25, \ldots\}$ **40.** $\{10, 20, 30, 40, \ldots\}$

41. $\{3, 6, 9, \ldots, 96\}$ **42.** $\{0\}$

43. $\{0, 1\}$

44. Do your answers to problems 37 through 43 suggest a general pattern concerning the closure of addition in subsets of whole numbers?

45. One way to obtain the sum of four numbers, a, b, c, and d, is to make the following associations:

$$[(a + b) + (c + d)] = n$$

The sets of inner parentheses indicate that we first associate a and b and compute $a + b$ and then we associate c and d and compute $c + d$. Finally n is found by adding these sums.

    Use parentheses as was done in the preceding discussion to show how you might find the sum of the elements of the following set of whole numbers: $\{3, 4, 7, 8, 14, 6, 5\}$.

3.3 Subtraction

Every day we perform certain operations that can be "undone." Putting on your shoes can be undone by taking off your shoes. Closing a book can be undone by opening the book. A pair of operations that undo each other are called *inverse operations*. In mathematics we find many pairs of inverse operations. As a first example, we shall define the operation *subtraction*, denoted by the minus sign, "$-$," to be the inverse of the operation of addition. That is, for each of the whole numbers, a, b, and c,

$$a - b = c \text{ if and only if* } c + b = a.$$

Example: The sentence "$6 - 4 = n$" has a solution if and only if we can find a whole number n such that $n + 4 = 6$. Since the sum of 2 and 4 is 6, we can state that $6 - 4 = 2$.

To solve a subtraction problem amounts to solving an addition problem knowing an addend and the sum. The missing addend is the result of subtraction and is called the *difference*.

Example: Solve "$8 - 5 = n$."

Solution: First restate the subtraction problem as the corresponding addition problem "$n + 5 = 8$." To what whole number can we add 5 to obtain a sum of 8? Since $3 + 5 = 8$, we have $8 - 5 = 3$.

Example: Solve "$4 - 6 = n$."

Solution: Restating the sentence as an addition statement "$n + 6 = 4$," we see that there is no whole number whose sum with 6 is 4. Hence the sentence "$4 - 6 = n$" has no whole-number solution.

The last example indicates that subtraction of whole numbers cannot always be performed. For "$a - b$" to name a whole number, a must be a whole number greater than or equal to the whole number b.

The binary operation subtraction is illustrated in Figure 3.4.

*Here again is the phrase "if and only if," which was discussed on page 17. In this context it means "if $a - b = c$, then $c + b = a$" as well as "if $c + b = a$, then $a - b = c$."

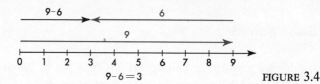

9-6=3   FIGURE 3.4

Question: Figure 3.1 is accompanied by a discussion that interprets addition as a combining of line segments. Can such an interpretation be made for subtraction using Figure 3.4?

Question: Figures 3.1 and 3.4 illustrate addition and subtraction, respectively. Can you use these figures to interpret addition and subtraction in terms of counting?

Exercises 3.3

Find a word or phrase that correctly completes each of the following sentences.

1. Subtraction is a(n) _____ operation.
2. The whole number b can be subtracted from the whole number a if and only if _____.
3. The result of subtracting _____ from a is a.
4. Addition and subtraction of whole numbers are _____ operations.
5. When b is subtracted from c, the result is called the _____ between c and b.
6. If any whole number is subtracted from itself, the difference is _____.

Each of the following generalizations about subtraction is false. For each statement, provide a counterexample to verify its falsity.

7. Subtraction of whole numbers is a closed operation.
8. Subtraction of whole numbers is a commutative operation.
9. Subtraction of whole numbers is an associative operation.

The inverse relationship between addition and subtraction is suggested by each of the following sentences. Fill in the blanks in these sentences to make true statements.

10. $(5 + 8) - \_\_ = 5$ 11. $(13 + 26) - 26 = \_\_$
12. $(10 + \_\_) - 7 = 10$ 13. $(\_\_ + 9) - 9 = \_\_$
14. $(7 - 2) + \_\_ = 7$ 15. $(23 - 4) + 4 = \_\_$
16. $(19 - \_\_) + 3 = 19$ 17. $(\_\_ - 8) + 8 = \_\_$

Solve the following sentences graphically. That is, use the number line as was done in Figure 3.4 to find n. $n \in W$.

18. $12 - 7 = n$ **19.** $26 - 18 = n$
20. $13 - n = 5$ **21.** $n - 14 = 16$
22. $32 - 19 = n$ **23.** $18 - n = 7$
24. $16 - n = 20$ **25.** $n - 12 = 9$

For each of the whole numbers, x and y, tell whether $x < y$, $x > y$, or $x = y$ in each of the following sentences.

26. $8 + x = y$ **27.** $x - 3 = y$
28. $(5 + x) - y = 4$ **29.** $(0 + x) - y = 0$
30. $x + 6 = y - 5$ **31.** $x = y - x$
32. $x + y = x + x$ **33.** $(x + 3) - y = (y + 3)$

For each of the following operations, state the inverse operation if one exists.

34. Opening a door.   **35.** Driving to work.
36. Boiling an egg.   **37.** Cutting down a tree.
38. Turning on a light.   **39.** Tying a knot.
40. Raising children.   **41.** Walking 2 miles due north.

3.4 The Addition Algorithm

We have spent some time discussing the operation of addition. We know that to find the sum of two numbers, say 639 and 437, we need only to determine the number of elements in the union of two disjoint sets A and B such that $n(A) = 639$ and $n(B) = 437$. But how is that done? Certainly counting will work, but the labor involved is time-consuming.

$639 + 437 = (600 + 30 + 9) + (400 + 30 + 7)$	[the numbers 639 and 437 are renamed]
$= (600 + 400) + (30 + 30) + (9 + 7)$	[the commutative and associate properties of addition allow us to regroup the numbers]
$= 1000 + 60 + 16$	[$6 + 4 = 10$, $3 + 3 = 6$, $9 + 7 = 16$]
$= 1000 + 60 + (10 + 6)$	[16 is renamed as $10 + 6$]
$= 1000 + (60 + 10) + 6$	[regroup again using the associative property]
$= 1000 + 70 + 6$	[$6 + 1 = 7$]
$= 1076$	[rename $1000 + 70 + 6$]

FIGURE 3.5

What we need is a process for finding a sum without counting. Such a process is called an *algorithm* for addition. A step-by-step development of the algorithm and the reasons for each step are shown in Figure 3.5. A shorthand description of the addition algorithm is shown in Figure 3.6.

639

+ 437

(9 + 7) ones	16		639
(3 + 3) tens	60	partial sums	+437
(6 + 4) hundreds	1000		1076
	1076		FIGURE 3.6

The step-by-step approach to the addition algorithm illustrated in Figure 3.5 is designed to emphasize that first, to add whole numbers, one must commit to memory the facts of addition for the numbers zero through nine (see the table on page 49), and that second, the addition algorithm is dependent upon the properties of addition of whole numbers discussed in Section 3.2.

Exercises 3.4

Use the step-by-step procedure of Figure 3.5 to solve each of the following sentences. $n \in W$.

1. $26 + 12 = n$ **2.** $58 + 46 = n$
3. $268 + 31 = n$ **4.** $23 + 198 = n$

Use the addition algorithm to solve the following sentences. $n \in W$.

5. $42 + 16 = n$ **6.** $38 + 156 = n$
7. $240 + 376 = n$ **8.** $8464 + 798 = n$
9. $10{,}096 + 7758 = n$ **10.** $9874 + 7498 = n$

11. Observe that each addend in problems 5 to 10 were even numbers. Does this suggest some general pattern about the addition of two even numbers?

Solve each of the following sentences. $n \in W$.

12. $11 + 15 = n$ **13.** $27 + 35 = n$
14. $151 + 87 = n$ **15.** $7063 + 5841 = n$
16. $21{,}009 + 63{,}547 = n$ **17.** $12{,}345 + 54{,}321 = n$

18. Observe that each addend in problems 12 through 17 were odd numbers. Does this suggest some general pattern about the addition of two odd numbers?

Solve each of the following sentences. $n \in W$.

19. $10 + 15 = n$ 20. $27 + 36 = n$
21. $151 + 84 = n$ 22. $7063 + 5848 = n$
23. $1056 + 2385 = n$ 24. $85{,}633 + 398 = n$

25. What general pattern about addition of whole numbers is suggested by problems 19 through 24?

Solve the following sentences. $n \in W$.

26. $10 + 20 = n$ 27. $50 + 170 = n$
28. $500 + 980 = n$ 29. $4760 + 53{,}680 = n$

30. How are the sentences in problems 26 through 29 and their solutions related to problem 40 of Exercises 3.2?
31. How are the sentences "$5 + 10 = n$," "$15 + 10 = n$," and "$85 + 35 = n$" related to problem 39 of Exercises 3.2?

Arrange each set of numbers in a column to find the following sums.

32. $7 + 6 + 9$
33. $53 + 69 + 74$
34. $562 + 875 + 761 + 438$
35. $656 + 748 + 203 + 252 + 344$
36. $4785 + 2967 + 5215 + 7133 + 8080$
37. $23{,}456 + 34{,}567 + 45{,}678 + 56{,}789$
38. $437{,}298 + 437{,}702 + 563{,}764 + 563{,}236$
39. $654{,}321 + 754{,}321 + 13{,}642 + 67{,}676$
40. $45 + 873 + 6 + 7983 + 54{,}789 + 564 + 2006$

41. An algorithm for addition called the scratch method is shown below. Determine how it works and use it on problem 35.

$$
\begin{array}{r}
528 \\
315 \\
486 \\
\hline
12\cancel{1}9 \\
\cancel{1}\cancel{1} \\
32
\end{array}
$$

3.5 The Subtraction Algorithm

The inverse relationship between the subtraction and addition operations permits us to restate a subtraction problem as an addition problem. We can, therefore, develop an algorithm for subtraction from the addition algorithm.

Suppose we wish to find the difference $647 - 421$. The number we seek, call it n, is that number whose sum with 421 is 647, that is, $n + 421 = 647$. To find the number n, we can rename it as $a + b + c$, where a is the number of hundreds, b the number of tens, and c the number of ones in n. Now we apply the addition algorithm to $n + 421$ as follows:

$$n + 421 = (a + b + c) + (400 + 20 + 1)$$
$$= (a + 400) + (b + 20) + (c + 1)$$

How do we find a, b, and c? Since $n + 421 = 647$, we can say

$$
\begin{array}{lll}
a + 400 = 600 & \text{or} & 600 - 400 = a \\
b + 20 = 40 & \text{or} & 40 - 20 = b \\
c + 1 = 7 & \text{or} & 7 - 1 = c
\end{array}
$$

Thus

$$647 - 421 = (600 + 40 + 7) - (400 + 20 + 1)$$
$$= n$$
$$= a + b + c$$
$$= (600 - 400) + (40 - 20) + (7 - 1)$$
$$= 200 + 20 + 6$$
$$= 226$$

This problem is illustrated in algorithmic form in Figure 3.7.

Subtraction, like addition, is a simple operation whose algorithm was based on the properties of the addition operation as well as the definition of subtraction. Of course, the algorithm is useless to anyone who does not know the basic subtraction facts for the set of whole numbers. You should develop a table, similar to that shown on page 49, for the subtraction operation.

As a further illustration of the subtraction algorithm, let us compute the difference $917 - 485$. Now

$$917 - 485 = (900 + 10 + 7) - (400 + 80 + 5)$$
$$= (900 - 400) + (10 - 80) + (7 - 5)$$

Before we proceed further, we note that $10 - 80$ does not name any whole number. Let us back up, then, and rewrite 917, not as $900 + 10 + 7$, but as $800 + 100 + 10 + 7$ or, equivalently, $800 + 110 + 7$. Then

$$917 - 485 = (800 + 110 + 7) - (400 + 80 + 5)$$
$$= (800 - 400) + (110 - 80) + (7 - 5)$$
$$= 400 + 30 + 2$$
$$= 432$$

This last example is also illustrated in Figure 3.7.

$$647 - 421 = 226$$

$$
\begin{array}{r}
647 \\
-421 \\
\hline
226
\end{array}
\left[
\begin{array}{l}
= (600 + 40 + 7) \\
= (400 + 20 + 1) \\
= (200 + 20 + 6)
\end{array}
\right]
$$

$$917 - 485 = 432$$

FIGURE 3.7
$$
\begin{array}{r}
917 \\
-485 \\
\hline
432
\end{array}
\left[
\begin{array}{l}
= (900 + 10 + 7) = (800 + 110 + 7) \\
= (400 + 80 + 5) = (400 + 80 + 5) \\
= (400 + 30 + 2)
\end{array}
\right]
$$

An alternative way to find the difference $917 - 485$ is as follows:

$$917 - 485 = (900 + 10 + 7) - (400 + 80 + 5)$$
$$= (900 + 110 + 7) - (500 + 80 + 5)$$
$$= (900 - 500) + (110 - 80) + (7 - 5)$$
$$= 400 + 30 + 2$$
$$= 432$$

Here 10 tens were added to 917, making the sum equivalent to $900 + 110 + 7$, and 1 hundred was added to 485, making the sum equivalent to $500 + 80 + 5$. This method of computing a difference is occasionally referred to as the *equal-additions method*, whereas the first method is usually called the *borrowing method*. You should supply an argument to justify the equal-additions method for subtracting.

Exercises 3.5

Use the step-by-step development preceding Figure 3.7 to solve each of the following sentences. $n \in W$.

1. $78 - 26 = n$ **2.** $485 - 322 = n$
3. $671 - 468 = n$ **4.** $7506 - 687 = n$
5. $2004 - 625 = n$ **6.** $80,060 - 7273 = n$

Use the subtraction algorithm to solve each of the following sentences. $n \in W$.

7. $92 - 51 = n$ **8.** $43 - 18 = n$
9. $315 - 128 = n$ **10.** $800 - 64 = n$
11. $7603 - 856 = n$ **12.** $64,117 - 5860 = n$
13. $746,321 - 635,844 = n$ **14.** $400,001 - 234,567 = n$

15. Complete this table of subtraction facts for the whole numbers zero through nine. The symbol "$*$" has been entered when a difference does not exist.

−	0	1	2	3	4	5	6	7	8	9
0	0			*						
1	1	0					*			
2		1						*		
3										
4	4						*			
5			3		1					*
6										
7						2		0		*
8										
9		8								0

16. How can the addition table of Figure 3.6 be used as a subtraction table?

17. Your answers to problems 11, 18, and 25 of Exercises 3.4 are general statements about the sum of two even numbers, the sum of two odd numbers, and the sum of an even and an odd number. They suggest similar statements about subtraction. Provide these statements and indicate why they are true.

18. The following subtraction algorithm was used in Austria in the nineteenth century and is called the *Austrian method of subtracting*.

Solve $738 - 456 = n$, $n \in W$.

$$
\begin{array}{r}
456 \\
\underline{2} \\
458 \\
\underline{80} \\
538 \\
\underline{200} \\
738
\end{array}
\quad \Big\} \; 282 = n
$$

The algorithm can be performed quickly in the following way.

$$
\begin{array}{r}
738 \\
- 456 \\
\hline
282
\end{array}
$$

6 plus 2 is 8

5 plus 8 is 13 (carry 10 tens to 4 hundreds)

5 plus 2 is 7

Why does this technique work?

Solve the following sentences using the Austrian method for subtracting. $n \in W$.

19. $86 - 48 = n$ **20.** $534 - 276 = n$

21. $8207 - 3645 = n$ **22.** $10{,}883 - 6427 = n$

23. Another subtraction algorithm, the scratch method, is described below.

$$
\begin{array}{r}
635 \\
- 478 \\
\hline
2 \\
16 \\
57
\end{array}
\qquad \text{or} \qquad
\begin{array}{r}
635 \\
- 478 \\
\hline
267 \\
15
\end{array}
$$

Does it work?   Use it to solve $4852 - 3684 = n$, $n \in W$.

3.6 Multiplication

In Chapter Two we discussed the Cartesian product of two sets.   We would like to use this operation on sets to develop the concept of multiplication of two whole numbers.

Suppose $A = \{a, b, c\}$ and $B = \{x, y\}$.   Then $n(A) = 3$ and $n(B) = 2$. Also $A \times B = \{(a, x), (a, y), (b, x), (b, y), (c, x), (c, y)\}$ and $n(A \times B) = 6$. We shall call this number 6 the *product* of 3 and 2.   The numbers 3 and

2 are called *factors* of 6. The process of finding a product of two whole numbers is a binary number operation called *multiplication*.

To be more general, suppose $n(A) = a$ and $n(B) = b$. Then the product, $a \cdot b$, of a and b is the number associated with the set $A \times B$, that is, $a \cdot b = n(A \times B)$. [Read "$a \cdot b$" as "the product of a and b" or "a times b."]

The properties of the operation of multiplication of whole numbers will be considered next.

Closure Property

The product of each pair of whole numbers is a whole number.

The reader should develop an argument similar to the one that supported the closure property for the addition of whole numbers.

Commutative Property

For each of the whole numbers a and b, $a \cdot b = b \cdot a$.

That is, the order in which two whole numbers are multiplied does not affect their product. To verify this, we let A and B be any two sets such that $n(A) = a$ and $n(B) = b$. Since the product $a \cdot b$ is defined as $n(A \times B)$, and, by Section 2.4, $n(A \times B) = n(B \times A)$, we have

$$a \cdot b = n(A \times B)$$
$$= n(B \times A)$$
$$= b \cdot a$$

We now ask how to obtain the product of three whole numbers a, b, and c. Since multiplication is a binary operation we can only multiply two numbers at a time. We must, therefore, as was done for addition, first associate two of the numbers, find their product, and then obtain the product of this number with the remaining number. Specifically, $a \cdot b \cdot c$ is meaningful as $(a \cdot b) \cdot c$ or as $a \cdot (b \cdot c)$.

Example:

$$6 \cdot 3 \cdot 2 = (6 \cdot 3) \cdot 2 = 18 \cdot 2 = 36$$

or

$$6 \cdot 3 \cdot 2 = 6 \cdot (3 \cdot 2) = 6 \cdot 6 = 36$$

This example leads us to suspect that for the operation of multiplication of whole numbers we have an

Associative Property

For each of the whole numbers, a, b, and c, $(a \cdot b) \cdot c = a \cdot (b \cdot c)$.

The validity of the associative property can be established by letting A, B, and C be sets such that $n(A) = a$, $n(B) = b$, and $n(C) = c$. In Section 2.4 we established the fact that $n[(A \times B) \times C] = n[A \times (B \times C)]$. Therefore,

$$(a \cdot b) \cdot c = n[(A \times B) \times C]$$
$$= n[A \times (B \times C)]$$
$$= a \cdot (b \cdot c)$$

Identity Property

For each whole number a, $a \cdot 1 = a$.

The number 1 is called the *multiplicative identity* element for the set of whole numbers. Write an argument to support the validity of the identity property (see Section 2.4).

Zero-factor Property

For each whole number a, $a \cdot 0 = 0$.

This property can be shown by letting A be any set such that $n(A) = a$. We know from Section 2.4 that $n(A \times \varnothing) = n(\varnothing) = 0$. Hence we can say

$$a \cdot 0 = n(A \times \varnothing)$$
$$= 0$$

We conclude this section with a discussion of a distributive property that relates multiplication and addition.

Distributive Property

For each of the whole numbers, a, b, and c, $a \cdot (b + c) = (a \cdot b) + (a \cdot c)$.

Example:

$$6 \cdot (4 + 5) = 6 \cdot 9 = 54$$

$$(6 \cdot 4) + (6 \cdot 5) = 24 + 30 = 54$$

so

$$6 \cdot (4 + 5) = (6 \cdot 4) + (6 \cdot 5)$$

Example: Let $A = \{a, b\}$, $B = \{r, s, t\}$, and $C = \{x, y\}$. Find $n[A \times (B \cup C)]$ and $n[(A \times B) \cup (A \times C)]$.

Solution:

$$B \cup C = \{r, s, t, x, y\}$$
$$A \times (B \cup C) =$$
$$\{(a, r), (a, s), (a, t), (a, x), (a, y), (b, r), (b, s), (b, t), (b, x), (b, y)\}$$

so

$$n[A \times (B \cup C)] = 10$$

$$A \times B = \{(a, r), (a, s), (a, t), (b, r), (b, s), (b, t)\}$$
$$A \times C = \{(a, x), (a, y), (b, x), (b, y)\}$$
$$(A \times B) \cup (A \times C)$$
$$= \{(a, r), (a, s), (a, t), (b, r), (b, s), (b, t), (a, x), (a, y), (b, x), (b, y)\}$$

so

$$n[(A \times B) \cup (A \times C)] = 10$$

Note that $A \times B$ and $A \times C$ are disjoint sets. (Why?)

Since it is true that for each of the sets A, B, and C, $A \times (B \cup C) = (A \times B) \cup (A \times C)$, it follows that, if $n(A) = a$, $n(B) = b$, and $n(C) = c$, and B and C are disjoint sets,

$$\begin{aligned} a \cdot (b + c) &= n[A \times (B \cup C)] \\ &= n[(A \times B) \cup (A \times C)] \\ &= n(A \times B) + n(A \times C) \\ &= (a \cdot b) + (a \cdot c) \end{aligned}$$

Arrays were used in Chapter Two (see Figures 2.8 and 2.9) to illustrate certain facts about the Cartesian product. We use them again here to illustrate the multiplication operation and our distributive property.

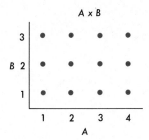

FIGURE 3.8 $4 \cdot 3 = n(A) \cdot n(B) = n(A \times B)$

Figure 3.8 can be thought of as an array representing $A \times B$, where $A = \{1, 2, 3, 4\}$ and $B = \{1, 2, 3\}$. Since $n(A \times B) = 12$, Figure 3.8 is also an illustration of the multiplication fact "$4 \cdot 3 = 12$."

We leave it to you to interpret Figure 3.9 in terms of the Cartesian product of a set A and the union of two disjoint sets B and C.

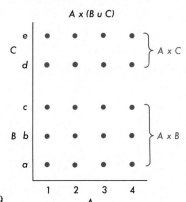

FIGURE 3.9

Exercises 3.6

For each pair of values given below, name two sets A and B such that $n(A) = a$ and $n(B) = b$. Then use these sets to solve the sentence "$a \cdot b = n(A \times B)$" by forming $A \times B$.

Example: $3 \cdot 5 =$

Solution: Let $A = \{a, b, c\}$ and $B = \{1, 2, 3, 4, 5\}$. Then the graph of $A \times B$ is as shown below and $n(A \times B) = 15$. Hence $3 \cdot 5 = 15$.

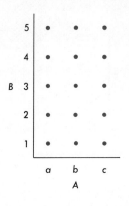

1. $2 \cdot 8 =$ **2.** $7 \cdot 3 =$
3. $9 \cdot 6 =$ **4.** $6 \cdot 7 =$

Each of the following sentences is an instance of one of the following properties of multiplication of whole numbers: the commutative property, the associative property, the identity property, the distributive property for multiplication over addition. For each sentence, identify the property and verify that the sentence is true.

5. $4 \cdot 3 = 3 \cdot 4$ **6.** $7 \cdot 1 = 7$
7. $(3 \cdot 7) \cdot 2 = 3 \cdot (7 \cdot 2)$ **8.** $8 \cdot 1 = 1 \cdot 8$
9. $1 \cdot 1 = 1$ **10.** $(5 \cdot 0) \cdot 7 = 5 \cdot (0 \cdot 7)$
11. $(6 + 3) \cdot 9 = 9 \cdot (6 + 3)$ **12.** $6 \cdot (9 + 1) = (6 \cdot 9) + (6 \cdot 1)$
13. $63 = 63 \cdot 1$ **14.** $4 \cdot (3 \cdot 2) = (4 \cdot 3) \cdot 2$
15. $(12 + 6) \cdot 1 = 12 + 6$ **16.** $(12 \cdot 6) \cdot 1 = 12 \cdot 6$
17. $1 \cdot (12 + 6) = 1 \cdot 12 + 1 \cdot 6$ **18.** $(12 \cdot 6) \cdot 1 = 12 \cdot (6 \cdot 1)$
19. $1 \cdot 1 + 1 \cdot 1 = (1 + 1) \cdot 1$ **20.** $1 \cdot (1 \cdot 1) = (1 \cdot 1) \cdot 1$

Which of the following sentences are true?

21. $1 \cdot 9 = 9$ **22.** $1 \cdot 11 = 11$
23. $64 = 1 \cdot 64$ **24.** $23 = 1 \cdot 23$
25. On the basis of problems 21 through 24, it seems reasonable that, for each whole number a, $1 \cdot a = a$. Using the basic properties discussed in this section, provide an argument to support this assertion.
26. Here is the start of a table of multiplication facts for the whole numbers zero through nine. Copy and complete the table.

•	0	1	2	3	4	5	6	7	8	9
0				0						
1						5				
2								14		
3										27
4		4								
5					20					
6							36			
7									56	
8	0									
9			18							

27. Imagine a diagonal line being drawn from the upper left corner of your multiplication table to the lower right corner. What do you note about the corresponding entries on either side of this line? What property of multiplication supports this observation?
28. Do the entries in the first row and the first column suggest a property of multiplication?
29. Do the entries in the second row and second column of your table suggest any properties of multiplication?

Each of the following sentences is true because it is a consequence of one or more properties of multiplication. For each sentence, name the property or properties.

30. $687 = 1 \cdot 687$
31. $(5 \cdot 2) \cdot (1 \cdot 0) = 0$
32. $(2 \cdot 7) \cdot 5 = (2 \cdot 5) \cdot 7$
33. $(2 \cdot 7) \cdot 5 = 5 \cdot (7 \cdot 2)$
34. $(3 + 2) \cdot 4 = 4 \cdot (3 + 2)$
35. $4 \cdot (3 + 2) = 4 \cdot 3 + 4 \cdot 2$
36. $4 \cdot 3 + 4 \cdot 2 = 3 \cdot 4 + 2 \cdot 4$
37. $(3 + 2) \cdot 4 = 3 \cdot 4 + 2 \cdot 4$

38. Supply an argument to support the assertion that, for each whole number a, $0 \cdot a = 0$.
39. Supply an argument to support the assertion that, for each of the whole numbers, a, b, and c, $(a + b) \cdot c = a \cdot c + b \cdot c$. (See problems 34 through 37.)

3.7 Division

The sentence "$14 \div 2 = n$" has a solution if and only if there is a whole number n such that $n \cdot 2 = 14$.   The symbol "÷," read "divided by," is used to denote the binary operation *division* which we define to be the inverse of the multiplication operation.

For each of the whole numbers a, b ≠ 0, and c, a ÷ b = c if and only if c • b = a. The number c is called the **quotient** *of a divided by b.*

Just as a subtraction sentence can be restated as an addition sentence, so can a division sentence be restated as a multiplication sentence.

Example: Find the quotient $14 \div 2$. This question can be restated as "Find the number n such that n times 2 is 14" or "$n \cdot 2 = 14$."   The sentence "$n \cdot 2 = 14$" is a multiplication sentence and has a solution 7.

Example: The sentence "$9 \div 4 = n$" has no solution because there is no whole number n such that $n \cdot 4 = 9$.

Example: The sentence "$3 \div 6 = n$" has no solution because there is no whole number n such that $n \cdot 6 = 3$.

Example: "$6 \div 0 = n$" is equivalent to "$n \cdot 0 = 6$." But, for any n, $n \cdot 0 = 0$ and $0 \neq 6$. Consequently $6 \div 0$ does not name a whole number. On the other hand, the sentence "$0 \div 0 = n$" is equivalent to "$n \cdot 0 = 0$." But every whole number is a solution of the latter sentence. Since we want the division operation to yield a *unique whole number*, we say division by zero cannot be performed, or *division by zero is undefined.*

We can use an array to illustrate a division sentence in a manner similar to the way we illustrate a multiplication sentence. Figure 3.10 is an array that illustrates the division fact $15 \div 3 = 5$ as well as the multiplication fact $5 \cdot 3 = 15$.

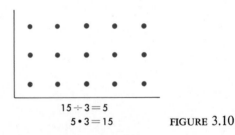

$$15 \div 3 = 5$$
$$5 \cdot 3 = 15$$

FIGURE 3.10

Exercises 3.7

Find a word or phrase that correctly completes each of the following sentences.

1. The result of dividing the whole number a by _____ is a.
2. Multiplication and division of whole numbers are _____ operations.
3. Division of whole numbers is a(n) _____ operation.
4. The whole number a divided by the whole number b is a whole number c if and only if _____.
5. The result of dividing when division can be performed, is called a(n) _____.
6. If any nonzero whole number is divided by itself, the result is _____.

Each of the following generalizations about division is false. For each statement, provide a counterexample to verify its falsity.

7. Division of whole numbers is a closed operation.
8. Division of whole numbers is a commutative operation.
9. Division of whole numbers is an associative operation.

The inverse relationship between multiplication and division is suggested by each of the following sentences. Fill in the blanks in these sentences to make true statements.

10. $(28 \cdot 4) \div 4 =$ ___
11. $(56 \div 7) \cdot 7 =$ ___
12. $(144 \div 12) \cdot 12 =$ ___
13. $(\text{___} \cdot 16) \div 16 = 28$
14. $(\text{___} \div 25) \cdot 25 = 750$
15. $(12 \cdot \text{___}) \div 42 = 12$
16. $(\text{___} \div 9) \cdot 9 =$ ___
17. $(24 \div \text{___}) \cdot \text{___} = 24$

Solve each of the following sentences by first restating it as a multiplication sentence. $n \in W$.

18. $14 \div 2 = n$
19. $99 \div 0 = n$
20. $48 \div 12 = n$
21. $836 \div 209 = n$
22. $1000 \div 200 = n$
23. $5000 \div 500 = n$
24. $115 \div 345 = n$
25. $345 \div 115 = n$
26. $345 \div n = 115$
27. $0 \div 10 = n$
28. $n \div 782 = 0$
29. $782 \div n = 0$

30. Problems 27 and 28 suggest a general property about division. State the property and supply an argument to justify its validity.
31. Without referring to the text, explain why division by zero is undefined.

3.8 The Multiplication Algorithm

The product $8 \cdot 3$ can be computed by addition as the sum of three eights because $8 \cdot 3 = 8(1 + 1 + 1) = 8 + 8 + 8$ by the distributive law. Likewise we can interpret the product $24 \cdot 13$ as the sum of 13 twenty-fours. As our factors get larger however, we begin to ask if there might be a better way to compute a product. We seek a multiplication algorithm.

$24 \cdot 13 = (20 + 4) \cdot (10 + 3)$ [the factors are renamed]

$= (20 + 4) \cdot 10 + (20 + 4) \cdot 3$ [distributive property; the factor $(20 + 4)$ is distributed over the addends 10 and 3]

$= [(20 \cdot 10) + (4 \cdot 10)] + [(20 \cdot 3) + (4 \cdot 3)]$ [distributive property; the factor 10 is distributed over the addends 20 and 4, and the factor 3 is distributed over the addends 20 and 4]

$= (200 + 40) + (60 + 12)$ [multiplication facts]

$= [200 + (40 + 60)] + 12$ [associative property of addition]

$= (200 + 100) + 12$ [addition fact]

$= 300 + 12$ [addition fact]

$= 312$ [renaming]

The algorithm is shown in Figure 3.11 in concise form.

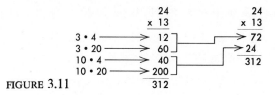

FIGURE 3.11

As another illustration (see Figure 3.12) we note that

$$28 \cdot 42 = (20 + 8) \cdot (40 + 2)$$
$$= (20 + 8) \cdot 40 + (20 + 8) \cdot 2$$
$$= [(20 \cdot 40) + (8 \cdot 40)] + [(20 \cdot 2) + (8 \cdot 2)]$$
$$= [800 + 320] + [40 + 16]$$
$$= [800 + 300] + [20 + 40 + 10] + 6$$
$$= 1100 + 70 + 6$$
$$= 1176$$

```
      28          28
    x 42        x 42
      16          56
      40         112
     320        1176
     800
```
FIGURE 3.12 1176

Exercises 3.8

Use the step-by-step procedure for multiplication developed in Section 3.8 to solve the following sentences. $n \in W$.

1. $22 \cdot 5 = n$ **2.** $36 \cdot 12 = n$
3. $145 \cdot 68 = n$ **4.** $782 \cdot 345 = n$

Use the multiplication algorithm to find each of the following products.

5. $42 \cdot 53$ **6.** $456 \cdot 37$
7. $4056 \cdot 7$ **8.** $687 \cdot 993$
9. $29,808 \cdot 447$ **10.** $2345 \cdot 4325$

Solve each of the following sentences. $n \in W$.

11. $10 \cdot 6 = n$ **12.** $10 \cdot 60 = n$
13. $100 \cdot 60 = n$ **14.** $10 \cdot 23 = n$
15. $100 \cdot 23 = n$ **16.** $1000 \cdot 23 = n$
17. $10 \cdot 58 = n$ **18.** $100 \cdot 421 = n$
19. $764 \cdot 1000 = n$ **20.** $1000 \cdot 1000 = n$

21. Do the sentences in problems 11 through 20 suggest any pattern?
State it.

Solve each of the following sentences. $n \in W$.

$\quad$ **22.** $n = 2 \cdot 7$ $\qquad$ **23.** $2 \cdot 26 = n$

$\quad$ **24.** $2 \cdot 175 = n$ $\qquad$ **25.** $n = 4 \cdot 83$

$\quad$ **26.** $n = 32 \cdot 51$ $\qquad$ **27.** $86 \cdot 143 = n$

$\quad$ **28.** $108 \cdot 926 = n$ $\qquad$ **29.** $n = 6042 \cdot 2812$

$\quad$ **30.** $n = 208 \cdot 81{,}047$ $\qquad$ **31.** $606 \cdot 11 = n$

32. What generalization about multiplication is suggested by problems
22 through 31?

Solve each of the following sentences. $n \in W$.

$\quad$ **33.** $5 \cdot 4 = n$ $\qquad$ **34.** $n = 5 \cdot 5$

$\quad$ **35.** $n = 5 \cdot 21$ $\qquad$ **36.** $68 \cdot 5 = n$

$\quad$ **37.** $32 \cdot 15 = n$ $\qquad$ **38.** $n = 75 \cdot 47$

$\quad$ **39.** $n = 125 \cdot 862$ $\qquad$ **40.** $2505 \cdot 6426 = n$

41. What generalization about multiplication is suggested by problems
33 through 40?

Solve the following sentences. $n \in W$.

$\quad$ **42.** $3 \cdot 7 = n$ $\qquad$ **43.** $n = 11 \cdot 5$

$\quad$ **44.** $n = 21 \cdot 43$ $\qquad$ **45.** $57 \cdot 103 = n$

$\quad$ **46.** $789 \cdot 463 = n$ $\qquad$ **47.** $n = 8009 \cdot 547$

48. What generalization about multiplication is suggested by problems
42 through 47?

49. Multiplication of whole numbers is occasionally thought of as repeated addition. For example, we can interpret $2 \cdot 3$ as $2 + 2 + 2$.

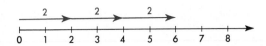

$\qquad$ The figure uses the number line to illustrate the repeated addition
interpretation. Use the number line and the repeated addition interpretation to illustrate the truth of each of the following sentences.

$\qquad$ **(a)** $4 \cdot 6 = 6 \cdot 4$ $\qquad$ **(b)** $(2 \cdot 5) \cdot 4 = 2 \cdot (5 \cdot 4)$

50. The distributive property is a useful tool in "mental multiplication."
The sentence "$n = 7 \cdot 15$" can be thought of as "$n = 7 \cdot (10 + 5)$,"
which is equivalent to "$n = 70 + 35$." Hence $n = 105$.

Use the distributive property to solve each of the following sentences mentally. $n \in W$.

(a) $n = 12 \cdot 8$ (b) $23 \cdot 6 = n$
(c) $234 \cdot 5 = n$ (d) $n = 13 \cdot 13$
(e) $n = 25 \cdot 12$ (f) $48 \cdot 32 = n$

51. Use the basic properties of multiplication to show that $8 \cdot 146 = (8 \cdot 100) + (8 \cdot 40) + (8 \cdot 6)$.
52. Is the generalization,

For each five whole numbers, a, b, c, d, and e,
$a \cdot (b + c + d + e) = (a \cdot b) + (a \cdot c) + (a \cdot d) + (a \cdot e)$

a true generalization ?   Provide an example to support your answer.

Which of the following sets are closed under the ordinary multiplication operation on whole numbers?

53. $\{0, 1, 2, 3, 4, 5, \ldots\}$ 54. $\{0, 1, 2, 3, \ldots, 100\}$
55. $\{0, 2, 4, 6, 8, \ldots\}$ 56. $\{0, 1, 3, 5, 7, \ldots\}$
57. $\{0, 1, 2, 3, \ldots, 865\}$ 58. $\{0, 1\}$

59. Two multiplication algorithms are shown below.   The first is called the scratch method and the second was used in Europe 500 years ago.   Determine how they work.

<pre>
          245   245
           83   83
        16000   166
         3200   332
           92   415
          400   20335
            6
          600
           12
           10
            2
          120
            3
           15
        20335
</pre>

3.9 The Division Algorithm

We shall develop a division algorithm by restating a division problem in terms of its inverse operation multiplication. We shall then solve the multiplication problem and note the pattern that develops.

Example: Solve the sentence $595 \div 7 = n$.

Solution: If $595 \div 7 = n$, then $n \cdot 7 = 595$. We note that $100 \cdot 7 = 700$, $90 \cdot 7 = 630$, and $80 \cdot 7 = 560$. Therefore, $80 < n < 90$.

Let $n = a + b$, where a is the number of tens and b is the number of ones in n. a must be 80. Then $n \cdot 7 = (a + b) \cdot 7 = (80 + b) \cdot 7$. Now we have

$$(80 + b) \cdot 7 = 595 \qquad \text{[renaming } n \text{ as } 80 + b]$$
$$560 + b \cdot 7 = 595 \qquad \text{[distributive law]}$$
$$b \cdot 7 = 595 - 560 \qquad \text{[restating addition problem as a}$$
$$\text{subtraction problem]}$$
$$b \cdot 7 = 35 \qquad \text{[subtraction performed]}$$
$$b = 5 \qquad \text{[basic multiplication fact]}$$
$$n = 85 \qquad \text{[renaming } a + b \text{ as n]}$$

The pattern established in the above example is a division algorithm. The algorithm is shown in Figure 3.13 in compact form. In the figure 7 is called the *divisor*, 595 the *dividend*, 85 the *quotient*, and 0 the *remainder*.

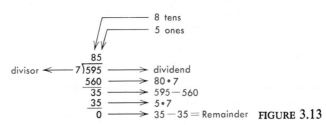

FIGURE 3.13

Division is said to be performable in the set of whole numbers if and only if the division algorithm yields a zero remainder.

Example: Solve the sentence $3082 \div 23 = n$.

Solution: We shall follow the pattern of the above example. Since $n \cdot 23$

$= 3082$, it follows that $100 < n < 200$. Let $n = 100 + a + b$, where a is the number of tens in n and b is the number of ones in n. Now

$n \cdot 23 = (100 + a + b) \cdot 23 = 3082$ [renaming n as $100 + a + b$]

$2300 + (a + b) \cdot 23 = 3082$ [distributive law]

$(a + b) \cdot 23 = 3082 - 2300$ [restating addition problem as subtraction problem]

$(a + b) \cdot 23 = 782$ [subtraction]

$30 < (a + b) < 40$ [multiplication fact]

$(30 + b) \cdot 23 = 782$ [renaming $a + b$]

$690 + b \cdot 23 = 782$ [distributive law]

$b \cdot 23 = 782 - 690$ [restating addition problem as subtraction problem]

$b \cdot 23 = 92$ [subtraction]

$b = 4$ [multiplication fact]

$n = 134$ [renaming $100 + a + b$ as 134]

The compact algorithmic form of the above pattern is shown in **Figure 3.14.**

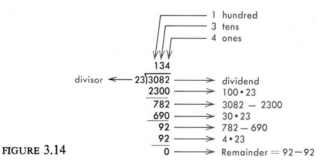

FIGURE 3.14

Exercises 3.9

Use the step-by-step development of the division algorithm (see the examples of this section) to solve each of the following sentences. $n \in W$.

      1. $288 \div 12 = n$ **2.** $625 \div 25 = n$

      3. $196 \div 14 = n$ **4.** $1024 \div 32 = n$

Use the division algorithm to solve each of the following sentences. $n \in W$.

5. $n = 30 \div 5$	**6.** $225 \div 5 = n$
7. $136 \div 5 = n$	**8.** $229 \div 5 = n$
9. $n = 1080 \div 5$	**10.** $n = 40 \div 10$
11. $115 \div 10 = n$	**12.** $n = 270 \div 10$
13. $524 \div 10 = n$	**14.** $5460 \div 10 = n$

15. What generalizations about division by 5 and by 10 are suggested by problems 5 through 14?

16. How can the multiplication table you made in problem 26 of Exercises 3.6 be used as a table of division facts?

Solve each of the following sentences. $n \in W$.

17. $n = 15 \div 3$	**18.** $33 \div 11 = n$
19. $91 \div 7 = n$	**20.** $n = 299 \div 23$
21. $n = 627 \div 57$	**22.** $1591 \div 43 = n$
23. $5085 \div 45 = n$	**24.** $79,083 \div 783 = n$

25. What generalization about division is suggested by problems 17 through 24?

Solve each of the following sentences. $n \in W$.

26. $n = 135 \div 4$	**27.** $359 \div 16 = n$
28. $477 \div 22 = n$	**29.** $1083 \div 28 = n$

30. What generalization about division is suggested by problems 26 through 29?

31. Provide a counterexample to show that the generalization,

Division of an even number by an uneven number, if it is possible, always results in an even quotient

is false.

It is possible to show that division is distributive over addition. We recall that multiplication and division are inverse operations; that is, they undo each other. Symbolically, $(x \div y) \cdot y = x$, for $y \neq 0$ provided $(x \div y) \in W$. Using this fact we can write

$$a + b = (a \div c) \cdot c + (b \div c) \cdot c \qquad [c \neq 0]$$
$$= [(a \div c) + (b \div c)] \cdot c$$

But by the definition of division,

$$a + b = [(a \div c) + (b \div c)] \cdot c \qquad [c \neq 0]$$

is equivalent to

$$(a + b) \div c = (a \div c) + (b \div c) \qquad [c \neq 0]$$

and the assertion is proved.

We can use the distributive property for division over addition to perform some divisions mentally. For example,

$$
\begin{aligned}
132 \div 12 &= (120 + 12) \div 12 \\
&= (120 \div 12) + (12 \div 12) \\
&= 10 + 1 \\
&= 11
\end{aligned}
$$

Solve each of the following sentences mentally. $n \in W$.

32. $n = 165 \div 15$ **33.** $264 \div 22 = n$
34. $117 \div 9 = n$ **35.** $n = 154 \div 11$
36. $n = 2525 \div 25$ **37.** $1648 \div 16 = n$

Another property of division is that division is distributive over subtraction. An instance of this property is

$$(30 - 12) \div 3 = (30 \div 3) - (12 \div 3)$$

Use the property to mentally solve the following sentences. $n \in W$.

38. $135 \div 15 = n$ **39.** $n = 117 \div 13$
40. $306 \div 34 = n$ **41.** $n = 950 \div 25$

42. A division algorithm developed over 500 years ago is shown below. How does it work? Use it to solve problem 23.

$$
\begin{array}{l}
884 - 13 \\
068 \\[4pt]
88 \\
\underline{78} \\
\overline{104} \\
\underline{104}
\end{array}
$$

3.10 Solving Worded Problems

Consider the following statement of a problem.

A certain junior college has 9843 students enrolled as full time day students. It also has a certain number of students enrolled in the evening division. How many students are enrolled in the evening division if the combined day-evening enrollment is 16,473?

To obtain a solution we may think as follows:

(**a**) Analyze the statement of the problem for numerical data and quantitative relationships.

> Day enrollment: 9483
> Evening enrollment: ?
> Combined enrollment: 16,473

(**b**) Restate the problem mathematically.

(day enrollment) + (evening enrollment) = (combined enrollment)
$9483 + n = 16,473$

(**c**) Solve the mathematical problem.

Since $9483 + n = 16,473$ is equivalent to $n = 16,473 - 9483$, subtraction will produce the solution 6990.

(**d**) Interpret the solution in terms of the original statement of the problem.

The evening division enrollment is 6990 students.

Here is a second illustration of the problem-solving technique.

Chairs are to be placed in an auditorium whose width restricts the side-to-side placement of chairs to 25 in each row. If there are as many rows as chairs in each row, how many people can be accommodated in the auditorium?

Solution:

(**a**) As before we read the problem for numerical data and quantitative relationships.
Data: 25 chairs in each row
Quantitative relationship: as many rows as chairs in each row

These two bits of information give us the following data: 25 rows is the maximum

(**b**) To restate the problem mathematically, we use the information in
   (a) together with the question "How many people can be accommodated in the auditorium?" which tells us what it is that we wish
   to find. We can now restate the problem mathematically as the
   following sentence:

$$25 \cdot 25 = n$$

This is so because the number of chairs in each row multiplied by the
number of rows is the number of people that can be accommodated
by the auditorium.

(**c**) Solve the mathematical problem.

$$
\begin{array}{r}
25 \\
\times\ 25 \\
\hline
125 \\
50\ \ \\
\hline
625 \\
\end{array}
$$

(**d**) Interpret the solution in (c) in terms of the original statement of
   the problem.

   The auditorium can accommodate 625 people.

   Although we can, conceivably, tackle each problem in this systematic
manner, and frequently we do, we usually do not write down each thought
we may have. Nevertheless, in beginning to acquire skill in problem
solving, it is very helpful to write down as many things as may seem to be
useful in solving the problem. As skills increase, you will write down less
and less to solve problems of the same order of difficulty. The attainment
of such skills should be the goal of each reader of this text.

Example: To reach his destination Mr. Sell has to travel 60 miles more
than twice the distance he has already traveled. If he already traveled
85 miles how much farther must he go?

Solution: Let n represent the distance to be traveled. Then

$$
\begin{aligned}
n &= 60 + 2 \cdot 85 \\
  &= 60 + 170 \\
  &= 230 \text{ miles}
\end{aligned}
$$

Hence Mr. Sell must travel 230 miles to his destination.

Exercises 3.10

Solve each of the following problems.

1. In looking over his checkbook, Mr. Davis found that he had written checks of $100, $10, $8, $56, $24, and $77 during the past week. How much did Mr. Davis spend by check during the past week?

2. If it costs Mr. Davis (see problem 1) 8 cents for each check he writes, what was his checking service charge for the past week?

3. If Mr. Davis had $427 in his account at the beginning of the past week, what is his current balance if he has not yet paid his service charge?

4. An assembly hall has 2802 seats but only 1928 seats are taken. How many more persons can be seated?

5. The product of two numbers is 1296. If one of the numbers is 48, find the other.

6. The perimeter of a triangle is 53 inches. If one side is 12 inches long and a second side is 25 inches long, how long is the third side?

7. A rectangle has a length of 36 feet and a width of 24 feet. Find its perimeter, P, and its area, A. $[P = 2 \cdot (l + w); A = l \cdot w]$

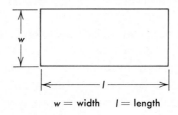

w = width   l = length

8. Find the area of the figure.

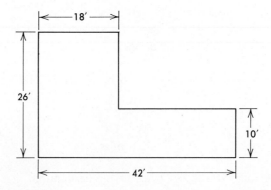

9. A light airplane flies from city *A* to city *B*, 556 miles apart, in 4 hours. Find the airplane's average speed for the trip.

10. In flying from city *R* to city *S*, a 924-mile trip, a light airplane whose airspeed is 108 miles per hour is aided by a 24-mph tailwind. How long will the trip from city *R* to city *S* take? How long will the return trip take if the plane is slowed down by a 24-mph headwind?

11. Mr. Larson made a 252-mile trip in his station wagon using 18 gallons of gasoline. He made the same trip in his compact coupe using only 12 gallons of gasoline. How far will each car travel on 1 gallon of gasoline?

12. The walls of three rectangularly shaped rooms, one bedroom 15 by 13 feet, one bedroom 12 by 10 feet, and a living room 18 by 16 feet, are to be painted. The ceiling height in each room is 9 feet. If 1 gallon of the chosen paint covers 420 square feet, how many gallons of paint are required for the paint job?

13. A listing of Mr. Karmon's stocks with the year's gain or loss in dollars per share of stock is shown in the table. Find Mr. Karmon's net gain or loss for the year.

Stock	Number of Shares	Gain	Loss
A	25		15
B	50	12	
C	10	14	
D	100	3	
E	30		11

14. Mr. Jackson had a "golden bucket" containing $100 from which he could draw $10 in the morning with the assurance that $5 would be replaced at night if there was any money left in the bucket. How long could Mr. Jackson continue to draw $10 a day before his golden bucket was emptied? How much did he take out? How much was put back in?

15. A certain airline has the following baggage limitations:

Two bags per person and a maximum of 120 pounds of baggage per person. Penalties are assessed at the rate of $8 per bag for each bag in excess of two and $4 for every 10 pounds in excess of 120 pounds.

Miss Starr has 15 bags each weighing 32 pounds. What is her baggage penalty?

16. In the freshman class at Clever College there are 183 students enrolled in Psychology 1, 167 students enrolled in Biology 1, and 229
students enrolled in English 1. Now of these students, 133 are enrolled in both Biology 1 and English 1, 149 are enrolled in both
Psychology 1 and Biology 1, and 148 are enrolled in both Psychology
1 and English 1. If there are 117 freshman students enrolled in
all three of these subjects and there are 286 freshman students in
all, how many freshmen are not taking any of these courses? (*Hint:*
Use Venn diagrams and set intersection.)

3.11 Summary

The common arithmetic operations were discussed from a developmental
point of view. We hope that the discussion has helped you to gain some
insight into the basic arithmetic computations that we frequently take for
granted. Also it is hoped that a knowledge and consideration of the
concepts involved in these operations will help to clarify them for you.

In review, let us recall that the sum of two whole numbers was defined
in terms of the cardinality of the union of two disjoint sets. The properties for addition—closure, commutativity, associativity, and identity—
were investigated. Then an algorithm for rapidly computing sums was
established, using the properties, some basic addition facts, and the place-
value principle.

We then defined the product of two whole numbers in terms of the cardinality of a Cartesian product set, and explored the properties of multiplication—closure, commutativity, associativity, and identity. To relate the
two binary operations of multiplication and addition, we found that a
distributive property holds. Then using these properties, together with
the place-value principle and some basic multiplication facts, we developed
an algorithm for multiplication.

Next we defined the subtraction and division operations in such a way
that they are inverse operations for addition and multiplication, respectively.
For example, subtracting a number nullifies the effect of adding that number. It was also noted that these operations are not closed operations
in the set of whole numbers; hence there is some limitation of their use-
fulness.

Last, we considered some applications of our operations to problem
solving. Since so many problems of our current technological society
have mathematical solutions, you are well advised to gain as much skill
in problem solving as possible.

Exercises 3.11—Review

Complete each sentence.

1. To find the sum of two numbers a and b, find two _____ sets A and B such that $n(A) = a$ and $n(B) = b$. Then $a + b =$ _____.

2. The binary operation of addition is _____ in the set of whole numbers because the sum of two whole numbers is always a whole number.

3. It is possible to add three whole numbers a, b, and c by first grouping them as $(a + b) + c$ or $a + (b + c)$. The _____ property for addition guarantees that both sums are the same.

4. _____ is the additive identity.

5. Subtraction is the _____ operation for addition.

6. We say $a - b = n$ if and only if _____.

7. Since the sentence "$a - b = n$" does not always have a solution in the set of whole numbers, we say subtraction is _____ in the set of whole numbers.

8. If $a = n(A)$ and $b = n(B)$, then $a \cdot b =$ _____.

9. The binary operation multiplication and its algorithm are based on the set operation _____.

10. Since $n(A \times B) = n(B \times A)$, we say multiplication is _____.

11. Let B be a set containing one element. Then $n(A \times B) =$ _____.

12. $a \div b = n$ if and only if _____.

13. An algorithm is _____.

Show that each of the following addition sentences are true by

(a) Finding sets A, B, and $A \cup B$ so that $n(A) = a$, $n(B) = b$, and $n(A \cup B) = a + b$.

(b) Drawing a number-line diagram similar to Figure 3.1.

14. $4 + 3 = 7$	**15.** $3 + 6 = 9$
16. $8 + 2 = 10$	**17.** $5 + 7 = 12$

Show that each of the following multiplication sentences are true by

(a) Finding sets A, B, and $A \times B$ so that $n(A) = a$, $n(B) = b$, and $n(A \times B) = a \cdot b$.

(b) Drawing an array similar to Figure 3.9.

18. $2 \cdot 4 = 8$	**19.** $7 \cdot 1 = 7$
20. $5 \cdot 3 = 15$	**21.** $4 \cdot 6 = 24$

Solve each of the following sentences, if possible, by first stating it in terms of the inverse operation. The domain of n is W, the set of whole numbers.

22. $8 - 4 = n$	**23.** $8 \div 4 = n$
24. $6 - 9 = n$	**25.** $9 \div 9 = n$
26. $9 \div 8 = n$	**27.** $108 - 56 = n$
28. $0 \div 5 = n$	**29.** $5 \div 0 = n$

Perform each of the following computations in algorithmic form. Supply reasons for each step. Use the developments on pages 53–54 and 68–69 as guides.

30. $52 \cdot 18$	**31.** $68 + 46$
32. $184 + 769$	**33.** $108 \cdot 25$

Each of the following sentences illustrates a property for addition or multiplication. State the property.

34. $(6 \cdot 4) \cdot 3 = 6 \cdot (4 \cdot 3)$	**35.** $8 + 2 = 2 + 8$
36. $0 + 5 = 5$	**37.** $2 \cdot (6 + 4) = 2 \cdot 6 + 2 \cdot 4$
38. $8 + (2 + 3) = (8 + 2) + 3$	**39.** $3 \cdot 1 = 3$

chapter four

INTEGERS

4.0 Introduction

Having established the whole-number system, we have been able to solve many types of mathematical problems. However, as we noted, it is not always possible to compute differences or quotients in the set of whole numbers. That is, the subtraction and division operations are not closed in the set of whole numbers.

To remedy the lack of closure for subtraction, we shall, in this chapter, extend our number system by "inventing" a new type of number, called an *integer*. We shall do this in such a way that the properties for the operations previously discussed will still be valid in the set of integers, and, in addition, subtraction will be closed in the set of integers. Then we shall explore some of the interpretations and uses of this new set of numbers.

4.1 Integers

The sentence "$3 - 4 = n$" has no solution in the set of whole numbers because there is no whole number n such that $3 = n + 4$. Obtaining a solution to such a sentence forms the major portion of the subject matter of this chapter.

The phrase "fifty feet below sea level" is meaningful to you. It refers to a place 50 feet below some position called sea level, which is arbitrarily given the elevation zero. If, in referring to the elevation of some place, we write the numeral 50, it would be assumed that we mean 50 feet above sea level. ⁻50, read "negative fifty," is the numeral that would usually be used to indicate 50 feet below sea level. Here 50 and ⁻50 indicate the same magnitude or size but opposite directions. The number negative fifty might be thought of as a number newly invented for the purpose of indicating opposite direction. In fact, we can invent a set of negative numbers, {⁻1, ⁻2, ⁻3, . . .} such that each nonzero whole number would have a correspondent in this new set to indicate opposite direction.

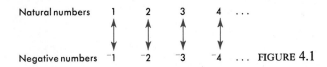

FIGURE 4.1

Figure 4.1 shows a one-to-one correspondence between the set of natural numbers and the set of their negatives. If we form the union of this set of negative numbers with the set of whole numbers we obtain the set of *integers*, *J*. Hence $J = \{. . . , {}^-4, {}^-3, {}^-2, {}^-1, 0, 1, 2, 3, 4, . . .\}$. The natural numbers will occasionally be referred to as positive integers. Each nonzero number in *J* has two notions associated with it, magnitude (size) and direction. With this in mind it is easy to devise a graph of the set *J*. All we need do is extend the number line to the left of zero. For example, negative five, which corresponds to five, is graphed five units to the left of the graph of zero (the origin), and ⁻3 is graphed three units to the left of the origin.

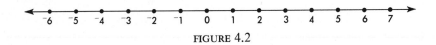

FIGURE 4.2

We shall very often be concerned only with the magnitude of the integer *a*. To indicate this particular concern we shall use the absolute value symbol, "| |."

Example: " |⁻3| = 3" is read "The absolute value of negative three is three." The statement means that the graph of ⁻3 is three units from the origin.

Example: " |10| = 10" is read "The absolute value of ten is ten."

The graph of *J* shown in Figure 4.2 suggests an ordering of the elements of *J* that is consistent with the way in which the whole numbers were ordered. For each of the integers *a* and *b*, if the graph of *a* is to the left of the graph of *b* on the number line, then *a* < *b*. On the other hand, if *a* < *b*, then *a* is graphed to the left of the graph of *b*.

Example: Replace the question mark by either of the symbols >, <, or =.

(a) ⁻6 ? 3   ⁻6 < 3
(b) ⁻2 ? ⁻5   ⁻2 > ⁻5
(c) ⁻3 ? 0   ⁻3 < 0
(d) |⁻3| ? 0 |⁻3| > 0
(e) |⁻2| ? ⁻5 |⁻2| > ⁻5
(f) |⁻6| ? 3 |⁻6| > 3
(g) |⁻12| ? 12 |⁻12| = 12

Example: Graph ⁻7, 3, ⁻2, 6 on a number line.

Solution:

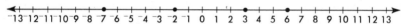

Exercises 4.1

Complete each of the following sentences to make true statements.

1. The set of integers can be formed as the union of the set of _____ and their _____.
2. The set of integers contains the set of whole numbers as a _____.
3. A negative integer is always _____ zero.
4. A positive integer is always _____ zero.
5. A negative integer is always _____ a positive integer.
6. "Natural number" is simply another name for "_____."
7. If "6" indicates 6 miles due north, then "_____" indicates 6 miles due south.
8. If "2000" represents an elevation of 2000 feet above sea level, then "−500" represents _____.

Replace each question mark with one of the symbols, >, <, or =, to make true statements.

         9. 1 ? ⁻1   **10.** ⁻18 ? 1
        11. ⁻15 ? ⁻11   **12.** 3 ? 3

13. 3 ? ⁻3   14. 0 ? ⁻4
15. ⁻926 ? ⁻1005   16. ⁻8 ? 8
17. ⁻(5 + 4) ? 0   18. ⁻(6 + 14) ? (2 + 8)

Graph each of the following sets of integers on a number line.

19. {⁻3, ⁻5}   20. {⁻1, 2}
21. {⁻6, ⁻2, 2, 6}   22. {⁻7, ⁻5, ⁻3, ⁻1, 1, 3, 5, 7}
23. {⁻6, ⁻9, ⁻12, 0, 6, 3}   24. {⁻106, ⁻108, 0, 5}
25. {⁻1057, 896, 904}   26. {⁻(3 + 1), (⁻5 + ⁻3)}

Indicate the solution set for each of the following sentences. The domain for n is the set J.

27. ⁻6 > n 28. n < ⁻3
29. 0 ≥ n 30. n > ⁻3 or n < 3
31. n < ⁻8 or n > ⁻12   32. n ≥ 0 or n ≤ 5

Replace each of the question marks with one of the symbols >, <, or =.

33. |⁻3| ? 2   34. |⁻15| ? |11|
35. 5 ? |10| 36. |⁻13| ? |⁻5|
37. |⁻4| ? |4| 38. |8 + 3| ? |⁻6|
39. |⁻12| ? |12| 40. |8 − 3| ? |⁻6|
41. 7 ? |7|

Draw Venn diagrams for each of the following sets. Indicate an appropriate universal set in each case.

42. A = {0, 1}, B = {0, ⁻1, ⁻5, ⁻7}, C = {⁻1, 1, 5}
43. A = {2, 4, 6, 8, 10}, B = {⁻2, ⁻4, ⁻6, ⁻8, ⁻10}
44. A = {⁻5, ⁻4, ⁻1, 3, 6, 9}, B = {⁻3, ⁻6, ⁻3, ⁻5}, C = {1, 3, 4, 5, ⁻6, ⁻91}
45. State five applications for negative whole numbers.
46. The discussion in Section 4.1 implies that there is something special and real about the natural numbers and something artificial about the integers. Can you justify this implication?

4.2 Addition of Integers

A method for solving the sentence "3 + 2 = n" using the number line was discussed on page 44. We wish to extend that method for solving addition problems involving integers.

Each integer can be represented by the length of a directed line segment.

Example: Four is represented by each of the directed line segments shown in Figure 4.3. Each segment has a length of four units and is directed toward the right.

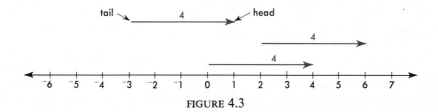

FIGURE 4.3

Example: Negative three is represented by each of the directed line segments shown in Figure 4.4. Each segment is three units long and is directed toward the left.

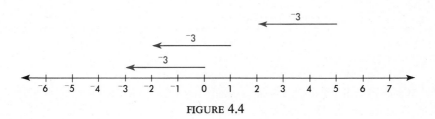

FIGURE 4.4

In general each nonzero integer a shall be represented by a line segment $|a|$ units long. If a is a positive, the segment is directed toward the right. If a is a negative, the segment is directed toward the left. Thus a correspondence is developed between the set of integers and the set of directed line segments whose lengths are whole numbers.

For each of the integers a and b, the sum, $a + b$, shall be obtained in the following way:

1. Find two directed line segments corresponding to a and b, respectively.
2. Place the tail of the directed line segment corresponding to a at the origin.
3. Place the tail of the directed line segment corresponding to b at the head of the first directed line segment.
4. The sum, $a + b$, is represented by the directed line segment whose tail is at the origin and whose head is at the head of the second directed line segment.

Example: $4 + {}^-3 = 1$ (see Figure 4.5).

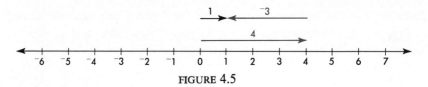

FIGURE 4.5

Example: $^-4 + ^-3 = ^-7$ (see Figure 4.6).

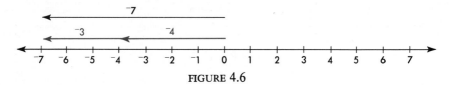

FIGURE 4.6

Example: $^-4 + 3 = ^-1$ (see Figure 4.7).

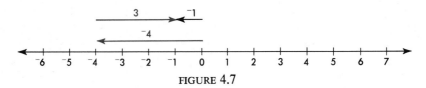

FIGURE 4.7

We shall call a directed line segment a *vector* and the method of addition exhibited in the preceding examples *vector addition*.

The four-step procedure on page 87 defines vector addition. It is a *binary operation* on directed line segments whose directed lengths represent the integers we wish to add. Vector addition allows us to add integers in a way that is consistent with the way we add whole numbers. That is, if we add two whole numbers by vector addition or by the addition algorithm we shall get the same sum.

Vector addition also has the properties of:

         1. Closure.   **2.** Commutativity.
         3. Associativity.   **4.** Identity.

These properties are the basic properties of addition in the whole numbers. It is not strange, therefore, that vector addition applied to whole numbers should yield the same result as the addition algorithm for whole numbers. But vector addition does more. It provides a way to compute the sum of any two integers.

We would like, however, to be able to compute the sum of any two integers without having to resort to a figure and vector addition each time. Each of the sentences in Figure 4.8 can be verified by vector addition. Study them carefully and see if you can find a pattern for adding integers before reading the next paragraph.

$$
\begin{array}{llll}
3 + 5 = 8 & 9 + 6 = 15 & 21 + 14 = 35 & 16 + 20 = 36 \\
{}^-3 + {}^-5 = {}^-8 & {}^-9 + {}^-6 = {}^-15 & {}^-21 + {}^-14 = {}^-35 & {}^-16 + {}^-20 = {}^-36 \\
{}^-3 + 5 = 2 & {}^-9 + 6 = {}^-3 & {}^-21 + 14 = {}^-7 & {}^-16 + 20 = 4 \\
3 + {}^-5 = {}^-2 & 9 + {}^-6 = 3 & 21 + {}^-14 = 7 & 16 + {}^-20 = {}^-4
\end{array}
$$

FIGURE 4.8

The patterns suggest the addition rule for integers which relates addition of integers to addition of whole numbers, an operation with which we are familiar.

ADDITION RULE FOR INTEGERS

For each of the integers a and b:

1. If $a > 0$ and $b > 0$, then $a + b = |a| + |b|$.
2. If $a < 0$ and $b < 0$, then $a + b = {}^-(|a| + |b|)$.
3. If $a > 0$ and $b < 0$ and $|a| > |b|$, then $a + b = |a| - |b|$.
4. If $a > 0$ and $b < 0$ and $|a| < |b|$, then $a + b = {}^-(|b| - |a|)$.

Example: Compute $8 + 3$.

Solution: Since $8 > 0$ and $3 > 0$, $8 + 3 = |8| + |3| = 11$.

Example: Compute ${}^-8 + {}^-3$.

Solution: Since ${}^-8 < 0$ and ${}^-3 < 0$,

$$
\begin{aligned}
{}^-8 + {}^-3 &= {}^-(|{}^-8| + |{}^-3|) \\
&= {}^-(8 + 3) \\
&= {}^-11
\end{aligned}
$$

Example: Compute $8 + {}^-3$.

Solution: Since $8 > 0$ and ${}^-3 < 0$ and $|8| > |{}^-3|$,

$$
\begin{aligned}
8 + {}^-3 &= |8| - |{}^-3| \\
&= 8 - 3 \\
&= 5
\end{aligned}
$$

Example: Compute $3 + {}^-8$.

Solution: Since $3 > 0$ and ${}^-8 < 0$ and $|3| < |{}^-8|$,

$$3 + {}^-8 = {}^-(|{}^-8| - |3|)$$
$$= {}^-(8 - 3)$$
$$= {}^-5$$

Example: Compute ${}^-8 + 3$.

Solution: By the commutative property for addition,

$${}^-8 + 3 = 3 + {}^-8$$
$$= {}^-5$$
by the previous example.

Since the magnitude of each integer is a whole number, we are now able to compute the sum of any two integers by using the properties of whole numbers, and the addition and subtraction algorithms.

Example: Compute ${}^-4387 + 3291$.

Solution:

$${}^-4387 + 3291 = 3291 + {}^-4387 \quad \text{[by the commutative property]}$$
$$= {}^-(4387 - 3291) \quad \text{[since } |{}^-4387| > |3291|]$$
$$= {}^-1096 \quad \text{[by the subtraction algorithm]}$$

Exercises 4.2

Use vector addition to solve each of the following sentences. $n \in J$.

1. $3 + {}^-5 = n$ 2. ${}^-7 + 2 = n$
3. ${}^-4 + 0 = n$ 4. ${}^-6 + {}^-8 = n$
5. $12 + {}^-4 = n$ 6. ${}^-38 + 15 = n$
7. ${}^-22 + {}^-16 = n$ 8. $286 + {}^-16 = n$
9. ${}^-147 + 23 = n$ 10. ${}^-36 + {}^-28 = n$

11–15. Use the addition rule for integers to solve each of the sentences in problems 6 through 10. $n \in J$.

Use either of the above methods to solve each of the following sentences.
$n \in J$.

  16. $48 + {}^-183 = n$ 17. ${}^-965 + 2804 = n$
  18. ${}^-819 + {}^-797 = n$ 19. ${}^-4821 + 3765 = n$
  20. $28{,}653 + {}^-4763 = n$

21. It is stated on page 88 that vector addition in the set of integers has
    the properties of (**1**) closure, (**2**) commutativity, (**3**) associativity,
    and (**4**) identity.   Provide examples to illustrate these properties.

    (*Hint:* To illustrate that vector addition is commutative, you might
    provide the following example.)

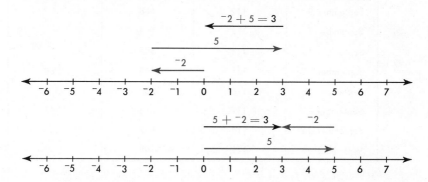

22. Give an example to show the fifth property of vector addition: (**5**)
    The sum of the vectors that correspond to the integers a and ${}^-a$ is
    the zero vector (additive identity element).   Property 5 can be
    restated as: Each integer a has an additive inverse, ${}^-a$, such that
    $a + {}^-a = 0$.

Use vector addition to solve the following sentences. $n \in J$.

  23. ${}^-2 + 0 + {}^-3 = n$ 24. $5 + {}^-7 + 2 = n$
  25. $11 + {}^-4 + 6 + {}^-7 = n$ 26. ${}^-8 + {}^-5 + 3 + {}^-3 = n$
  27. $15 + 2 + 0 + {}^-7 + {}^-2 = n$

28–32. Use the addition and subtraction algorithms and the properties
    of whole number addition to solve the sentences in problems 23
    through 27. $n \in J$.

Solve each of the following sentences. $n \in J$.

  33. $386 + {}^-754 = n$ 34. ${}^-821 + {}^-439 = n$
  35. ${}^-1028 + 653 = n$ 36. ${}^-2533 + {}^-12{,}463 = n$
  37. $7561 + {}^-9842 = n$ 38. ${}^-12 + {}^-83 + 15 = n$

39. $^-48 + 7 + 56 + ^-21 = n$

40. $245 + ^-783 + ^-45 + 83 = n$

41. $1046 + ^-759 + 11 + 82 + ^-906 = n$

42. $^-83 + ^-7 + ^-921 + ^-1856 + ^-29 = n$

43. Mr. Kay's checking account for the month of September has the entries shown. If Mr. Kay had $139 in his checking account at the beginning of September, how much money did he have in his account at the beginning of October ?

Date	Check No.	Amount of Check	Deposit
September 3	112	$68	
September 7	113	$14	
September 10	114	$85	
September 15	115	$165	$760
September 18	116	$220	
September 19	117	$12	$342
September 25	118	$57	
September 29	119	$108	

44. A salesman must leave city A to visit accounts in cities B, C, D, E, and F. The position of each city with respect to the previous city is given by a pair of numbers (a, b). The first number represents distance in the north-south direction and the second number represents distance in the east-west direction. A negative integer indicates that the distance considered is either south or west. For example: $B(10, ^-18)$ is interpreted to mean that city B is 10 miles north and 18 miles west of city A. If the locations of the remaining cities are $C(54, ^-67)$, $D(78, ^-35)$, $E(^-96, 52)$, and $F(^-37, 41)$, how far is city D from city A ?

45. Do the sentences "$4 + ^-3 = 1$" and "$4 - 3 = 1$" suggest some relationship between subtraction and the negative number sign?

46. Solve each of the following sentences by vector addition. $n \in J$.

$$\text{(a)} \ 4 + 3 = n \qquad \text{(b)} \ 4 + 2 = n$$
$$\text{(c)} \ 4 + 1 = n \qquad \text{(d)} \ 4 + 0 = n$$

Does the pattern established by the solutions to these sentences suggest how to solve sentences (e) and (f) ?

$$\text{(e)} \ 4 + ^-1 = n \qquad \text{(f)} \ 4 + ^-2 = n$$

47. Vector addition is defined as a four-step procedure on page 87. Write down all the similarities that you find between this definition and the addition rule on page 89.

4.3 Subtraction of Integers

The properties of addition of Section 4.2 provide us with an addition rule for integers. It allows us to interpret integer addition in terms of whole-number addition. We invented new numbers (the negative integers) to extend the set of whole numbers. Then we invented integer addition as an extension of whole-number addition. We can therefore add integers without having to change the way we add whole numbers. We shall now apply the operation of subtraction to the set of integers.

Subtraction in the set of whole numbers was defined as the inverse operation for addition. This definition is extended to subtraction in the set of integers.

The sentence "$4 - 3 = n$" has a solution if and only if there is an integer n such that $4 = n + 3$.

Consider the following sentences.

$$\textbf{1. } 4 - 3 = n. \qquad \textbf{2. } 4 - {}^-3 = n.$$
$$\textbf{3. } {}^-4 - {}^-3 = n. \qquad \textbf{4. } {}^-4 - 3 = n.$$

They are solved as follows:

1. $4 - 3 = n$ if and only if $4 = n + 3$. So, $n = 1 = 4 + {}^-3$.
2. $4 - {}^-3 = n$ if and only if $4 = n + {}^-3$. So, $n = 7 = 4 + 3$.
3. ${}^-4 - {}^-3 = n$ if and only if ${}^-4 = n + {}^-3$. So, $n = {}^-1 = {}^-4 + 3$.
4. ${}^-4 - 3 = n$ if and only if ${}^-4 = n + 3$. So, $n = {}^-7 = {}^-4 + {}^-3$.

Figure 4.9 summarizes the above results and suggests that every subtraction problem in the set of integers can be restated as an addition problem.

$$
\begin{array}{ll}
4 - 3 = 1 & 4 + {}^-3 = 7 \\
4 - {}^-3 = 7 & 4 + 3 = 7 \\
{}^-4 - {}^-3 = {}^-1 & {}^-4 + 3 = {}^-1 \\
{}^-4 - 3 = {}^-7 & {}^-4 + {}^-3 = {}^-7
\end{array}
$$

FIGURE 4.9

Figure 4.9 also suggests the alternative definition for subtraction of integers.

DEFINITION OF SUBTRACTION

To subtract the integer b from the integer a add the opposite of b to a. Symbolically, for each of the integers a and b, $a - b = a + (^-b)$.

Example:

(a) $12 - 7 = 12 + {}^-7 = 5$
(b) $12 - {}^-7 = 12 + {}^-({}^-7) = 12 + 7 = 19$
(c) $^-48 - {}^-24 = {}^-48 + {}^-({}^-24) = {}^-24$

Exercises 4.3

Solve each of the following sentences by interpreting subtraction as the inverse for addition. $n \in J$.

1. $7 - 14 = n$ **2.** $8 - {}^-12 = n$
3. $48 - {}^-32 = n$ **4.** $^-46 - 29 = n$
5. $^-84 - {}^-56 = n$

6–10. Solve the sentences of problems 1 through 5 by using the definition of subtraction for integers.

Compute each difference.

11. $486 - 942$ **12.** $359 - {}^-1148$
13. $^-8246 - 7531$ **14.** $^-7962 - {}^-18,604$
15. $83,670 - 200,400$ **16.** $343 - 237$
17. $^-343 - {}^-237$ **18.** $237 - 343$
19. $^-237 - {}^-343$ **20.** $(16 - {}^-8) - 21$
21. $16 - ({}^-8 - 21)$ **22.** $16 - ({}^-8 + 21)$
23. $8 - (21 - 16)$

The method used in solving problems 1 through 5 can be combined with vector addition to solve the sentence "$3 - 8 = n$." $3 - 8 = n$ if and only if $n + 8 = 3$ or, equivalently, $8 + n = 3$. By vector addition, $n = {}^-5$.

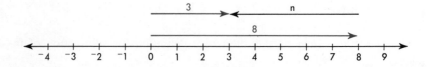

Use the above technique to solve each of the following sentences. $n \in J$.

24. $2 - 4 = n$ 25. $^-3 - 8 = n$

26. $1 - {}^-5 = n$ 27. $^-2 - {}^-4 = n$

28. Do problems 24 through 27 suggest to you how the method of vector addition can be adapted to solve subtraction problems? If so, solve the sentences in problems 24 through 27 by vector subtraction.

29. Provide examples to show that subtraction of integers is not (**a**) commutative, (**b**) associative.

30. What property does subtraction have in the set of integers that it does not have in the set of whole numbers?

Perform the following subtractions.

31.	264	32.	9846	33.	$^-541$
	$-\ ^-138$		$-\ 7483$		$-\ ^-375$

34.	$^-5832$	35.	28364
	$-\ 6771$		$-\ ^-9287$

36. Dr. Green's monthly gas mileage is as shown. Completely fill in the monthly mileage change column.

Month	Mileage	Change	Month	Mileage	Change
January	2320	-455	July	1706	
February	1865		August	1783	
March	2050		September	1865	
April	1986		October	2000	
May	2360		November	2437	
June	2504		December	2855	

37. Anchorage, Alaska, recorded a temperature high of 91° and a temperature low of $^-35°$ last year. What is the range between these two temperatures?

38. Chapter Four began with the statement that you will learn how to solve a sentence of the type "$3 - 4 = n$." You can now solve this sentence. Can you describe in a few sentences the development in Sections 4.1 through 4.3 that led to your being able to solve "$3 - 4 = n$"?

4.4 Multiplication of Integers

The set of whole numbers was extended to the set of integers J, to enable us to solve a sentence of the form "$a - b = n$," where a and b are whole numbers and $b > a$. We can say that subtraction is a closed operation in the set of integers.

Now that we have the set J we must learn how to perform multiplication in J. Can we extend whole number multiplication to multiplication in the integers by devising a few simple rules? It seems all we need to learn to do is

1. Find the product of a negative integer and a positive integer.

2. Find the product of two negative integers.

Note the following patterns:

I	II
$4 \cdot 3 = 12$	$3 \cdot 4 = 12$
$4 \cdot 2 = 8$	$2 \cdot 4 = 8$
$4 \cdot 1 = 4$	$1 \cdot 4 = 4$
$4 \cdot 0 = 0$	$0 \cdot 4 = 0$
$4 \cdot {}^-1 = ?$	${}^-1 \cdot 4 = ?$
$4 \cdot {}^-2 = ?$	${}^-2 \cdot 4 = ?$

The set of sentences in column I suggests that $4 \cdot {}^-1 = {}^-4$ (read "four times negative one equals negative four") and $4 \cdot {}^-2 = {}^-8$. The set of sentences in column II suggests that ${}^-1 \cdot 4 = {}^-4$ and ${}^-2 \cdot 4 = {}^-8$. Together the two sets of sentences suggest that multiplication in the integers be made commutative. They also suggest the following multiplication rule:

MULTIPLICATION RULE I

The product of a positive integer and a negative integer is a negative integer. It is the opposite of the product of the absolute values of the two integers.

Example: $56 \cdot {}^-38 = {}^-(56 \cdot 38)$ —┌ 56

                                   $= {}^-(2128)$ 38
                                                            ─────
                                   $= {}^-2128$ 448

                                                              168
                                                            ─────
                                                            └ 2128

Example: ${}^-104 \cdot 15 = {}^-(104 \cdot 15)$ —┌ 104

                                   $= {}^-1560$ 15
                                                            ─────
                                                              520

                                                              104
                                                            ─────
                                                            └ 1560

The examples suggest that the multiplication algorithm for whole numbers and multiplication rule I are all that is needed to find the product of a positive integer and a negative integer. *A new multiplication algorithm is not necessary.*

Observe these patterns:

I	II
${}^-4 \cdot 3 = {}^-12$	$3 \cdot {}^-4 = {}^-12$
${}^-4 \cdot 2 = {}^-8$	$2 \cdot {}^-4 = {}^-8$
${}^-4 \cdot 1 = {}^-4$	$1 \cdot {}^-4 = {}^-4$
${}^-4 \cdot 0 = 0$	$0 \cdot {}^-4 = 0$
${}^-4 \cdot {}^-1 = ?$	${}^-1 \cdot {}^-4 = ?$
${}^-4 \cdot {}^-2 = ?$	${}^-2 \cdot {}^-4 = ?$

The sentences in column I suggest that ${}^-4 \cdot {}^-1 = 4$ and ${}^-4 \cdot {}^-2 = 8$. The sentences in column II suggest that ${}^-1 \cdot {}^-4 = 4$ and ${}^-2 \cdot {}^-4 = 8$. Again commutativity of multiplication is suggested. These sentences also suggest that 1 is the multiplicative identity element in the set of integers and that the product of any integer and 0 is zero. A second multiplication rule is also suggested.

MULTIPLICATION RULE II

The product of two negative integers is a positive integer. It is the product of their absolute values.

Example: $^-96 \cdot {}^-27 = |{}^-96| \cdot |{}^-27|$ ───┌   96
                           $= 96 \cdot 27$ 27
                           $= 2592$ ────
                                                                 672
                                                                 192
                                                                ────
                                                                2592

Referring back to Section 3.6, we see that whole number multiplication is defined there in terms of the Cartesian product operation. To find the product $3 \cdot 2$, one forms the Cartesian product set $A \times B$ from a set $A = \{a, b, c\}$ containing three elements and a set $B = \{1, 2\}$ containing two elements. The number of elements in the Cartesian product set $A \times B = \{(a, 1), (a, 2), (b, 1), (b, 2), (c, 1), (c, 2)\}$ is the product sought. The properties of the multiplication operation are then obtained from the definition.

Our discussion of multiplication in the integers did not begin with a definition. We allowed some multiplicative patterns to indicate how multiplication might be extended from the whole numbers to the integers. What we really did was assume that, except for two new rules to handle negative numbers, multiplication in the integers is exactly the same as multiplication in the whole numbers.

To sum up: Multiplication in the set of integers is a binary operation that satisfies the following properties:

For each of the integers a, b, c,

1. $a \cdot b$ is an integer   [closure]
2. $a \cdot b = b \cdot a$ [commutativity]
3. $(a \cdot b) \cdot c = a \cdot (b \cdot c)$ [associativity]
4. $a \cdot 1 = a$ [identity]
5. $a \cdot 0 = 0$ [zero factor]
6. $a \cdot (b + c) = a \cdot b + a \cdot c$ [distributivity]
    $(a + b) \cdot c = a \cdot c + b \cdot c$

Example: Find the product of 3, $^-5$, and $^-12$.

Solution: $3 \cdot {}^-5 = {}^-15$
                                    ${}^-15 \cdot {}^-12 = 180$
So $(3 \cdot {}^-5) \cdot {}^-12 = 180$
Or ${}^-5 \cdot {}^-12 = 60$
                                    $3 \cdot 60 = 180$
So $3 \cdot ({}^-5 \cdot {}^-12) = 180$

Example: Use the distributive law to find the product of ⁻5 and 12.

Solution:
$$⁻5 \cdot 12 = ⁻5 \cdot (10 + 2)$$
$$= ⁻5 \cdot 10 + ⁻5 \cdot 2$$
$$= ⁻50 + ⁻10$$
$$= ⁻60$$

Example: Use the distributive law to solve the sentence "85 · 99 = *n*."

Solution:
$$85 \cdot 99 = 85 \cdot (100 + ⁻1)$$
$$= 85 \cdot 100 + 85 \cdot ⁻1$$
$$= 8500 + ⁻85$$
$$= 8415$$

We conclude this section with a comment on notation. A product such as ⁻5 · (10 + 2) is often written ⁻5(10 + 2) and is read "negative five times the quantity ten plus two."

Exercises 4.4

1. State the two multiplication rules of this section.

Use the multiplication rules to solve each of the following sentences. *n* ∈ *J*.

> **2.** ⁻8 · 6 = *n*   **3.** ⁻14(⁻5) = *n*
> **4.** 33(⁻48) = *n*   **5.** ⁻137(⁻259) = *n*
> **6.** ⁻1803 · 607 = *n*

Use the distributive law to solve each of the following sentences. *n* ∈ *J*. Do as many as you can mentally.

> **7.** 8 · 19 = *n*   **8.** 101(⁻12) = *n*
> **9.** ⁻31(⁻6) = *n*   **10.** 99 · 19 = *n*
> **11.** 198(⁻59) = *n*

Compute each of the indicated products.

> **12.** (2)(⁻5)(8)   **13.** (3)(8)(⁻2)(⁻25)
> **14.** (⁻12)(⁻6)(5)(⁻5)   **15.** (11)(⁻21)(9)
> **16.** (100)(10)(⁻5)(1000)

Compute each of the following in two different ways.

> **17.** ⁻(8 + 12 − 36)   **18.** ⁻(⁻6 − 23 + 104)
> **19.** ⁻(11 − 59 + 145 − 763)   **20.** ⁻(⁻13 + 29) + (⁻141 + 93)

21. Referring to your results for problems 17 through 20, can you make a generalization about the effect the opposite sign outside the grouping symbols has on the signs inside the grouping symbols?

22. Mr. Jones indicates a withdrawal from his bank account by writing an "opposite" before an amount withdrawn. "⁻123" appears thirty six times in his accounts as car payments. How much did he withdraw from his bank account to pay for the car?

23. An ocean rig begins drilling for oil at elevation ⁻136 feet. If the drill can descend 20 feet an hour, at what elevation will it be after 48 hours of drilling?

24. A certain freezing process requires that room temperature be lowered from 70 degrees Fahrenheit at the rate of 23°F every 2 hours. What is the room temperature 10 hours after the process begins?

25. (a) The first paragraph of Section 3.8 indicates how the product of two whole numbers is determined by repeated addition. Solve the sentence "⁻3 · 4 = n" by repeated addition.

   (b) The set of integers, J, contains the set W as a subset. Therefore multiplication in the integers should enjoy the same properties as whole-number multiplication. Assume integer multiplication is commutative and use part (a) to solve the sentence $4(⁻3) = n$.

   (c) Which multiplication rule of this section is suggested by parts (a) and (b) of this problem?

26. Assume multiplication in the integers enjoys the distributive property. Supply reasons for the results obtained in parts (a) through (e) below.

   (a) $3 + ⁻3 = 0$ Why?
   (b) $⁻4(3 + ⁻3) = 0$ Why?
   (c) $⁻4(3 + ⁻3) = ⁻4 · 3 + (⁻4)(⁻3) = 0$ Why?
   (d) $⁻4 · 3 = ⁻12$ Why?
   (e) $(⁻4)(⁻3) = 12$ Why?

   (f) Which multiplication rule of this section is suggested by parts (a) through (e) of this problem?

Replace the blank with an integer in each sentence to make a true statement.

27. $⁻3 · \underline{\ \ \ } = 27$ 28. $5 · \underline{\ \ \ } = ⁻35$

29. $\underline{\ \ \ } · (⁻8) = 56$ 30. $⁻12 · \underline{\ \ \ } = 132$

31. $\underline{\ \ \ } · 14 = ⁻266$

4.5 Division of Integers

Division of integers shall be thought of as the inverse of multiplication. If a and $b \neq 0$ are integers, the sentence "$a \div b = n$" has a solution if and only if $n \cdot b = a$ has a solution. We already know how to divide whole numbers, when the operation can be performed. Therefore to extend division from the set of whole numbers to the set of integers it is only necessary to establish how to divide:

1. A positive integer by a negative integer.
2. A negative integer by a positive integer.
3. A negative integer by a negative integer.

Example: Solve the sentence "$16 \div (^-8) = n$."

Solution: $16 \div (^-8) = n$ is equivalent to $n(^-8) = 16$. Hence $n = {}^-2$.

Example: Solve the sentence "$^-21 \div 3 = n$."

Solution: $^-21 \div 3 = n$ is equivalent to $n \cdot 3 = {}^-21$. Hence $n = {}^-7$.

Example: Solve the sentence "$^-5 \div 0 = n$."

Solution: $^-5 \div 0 = n$ is equivalent to $n \cdot 0 = {}^-5$. Since the product of any integer and zero is zero, the sentence "$^-5 \div 0 = n$" has no solution in the set of integers. Again we state that *division by zero is not defined.*

Example: Solve the sentence "$^-18 \div (^-6) = n$."

Solution: $^-18 \div (^-6) = n$ is equivalent to $n(^-6) = {}^-18$. Hence $n = 3$.

The examples suggest the following general division rules for integers:

DIVISION RULE I

If a division involving a positive integer and a negative integer can be performed, the quotient is always a negative integer.

DIVISION RULE II

If a division involving two negative integers can be performed, the quotient is always a positive integer.

(Note: A new division algorithm for the integers is not needed. We need only use whole number division and the division rules for integers.)

Example: Solve "$^-240 \div 15 = n$."

Solution: $n = {}^-(240 \div 15)$ by division rule I.   Perform the indicated division:

$$
\begin{array}{r}
16 \\
15\overline{)240} \\
15 \\ \hline
90 \\
90 \\ \hline
0
\end{array}
$$

Hence $n = {}^-(240 \div 15)$
$\quad\quad = {}^-16$

Example: Solve "$^-1272 \div (^-24) = n$."

Solution: $n = 1272 \div 24$ by division rule II.   Perform the indicated division:

$$
\begin{array}{r}
53 \\
24\overline{)1272} \\
120 \\ \hline
72 \\
72 \\ \hline
0
\end{array}
$$

Hence $n = 53$.

Example: Solve the sentence "$^-7 \div 3 = n$."   The domain for n is the set of integers.

Solution: $^-7 \div 3 = n$ is equivalent to $n \cdot 3 = {}^-7$.   But there is no integer n which when multiplied by 3 gives a product $^-7$.   We say therefore that the division, $^-7 \div 3$, cannot be performed in the set of integers.

Exercises 4.5

1. Write the two division rules discussed in this section.

Solve each of the following sentences using the division rules for integers $n \in J$.

    2. $56 \div (^-8) = n$ **3.** $^-80 \div 5 = n$

    4. $^-182 \div (^-13) = n$ **5.** $^-10,192 \div 364 = n$

    6. $^-238,003 \div (^-283) = n$

Indicate which of the following sentences has no solutions. $n \in J$.

    7. $426 \div (^-7) = n$ **8.** $0 \div (^-83) = n$

    9. $^-54 \div 0 = n$ **10.** $^-132 \div 12 = n$

    11. $^-18 \div (^-36) = n$ **12.** $^-135 \div 0 = n$

    13. $^-720 \div (^-24) = n$ **14.** $258 \div (^-18) = n$

15. Write ten pairs of integers (a, b) such that $a \div b = ^-3$. $(6, ^-2)$ is one such pair because $6 \div (^-2) = ^-3$.

16. Write ten pairs of integers (a, b) such that $a \div b = 7$.

17. Write ten pairs of integers (a, b) such that $a \div b = ^-11$.

18. An elevator descends into a mine shaft at the rate of 6 feet per second. If the descent begins from elevation 200, how long will it take to reach elevation $^-738$?

19. The temperature at 12 noon was 10 degrees above zero. If it decreased at the rate of 4 degrees per hour until midnight, at what time was the temperature 22 degrees below zero? What was the temperature at midnight?

20. Provide examples to show that division in the integers is not (**a**) closed, (**b**) commutative, (**c**) associative.

4.6 Summary

The major concern of this chapter has been to extend our number system in order that the subtraction operation be closed, without invalidating the other properties of the fundamental operations. This task was accomplished by assigning to each whole number an opposite. The new set of numbers, all the whole numbers together with their opposites, is called the set of integers. Each integer is either positive, zero, or negative, and the opposite of each integer is an integer. Associated with each integer is its magnitude, or absolute value. The absolute value of an integer is always nonnegative, that is, a whole number.

We defined vector addition to see how to add integers. With our knowledge of vector addition we developed some addition patterns for integers. These patterns helped us establish the addition rule for integers which allows us to add integers without recourse to vector addition. Addition was thus extended to the set of integers in which it was a closed operation and had the properties of commutativity, associativity, and additive identity.

We then extended the definition of multiplication from the set of whole numbers to include the product of any two integers. In so doing we preserved the properties of multiplication in the set of whole numbers.

Finally, subtraction and division were again introduced as the inverse operations for addition and multiplication, respectively. And subtraction was shown to be a closed operation in the set of integers.

Since many physical quantities have associated with them both a magnitude and a direction, the set of integers find many applications in our modern world, some of which were discussed in this chapter.

Exercises 4.6—Review

Complete each sentence:

1. The magnitude of a number is its _____.
2. The set $\{\ldots, {}^-4, {}^-3, {}^-2, {}^-1, 0, 1, 2, 3, 4, \ldots\}$ is the set of _____.
3. If the graph of a first number is to the right of the graph of a second number, then the first number is _____ than the second number.
4. The sum of each number and its opposite is _____.
5. The addition rule for integers relates addition of integers to addition of _____.
6. Addition and subtraction of integers are _____ operations.
7. Each subtraction problem can be converted to _____.
8. The product of each two integers is _____.
9. The inverse operation for multiplication of integers is _____.
10. Division of nonzero integers is not a _____ operation.

True or false?

11. $|{}^-7| < |7|$ **12.** ${}^-7 < 7$
13. ${}^-({}^-12)$ is a positive integer.   **14.** $({}^-3) + 5 = 5 + ({}^-3)$
15. $({}^-3) + 5 = |{}^-3| + |5|$ **16.** $({}^-16) + ({}^-12) < ({}^-100) + 98$
17. $({}^-16) \cdot ({}^-12) < ({}^-100) \cdot (98)$ **18.** $(3 + 4) - 5 = (3 - 5) + 4$
19. $({}^-3) \cdot (5) = |{}^-3| \cdot |5|$

20. $[(^-2) + (^-12)] \div [10 + (^-3)] = | [(^-63) \div (^-9)] - 9 |$
21. The quotient of each two nonzero integers is an integer.
22. Subtraction of integers is an associative operation.
23. The product of two nonpositive integers is a nonpositive integer.
24. Each integer is greater than its opposite.
25. Any integer can be the absolute value of some integer.
26. There is a first integer whose sum with any second integer is that second integer.
27. The quotient of two nonpositive integers, if it exists, is a nonnegative integer.
28. The sum of two nonnegative integers is a nonnegative integer.
29. The sum of two integers is greater than either integer.
30. The product of two integers is greater than or equal to one of the factors.

Compute each of the following.

31. $(^-63) + (^-28)$ **32.** $(^-59) + 46$
33. $27 - (^-33)$ **34.** $(^-632) - (^-321)$
35. $(^-44) \cdot (21)$ **36.** $(^-27) \cdot (^-27)$
37. $(^-693) \div (63)$ **38.** $(^-1024) + (^-16)$
39. $[(^-3) + (^-5)] \cdot [(^-3) - (^-5)]$ **40.** $[(^-36) + (^-72)] \div (^-12)$

Each of the following sentences illustrates some property for an operation in the set of integers. State the property.

41. $(^-538) + (^-457) = (^-457) + (^-538)$
42. $[(^-62) \cdot 39 + (^-38) \cdot 39] = [(^-62) + (^-38)] \cdot 39$
43. $(^-56) + [(^-56) + (^-79)] = [(^-56) + (^-56)] + (^-79)$
44. $375 \cdot 439 \cdot (^-564) \cdot 0 = 0$
45. $[5693 + (^-6572)] \cdot 1 = 5693 + (^-6572)$

chapter five

PRIME NUMBERS

5.0 Introduction

Before proceeding to the rational-number system, we shall investigate some additional properties of the arithmetic of whole numbers. We may then use these properties to aid us in performing computation with rational numbers.

In this chapter we shall separate the set of whole numbers into two major classes, prime numbers and composite numbers. Investigation of the factors of a number leads to the fundamental theorem of arithmetic, which tells us that every composite number can be renamed as a product of prime numbers. We shall then use this result to find the greatest common factor and the least common multiple of a pair of numbers, processes basic to computation in the rational number system.

5.1 Exponential Notation

Occasionally we encounter indicated products in which the same number is used more than once as a factor, for example, $2 \cdot 2 \cdot 2 = 8$ or $3 \cdot 3 \cdot 3 \cdot 3 \cdot 3 = 243$. Because such notation is rather cumbersome, we shall adopt the following

106

Definition:

The product of m factors of the number a, m ≥ 2, is the **mth power of a,** *written a^m. Symbolically,*

$$a = \underbrace{a \cdot a \cdot a \cdot \ldots \cdot a}_{m \ factors \ of \ a}$$

This form of expressing a continued product is called **exponential notation.**

The repeated factor a is called the **base** *and the number of factors m is called the* **exponent.**

Example 1: $2 \cdot 2 \cdot 2 = 2^3$
$\qquad 7 \cdot 7 \cdot 7 \cdot 7 \cdot 7 \cdot 7 = 7^6$
$\qquad 3 \cdot 3 \cdot 3 \cdot 3 \cdot 3 = 3^5$
$\qquad 12 \cdot 12 = 12^2$

Example 2: Express as a continued product (a) 2^5, (b) 5^4, (c) 9^2, (d) 18^8.

Solution:

(a) $2^5 = 2 \cdot 2 \cdot 2 \cdot 2 \cdot 2$
(b) $5^4 = 5 \cdot 5 \cdot 5 \cdot 5$
(c) $9^2 = 9 \cdot 9$
(d) $18^8 = 18 \cdot 18 \cdot 18 \cdot 18 \cdot 18 \cdot 18 \cdot 18 \cdot 18$

Example 3: Express as a continued product without exponents: (a) $2^3 \cdot 3^2 \cdot 5^2$, (b) $4^4 \cdot 6^3$.

Solution:

(a) $2^3 \cdot 3^2 \cdot 5^2 = 2 \cdot 2 \cdot 2 \cdot 3 \cdot 3 \cdot 5 \cdot 5$
(b) $4^4 \cdot 6^3 = 4 \cdot 4 \cdot 4 \cdot 4 \cdot 6 \cdot 6 \cdot 6$

Example 4: Express in exponential notation:

(a) $2 \cdot 2 \cdot 2 \cdot 2 \cdot 3 \cdot 3 \cdot 3 \cdot 3 \cdot 3$, (b) $2 \cdot 3 \cdot 2 \cdot 3 \cdot 2 \cdot 3 \cdot 2 \cdot 3 \cdot 3$.

Solution:

(a) $2 \cdot 2 \cdot 2 \cdot 2 \cdot 3 \cdot 3 \cdot 3 \cdot 3 \cdot 3 = (2 \cdot 2 \cdot 2 \cdot 2) \cdot (3 \cdot 3 \cdot 3 \cdot 3 \cdot 3)$
$$= 2^4 \cdot 3^5$$

(b) $2 \cdot 3 \cdot 2 \cdot 3 \cdot 2 \cdot 3 \cdot 2 \cdot 3 \cdot 3 = [(2 \cdot 3) \cdot (2 \cdot 3) \cdot (2 \cdot 3) \cdot (2 \cdot 3)] \cdot 3$
$$= (2 \cdot 3)^4 \cdot 3$$

or alternatively

$$2 \cdot 3 \cdot 2 \cdot 3 \cdot 2 \cdot 3 \cdot 2 \cdot 3 \cdot 3 = (2 \cdot 2 \cdot 2 \cdot 2) \cdot (3 \cdot 3 \cdot 3 \cdot 3 \cdot 3)$$
$$= 2^4 \cdot 3^5$$

How were the commutative and associative properties for multiplication used in Example 4?

Example 5: Simplify the indicated product, expressing the result in exponential notation: **(a)** $2^3 \cdot 2^2$, **(b)** $3^4 \cdot 5^2 \cdot 3^2 \cdot 5^3$.

Solution:

(a) $2^3 \cdot 2^2 = (2 \cdot 2 \cdot 2) \cdot (2 \cdot 2)$
$$= 2^5$$

(b) $3^4 \cdot 5^2 \cdot 3^2 \cdot 5^3 = 3^4 \cdot 3^2 \cdot 5^2 \cdot 5^3$
$$= (3 \cdot 3 \cdot 3 \cdot 3)(3 \cdot 3)(5 \cdot 5)(5 \cdot 5 \cdot 5)$$
$$= (3 \cdot 3 \cdot 3 \cdot 3 \cdot 3 \cdot 3)(5 \cdot 5 \cdot 5 \cdot 5 \cdot 5)$$
$$= 3^6 \cdot 5^5$$

Example 6: Simplify the indicated quotient, expressing the result in exponential notation: **(a)** $5^3 \div 5^2$, **(b)** $(3^4 \cdot 7^3) \div (3^2 \cdot 7)$.

Solution:

(a) $5^3 \div 5^2 = (5 \cdot 5 \cdot 5) \div (5 \cdot 5) = q$ if and only if $q \cdot (5 \cdot 5) = (5 \cdot 5 \cdot 5)$ for some $q \in J$
Hence $q = 5$, by inspection.

(b) $(3^4 \cdot 7^3) \div (3^2 \cdot 7) = q$ if and only if $q \cdot (3^2 \cdot 7) = 3^4 \cdot 7^3$, for some $q \in J$

Since $3^4 \cdot 7^3 = 3^2 \cdot 3^2 \cdot 7 \cdot 7^2$
$$= (3^2 \cdot 7^2) \cdot (3^2 \cdot 7)$$
$q \cdot (3^2 \cdot 7) = (3^2 \cdot 7^2) \cdot (3^2 \cdot 7)$
Hence $q = 3^2 \cdot 7^2$.

Definition:

For each integer a, a^2 is called the **square** *of a and a is called* **a square root** *of a^2.*

Example 7: $3^2 = 9$ and $(-3)^2 = 9$

    9 is the square of 3

    9 is the square of $^-3$

    3 is a square root of 9

    $^-3$ is a square root of 9

Definition:

For each integer a, a^3 is the **cube** *of a and a is the* **cube root** *of a^3.*

Example 8: $4^3 = 64$

    64 is the cube of 4

    4 is the cube root of 64

Frequently we are concerned with powers of products and powers of powers.

Example 9: Express $(2 \cdot 3)^4$ as a product of powers.

Solution:
$$(2 \cdot 3)^4 = (2 \cdot 3) \cdot (2 \cdot 3) \cdot (2 \cdot 3) \cdot (2 \cdot 3)$$
$$= (2 \cdot 2 \cdot 2 \cdot 2) \cdot (3 \cdot 3 \cdot 3 \cdot 3)$$
$$= 2^4 \cdot 3^4$$

Example 10: Simplify $(3^4)^2$.

Solution:
$$(3^4)^2 = 3^4 \cdot 3^4$$
$$= (3 \cdot 3 \cdot 3 \cdot 3) \cdot (3 \cdot 3 \cdot 3 \cdot 3)$$
$$= 3^8$$
$$= 3^{(4 \cdot 2)}$$

The preceding examples suggest some of the following properties of exponents, which we state without proof.

Properties of Exponents

For each of the integers a and b and for each of the whole numbers m and n.

1. $a^0 = 1, a \neq 0$
2. $a^1 = a.$
3. $a^m \cdot a^n = a^{m+n}.$
4. $a^m \div a^n = a^{m-n}$ for $m \geq n.$
5. $(ab)^m = a^m b^m.$
6. $(a^m)^n = a^{mn}.$

Exercises 5.1

Express each of the following as a product without using exponents.

1. 3^4
2. 5^6
3. $(-17)^3$
4. 100^6
5. 19^2
6. $(-4)^4$
7. 9^9
8. $(3^3)^3$
9. $3^2 \cdot 4^2 \cdot 5^2$
10. $(-7)^3 \cdot 9^2 \cdot (-11)$
11. $3^6 \cdot 2^2 \cdot 5^3$
12. $(-2)^6 \cdot 3^4 \cdot 7^3$

Express each of the following in exponential notation.

13. $3 \cdot 3 \cdot 3 \cdot 3 \cdot 3 \cdot 3$
14. $6 \cdot 6 \cdot 6 \cdot 6$
15. $23 \cdot 23 \cdot 23 \cdot 23 \cdot 23$
16. $100{,}000 \cdot 100{,}000$
17. $3 \cdot 3 \cdot 4 \cdot 4 \cdot 4 \cdot 5 \cdot 5 \cdot 5 \cdot 5 \cdot 5$
18. $6 \cdot 6 \cdot 6 \cdot 9 \cdot 9 \cdot 9 \cdot 11 \cdot 11$
19. $2 \cdot 2 \cdot 3 \cdot 3 \cdot 3 \cdot 4 \cdot 4 \cdot 4 \cdot 4 \cdot 5 \cdot 5$
20. $2 \cdot 3 \cdot 4 \cdot 3 \cdot 4 \cdot 2 \cdot 2 \cdot 3 \cdot 3 \cdot 4$
21. $7 \cdot 9 \cdot 7 \cdot 9 \cdot 9 \cdot 9 \cdot 7 \cdot 9$
22. $13 \cdot 17 \cdot 17 \cdot 17 \cdot 13 \cdot 13 \cdot 13 \cdot 17$
23. $3 \cdot 3 \cdot 5 \cdot 5 \cdot 7 \cdot 5 \cdot 7 \cdot 7 \cdot 3 \cdot 7 \cdot 5 \cdot 5 \cdot 7$
24. $3 \cdot 7 \cdot 5 \cdot 7 \cdot 7 \cdot 3 \cdot 9 \cdot 3 \cdot 8 \cdot 3 \cdot 5$

Simplify each indicated product, quotient, or power and express the result in exponential notation.

25. $2^2 \cdot 3^3 \cdot 2^5$
26. $2^4 \cdot 3^4 \cdot 3^2 \cdot 5$
27. $5^6 \cdot 7 \cdot 5 \cdot 7^4$
28. $3^2 \cdot 5^3 \cdot 7 \cdot 5 \cdot 7^3$
29. $3^7 \div 3^3$
30. $(-5)^{17} \div (-5)^8$
31. $(5^4 \cdot 7^3) \div (5 \cdot 7^2)$
32. $(11^7 \cdot 13^5) \div (11^3 \cdot 13^3)$
33. $(3^9 \cdot (-7^7)) \div (3^6 \cdot (-7^5) \cdot 3 \cdot (-7)^2)$

34. $(7^7 \cdot 8^9 \cdot 9^9) \div (7 \cdot 8^2 \cdot 9^6)$

35. $(2^3 \cdot 3^4)^3$ **36.** $(3^2 \cdot 5^3)^2 \cdot (3^3 \cdot 5^2)^3$

37. $[(3^4 \cdot 5^5)^6]^3$

Find the squares of each of the following.

38. 7	**39.** $^-3$
40. 13	**41.** 12
42. $^-6$	**43.** $^-15$
44. $^-25$	**45.** 19
46. $^-19$	**47.** 15
48. $(6 + 5)$	**49.** $(^-3 + 7)$
50. (ab) $\quad [a, b \in J]$	**51.** $(a + b)$ $\quad [a, b \in J]$

Find the square roots of each of the following.

52. 49	**53.** 121
54. 144	**55.** $^-16$
56. 8^2	**57.** $(^-4)^2$
58. $(19 - 5)^2$	**59.** $(5 - 19)^2$
60. $3^2 \cdot (^-4)^2$	**61.** $[(3) \cdot (^-4)]^2$
62. a^2 $\quad [a \in J]$	**63.** $(a + b)^2$ $\quad [a, b \in J]$
64. $(ab)^2$ $\quad [a, b \in J]$	**65.** $(a - b)^2$ $\quad [a, b \in J]$

Find the cubes of each of the following.

66. 5	**67.** $^-9$
68. $^-4$	**69.** 6
70. ab^2c^3 $\quad [a, b, c \in J]$	**71.** $3a$ $\quad [a \in J]$

Find the cube roots of each of the following.

72. 27	**73.** $^-64$
74. $^-125$	**75.** 216
76. $8a^3$ $\quad [a \in J]$	**77.** $343a^6b^3$ $\quad [a, b \in J]$

True or false ?

78. The square of each positive integer is positive.

79. The cube of each negative integer is negative.

80. The square of each integer is positive.

81. The fourth power of each negative integer is negative.

82. Each odd power of each negative integer is negative.

83. Each even power of each negative integer is negative.

84. Each even power of each integer is positive.

85. On the first day in September you have \$1. Each succeeding day in September you double your money. How much do you have on September 5? September 10? September 20? September 30?

86. Is "$2^2 + 3^2 = (2 + 3)^2$" true?

Is "$(5 + 1)^2 = 5^2 + 1^2$" true?

Is "$a^2 + b^2 = (a + b)^2$" true for all integers a and b?

5.2 Prime and Composite Numbers

Frequently we are interested in the factors of a whole number. For example, 1 is the only factor of 1. 2 has 1 and 2 as factors. The only factors of 3 are 1 and 3. 4 has factors 1, 2, and 4, etc.

Some whole numbers, you may have noted, have exactly two distinct factors, 1 and the number itself. 2, 3, and 5 are such numbers and are called *prime numbers*.

To find prime numbers, we can use a trial-and-error division process, testing each whole number less than the one in question.

Example: Is 91 a prime number?

Solution: 91 is prime if the only factors of 91 are 1 and 91. But 7 is a factor of 91 because $7 \cdot 13 = 91$. Hence 91 is not a prime number.

Example: Is 23 a prime number?

Solution: As in the first example we ask ourselves if there is a factor of 23 other than 1 and 23. Is 2 a factor of 23? No, there is no integer n such that $2 \cdot n = 23$. For the same reason, 3, 4, and 5 are not factors of 23. There is no need to test integers greater than 5, because any factor greater than 5 would have to be associated with a factor less than 5 to obtain 23 as a product. So we conclude that 23 has no factors other than 1 and 23. 23 is a prime number.

These examples exhibit a lengthy and undesirable process for determining whether a whole number is prime.

Another way to find prime numbers is to use what is called the *sieve of Eratosthenes*, which works as follows. Suppose we wish to find all the prime numbers less than 30. To do so we make a list of whole numbers 1 through 30 (see Figure 5.1).

1́	2	3	4	5	6	7	8	9	10
11	12	13	14	15	16	17	18	19	20
21	22	23	24	25	26	27	28	29	30

FIGURE 5.1

First we note that since 1 has only one factor, it is not prime, so we cross it off the list. Next 2, having exactly two factors, is prime. If, however, we begin counting by twos, we shall always end at an even number. This number cannot be prime, because it will always have at least three factors: 1, 2, and the number itself. Hence we cross out each of these numbers (see Figure 5.2).

1́	2	3	4́	5	6́	7	8́	9	1́0
11	1́2	13	1́4	15	1́6	17	1́8	19	2́0
21	2́2	23	2́4	25	2́6	27	2́8	29	3́0

FIGURE 5.2

The next number we find still in our list is 3, which is prime. (Why?) Counting by threes we can eliminate more numbers. (Why?) See Figure 5.3.

1́	2	3	4́	5	6́	7	8́	9́	1́0
11	1́2	13	1́4	1́5	1́6	17	1́8	19	2́0
2́1	2́2	23	2́4	25	2́6	2́7	2́8	29	3́0

FIGURE 5.3

Proceeding similarly with 5, 7, etc., we shall have only prime numbers left in the list when we finish: 2, 3, 5, 7, 11, 13, 17, 19, 23, 29 (see Figure 5.4).

1́	②	③	4́	⑤	6́	⑦	8́	9́	1́0
⑪	1́2	⑬	1́4	1́5	1́6	⑰	1́8	⑲	2́0
2́1	2́2	㉓	2́4	2́5	2́6	2́7	2́8	㉙	3́0

FIGURE 5.4

Natural numbers that are neither prime nor 1 are called *composite numbers*.

Exercises 5.2

How many factors has each of the following whole numbers?

1. 5	**2.** 9	**3.** 10	**4.** 12	**5.** 16	**6.** 18
7. 21	**8.** 23	**9.** 30	**10.** 31	**11.** 32	**12.** 33
13. 34	**14.** 35	**15.** 36	**16.** 37	**17.** 51	**18.** 81

19. Which of the numbers in problems 1 through 18 are prime numbers?

20. Use the sieve of Eratosthenes to find all the prime numbers less than or equal to 100.

21. Use the sieve of Erathosthenes to find all the prime numbers less than or equal to 250.

22. How many whole numbers less than 100 are prime numbers?

23. How many elements belong to the set $\{p \in W: p$ is a prime number and $100 < p < 200\}$?

24. Name the first 25 composite numbers.

25. Do any composite numbers have an odd number of factors?

26. Do any composite numbers have an even number of factors?

27. Is there a whole number that is a factor of every whole number?

28. Is each whole number a factor of itself?

29. Are any prime numbers even numbers?

30. Factors of a number that are less than the number are called *proper factors*. If the sum of the proper factors of a number is the number itself, then the number is called a *perfect number*. For example, 6 is the first perfect number, since the sum of the proper factors of 6—1, 2, and 3—is 6. Find the next two perfect numbers.

31. Whole numbers such as 1, 4, 9, 16, 25, 36, etc., are called *perfect squares* because $1 = 1^2$, $4 = 2^2$, $9 = 3^2$, etc. Name the first ten perfect squares and write down next to each perfect square its factors. Do you observe any patterns?

5.3 Factor Sets and Prime Factors

Suppose you are asked to list the elements of $\{x \in W: x$ is a factor of 12$\}$. Since you know the factors of 12 you can write

$$\{x \in W: x \text{ is a factor of } 12\} = \{1, 2, 3, 4, 6, 12\}$$

This set is called the *factor set* for 12.

Are any of the elements of this set prime numbers? 2 and 3 are. Can you express 12 as a product of only 2's and 3's? You might begin by noting $2 \cdot 3 = 6$ and $6 \cdot 2 = 12$, so $(2 \cdot 3) \cdot 2 = 12$, or, by the commutative and associative properties, $2 \cdot 2 \cdot 3 = 12$.

Using the exponential notation introduced in Section 5.1, you may write $2^2 \cdot 3 = 12$. 2 and 3 are called the *prime factors* of 12.

Example:

(a) Find the factor set of 18.

(b) Express 18 as a product of primes.

Solution:

(a) $\{x \in W: x \text{ is a factor of } 18\} = \{1, 2, 3, 6, 9, 18\}$.
(b) Since 2 and 3 are the only primes in the factor set for 18, and $2 \cdot 3 = 6$ and $6 \cdot 3 = 18$, it follows that $2 \cdot 3 \cdot 3 = 18$ or, more briefly, $2 \cdot 3^2 = 18$.

Example: Express 70 as a product of primes.

Solution:
$$70 = 2 \cdot 35$$
$$= 2 \cdot (5 \cdot 7)$$
$$= 2 \cdot 5 \cdot 7$$

Example: Express 144 as a product of primes.

Solution:

$$144 = 2 \cdot 72$$
$$= 2 \cdot (2 \cdot 36)$$
$$= 2^2 \cdot (2 \cdot 18)$$
$$= 2^3 \cdot (2 \cdot 9)$$
$$= 2^4 \cdot (3 \cdot 3)$$
$$= 2^4 \cdot 3^2$$
$$\text{or } 144 = 3 \cdot 48$$
$$= 3 \cdot (6 \cdot 8)$$
$$= 3 \cdot (3 \cdot 2) \cdot 2^3$$
$$= 3^2 \cdot 2^4 = 2^4 \cdot 3^2$$

Exercises 5.3

Using the examples of this section as a guide, (a) find the factor set for each of the following numbers, and (b) express each of the following numbers as a product of primes.

1. 4	**2.** 6	**3.** 8	**4.** 9	**5.** 10	**6.** 12
7. 14	**8.** 15	**9.** 16	**10.** 18	**11.** 20	**12.** 21
13. 22	**14.** 24	**15.** 25	**16.** 26	**17.** 27	**18.** 28
19. 30	**20.** 42	**21.** 72	**22.** 54	**23.** 96	**24.** 91
25. 76	**26.** 63	**27.** 81	**28.** 84	**29.** 85	**30.** 135

Find the factor set for each of the following indicated products.

Example: $2^3 \cdot 3$.

Solution: 1 is a factor. 2, 2^2, and 2^3 are factors. 3, $2 \cdot 3$, $2^2 \cdot 3$, and $2^3 \cdot 3$ are factors. Hence the factor set of $2^3 \cdot 3$ or 24 is $\{1, 2, 2^2, 2^3, 3, 2 \cdot 3, 2^2 \cdot 3, 2^3 \cdot 3\}$ or, more simply, $\{1, 2, 4, 8, 3, 6, 12, 24\}$.

31. $3^3 \cdot 5$ **32.** $3 \cdot 5^2 \cdot 7$ **33.** $2 \cdot 3^2 \cdot 5^3$

34. $2^4 \cdot 5$ **35.** $2 \cdot 3^4$

36. Express each of the numbers 4, 7, 10, 11, and 12 as a product of primes.

37. Express the squares of each of the numbers 4, 7, 10, 11, and 12 as a product of primes.

38. Compare the results of problems 36 and 37 and state, if you can, a general property of the factors of the square of a whole number.

39. Repeat problems 37 and 38 with the word "square" replaced by "cube."

5.4 The Fundamental Theorem of Arithmetic

Is it always possible to express a composite number as a product of primes? It seems reasonable to say so on the basis of your experience with the problems of Exercises 5.3. Can a composite number be expressed as a product of primes in more than one way? For example, we may note that 105 can be expressed as a product of primes in the following ways: $3 \cdot 5 \cdot 7$, $3 \cdot 7 \cdot 5$, $5 \cdot 3 \cdot 7$, $5 \cdot 7 \cdot 3$, $7 \cdot 5 \cdot 3$, and $7 \cdot 3 \cdot 5$. However, by the commutative and associative properties of multiplication, each of these expressions is equal to the first. If you *disregard the order* of the factors, you can say that there is only one prime factorization of 105.

These observations are summarized in the following fundamental theorem, the proof of which is beyond the scope of this text.

The Fundamental Theorem of Arithmetic

Each composite whole number can be expressed as a product of primes in exactly one way.

The fundamental theorem of arithmetic allows us to *rename every whole number in a unique way* as a product of its prime factors. Since we now know that a whole number has only one prime factorization, we no longer ask for a prime factorization of that number but for *the* prime factorization.

Example: Write *the* prime factorization of 28.

Solution:
$$28 = 2 \cdot 14$$
$$= 2 \cdot 2 \cdot 7$$
$$= 2^2 \cdot 7$$

Example: Write *the* prime factorization of 101101.

Solution:
$$101101 = 7 \cdot 14443$$
$$= 7 \cdot 11 \cdot 1313$$
$$= 7 \cdot 11 \cdot 13 \cdot 101$$

Each negative integer can be expressed as the product of $^-1$ and a whole number. For example, $^-7 = {}^-1 \cdot 7$, $^-12 = {}^-1 \cdot 12$ and $^-103 = {}^-1 \cdot 103$. For convenience, when we ask for the prime factorization of a negative integer, we shall mean the product of $^-1$ and the prime factorization of the corresponding whole number.

Example: Find the prime factorization of (**a**) $^-12$, (**b**) $^-18$.

Solution:
$$\text{(a) } ^-12 = {}^-1 \cdot 12$$
$$= {}^-1 \cdot 2 \cdot 6$$
$$= {}^-1 \cdot 2 \cdot 2 \cdot 3$$
$$= {}^-1 \cdot 2^2 \cdot 3$$
$$\text{(b) } ^-18 = {}^-1 \cdot 18$$
$$= {}^-1 \cdot 2 \cdot 9$$
$$= {}^-1 \cdot 2 \cdot 3^2$$

Exercises 5.4

Write *the* prime factorization of each of the following whole numbers.

1. 32	**2.** 33	**3.** 34	**4.** 35
5. 36	**6.** 38	**7.** 39	**8.** 40
9. 42	**10.** 44	**11.** 45	**12.** 46
13. 48	**14.** 49	**15.** 50	**16.** 51

17. 52	**18.** 54	**19.** 55	**20.** 56
21. 57	**22.** 58	**23.** 60	**24.** 80
25. 156	**26.** 243	**27.** 1024	**28.** 512
29. 256	**30.** 324	**31.** 1273	**32.** 1275
33. 4680	**34.** 5125	**35.** 999,999	**36.** 468

Write the prime factorizations for each of the following negative integers.

| **37.** -10 | **38.** -50 | **39.** -72 | **40.** -48 |
| **41.** -121 | **42.** -91 | **43.** -65 | **44.** -95 |

The concept of factor set can be extended to include all the integer factors of an integer. For each of the following integers, find its integer factor set.

Example: -18.

Solution: $-18 = -1 \cdot 2 \cdot 3^2$. Hence positive integer factors are 1, 2, 3, 6, 9, and 18. Negative integer factors are the opposites of these numbers: -1, -2, -3, -6, -9, -18. There the integer factor set of -18 is $\{-18, -9, -6, -3, -2, -1, 1, 2, 3, 6, 9, 18\}$.

| **45.** -10 | **46.** -25 | **47.** -36 | **48.** -40 |
| **49.** -60 | **50.** -56 | **51.** -80 | **52.** -119 |

5.5 The Least Common Multiple and The Greatest Common Factor

Consider

$$A = \{x \in N: 4 \text{ is a factor of } x\}$$
$$B = \{x \in N: 5 \text{ is a factor of } x\}$$

Note that

$$A = \{4, 8, 12, 16, 20, 24, 28, 32, 36, 40, 44, \ldots\}$$
$$B = \{5, 10, 15, 20, 25, 30, 35, 40, 45, \ldots\}$$

A and B are called *multiple sets* for 4 and 5, respectively.
Now find $A \cap B$.

$$A \cap B = \{20, 40, 60, 80, \ldots\}$$

You might also write

$$A \cap B = \{x \in N: 4 \text{ is a factor of } x \text{ and } 5 \text{ is a factor of } x\}$$

The set $A \cap B$ is called the set of *common multiples* of 4 and 5. Since 20 is the smallest member of $A \cap B$, we say that 20 is the *least common multiple* of 4 and 5.

Since 4 is a factor of each of its multiples, each of the prime factors of 4 must also be a factor of each multiple. Similarly, any common multiple of 4 and 5 must include not only 4 and 5 as factors but the prime factors of 4 and 5 as well. For example, $4 = 2^2$, $5 = 5$, and $20 = 2^2 \cdot 5$. Each multiple of 20 is the product of $2^2 \cdot 5$ with a natural number. Consequently the prime factorization of each multiple of 20 will include $2^2 \cdot 5$ and 20 is the smallest such number.

Example: Find the least common multiple of 45 and 72.

Solution: $45 = 3^2 \cdot 5$ and $72 = 2^3 \cdot 3^2$. Now each common multiple of 45 and 72 must include $3^2 \cdot 5$ and $2^3 \cdot 3^2$ in its prime factorization. That is, each common multiple of 45 and 72 must include in its prime factorization two factors of 3, three factors of 2, and one factor of 5, or $2^3 \cdot 3^2 \cdot 5$. The smallest such number is $2^3 \cdot 3^2 \cdot 5 = 360$, the least common multiple of 45 and 72. Observe also that if

$$
\begin{aligned}
A &= \{x \in N: 45 \text{ is a factor of } x\} \\
&= \{45, 90, 135, 180, 225, 270, 315, 360, 405, \ldots\} \\
B &= \{x \in N: 72 \text{ is a factor of } x\} \\
&= \{72, 144, 216, 288, 360, 432, \ldots\}
\end{aligned}
$$

then $A \cap B = \{360, 720, \ldots\}$ and 360 is the least common multiple.

Example: Find the least common multiple of 56 and 124.

Solution: $56 = 2^3 \cdot 7$ and $124 = 2^2 \cdot 31$. Hence the least common multiple of 56 and 124 is $2^3 \cdot 7 \cdot 31 = 1936$.

Now consider the factor sets of 8 and 12:

$$A = \{x \in W: x \text{ is a factor of 8}\}$$
$$= \{1, 2, 4, 8\}$$
$$B = \{x \in W: x \text{ is a factor } 12\}$$
$$= \{1, 2, 3, 4, 6, 12\}$$

The set $A \cap B = \{1, 2, 4\}$ is the set of factors of both 8 and 12, or the set of *common factors* of 8 and 12. The largest member of this set, 4, is called the *greatest common factor* of 8 and 12. Since $8 = 2^3$ and $12 = 2^2 \cdot 3$, each common factor of 8 and 12 can include no more than two factors of 2. The largest such number is 2^2, 4, the greatest common factor of 8 and 12.

Example: Find the greatest common factor of 36 and 54.

Solution: $36 = 2^2 \cdot 3^2$ and $54 = 2 \cdot 3^3$. Hence any common factor of 36 and 54 can include not more than one factor of 2 and two factors of 3, or $2 \cdot 3^2$. Hence $2 \cdot 3^2$, or 18, is the greatest common factor of 36 and 54.

Note that if

$$A = \{x \in W: x \text{ is a factor of 36}\}$$
$$= \{1, 2, 3, 4, 6, 9, 12, 18, 36\}$$
$$B = \{x \in W: x \text{ is a factor of 54}\}$$
$$= \{1, 2, 3, 6, 9, 18, 27, 54\}$$

then $A \cap B = \{1, 2, 3, 6, 9, 18\}$. Hence 18 is the greatest common factor of 36 and 54.

Exercises 5.5

Complete each of the following sentences to make them true statements.

1. The elements of $\{7, 14, 21, \ldots\}$ are called _____ of 7.
2. The _____ of 15 and 25 is 75.
3. The elements of $\{1, 3, 9, 27\}$ are called _____ of 27.
4. The _____ of 30 and 42 is 6.
5. $\{x \in W: x \text{ is a factor of 24}\}$ is called the _____ set for 24.
6. $\{x \in N: 6 \text{ is a factor of } x\}$ is called the _____ set for 6.

For each of the following pairs of whole numbers find
(a) The multiple set of each number.
(b) The factor set of each number.
(c) The set of common multiples.
(d) The set of common factors.
(e) The least common multiple.
(f) The greatest common factor.

Check parts (e) and (f) by finding the least common multiple and greatest common factor using prime factorizations.

7. 9, 12	**8.** 16, 25	**9.** 12, 16
10. 25, 35	**11.** 16, 36	**12.** 24, 54
13. 36, 48	**14.** 49, 91	**15.** 64, 144
16. 81, 144	**17.** 72, 156	**18.** 76, 95
19. 100, 250	**20.** 324, 256	**21.** 37, 39

For each of the following pairs of whole numbers, show that the product of the least common multiple multiplied by the greatest common factor is equal to the product of the numbers.

22. 54, 63   **23.** 64, 144   **24.** 60, 96   **25.** 48, 84

5.6 Summary

Each whole number, other than 0 or 1, is either a prime number or a composite number. It is prime if it has exactly two distinct factors, 1 and itself. Furthermore, every whole number can be renamed in a unique way as a product of primes. This last fact, which we call the fundamental theorem of arithmetic, provides us with a means for determining the least common multiple and greatest common factor of a pair of whole numbers.

Exercises 5.6—Review

Complete each sentence.

1. The indicated product, $5 \cdot 5 \cdot 5$, can be more conveniently expressed as _____.
2. The notational form that permits us to express the indicated product $a \cdot a \cdot a \cdot a$ as a^4 is called _____.
3. The product of a number multiplied by itself is called the _____ of the number.
4. A prime number has only 1 and _____ as factors.

5. If a natural number is not prime, then it is _____.
6. The first even prime number is _____.
7. The fundamental theorem of arithmetic states that _____.
8. If A is a set of whole numbers and each element of A is a factor of the whole number d, d is the _____ of the elements of A.
9. The smallest natural number that is a multiple of the elements of a set B of natural numbers is called the _____ of the elements of B.
10. A whole number b is called the _____ of the elements of a set D of whole numbers if it is the largest number that is a factor of each element in D.

Write each of the following without exponents.

11. $(-2)^5$ 12. $3^2 \cdot 5^3$ 13. $3^4 \cdot (-5)^3 \cdot 7^2$

Use exponential notation for each of the following.

14. $12 \cdot 12 \cdot 12 \cdot 12$ 15. $-6 \cdot -6 \cdot 8 \cdot 8 \cdot 8 \cdot 8 \cdot 3$
16. $1 \cdot 1 \cdot 1 \cdot 1 \cdot 5 \cdot 5 \cdot 5 \cdot 3 \cdot 3 \cdot 3 \cdot 3 \cdot 3$
17. Compute the products in problems 11 through 13.
18. Test the truth of the statement "$(a - b)^2 \geq 0$" for all integers a and b.
19. Test the truth of the statement "$(a - b)^3 \geq 0$" for all integers a and b.

Which of the following numbers are prime and which are composite?

20. 11   21. 15   22. 24
23. 73   24. 127   25. 171
26. Find the prime factorization for each composite number in problems 20 through 25.

Find prime factorizations for

27. -17 28. -96 29. -245

Find the least common multiple and greatest common factor for each of the following sets.

30. $\{6, 8\}$ 31. $\{12, 15, 20\}$
32. $\{14, 42, 56, 98\}$ 33. $\{15, 60, 90, 225\}$

chapter six

RATIONAL NUMBERS

6.0 Introduction

If you were to imagine that your knowledge about numbers and number systems included nothing more than the integers, you would be unable to solve the sentence "$3 \div 2 = n$." Remember that $3 \div 2 = n$ if and only if $n \cdot 2 = 3$ and there is no integer n that solves this last sentence. You would conclude that division is not a closed operation in the set of integers.

In this chapter we extend the set of integers to a larger set of numbers called the *rationals*. We say a number of the form $\frac{a}{b}$, where a and b are integers and b is not 0, is a rational number. Then we interpret $\frac{\text{"}a\text{"}}{b}$ as "$a \div b$." This means that "$3 \div 2 = n$" has a solution in the set of rationals, namely, $3 \div 2 = \frac{3}{2}$. Division becomes a closed operation in the set of nonzero rational numbers. Also the set of rationals includes the set of integers as a subset. For example, $\frac{3}{1} = 3 \div 1 = 3$. Each integer b can be written as the rational number $\frac{b}{1}$.

Since we wish to think of the rationals as an extension of the integers we shall carry over all the properties of addition and multiplication, etc., in

123

the integers into the set of rationals. Then we begin to investigate ways for adding, multiplying, subtracting, and dividing rationals.

6.1 Rational Numbers

The operation of division in the set of integers was defined in the following manner:

(*) *For each of the integers, a, b ≠ 0, c, a ÷ b = c if and only if c • b = a.*

Example: $27 \div 9 = 3$ if and only if $3 \cdot 9 = 27$; $16 \div 8 = 2$ if and only if $2 \cdot 8 = 16$.

It was noted, however, that this operation is not closed for the set of nonzero integers, since some quotients are not in this set.

Example: "$5 \div 3 = c$" has no solution in J since there is no integer c such that $c \cdot 3 = 5$.

So that we may be able to solve any sentence, "$a \div b = n$," where a and b are integers, $b \neq 0$, we again enlarge our set of numbers in such a way as to include the integers and to preserve the properties of the integers. The new set of numbers is called the set of *rational numbers, Q,* and contains all the numbers whose numerals may be written $\frac{"a"}{b}$, where a and b are integers and $b \neq 0$. We shall interpret $\frac{"a"}{b}$ as "$a \div b$."

Example: $\frac{2}{3}, \frac{0}{12}, \frac{5}{4}, \frac{-3}{2}, \frac{-5}{-9}, \frac{141}{1}, \frac{-2}{147}$, and $\frac{29}{-17}$ are all rational numbers.

The set of rational numbers is given symbolically by

$$Q = \left\{ \frac{a}{b} : a \in J, b \in J, b \neq 0 \right\}$$

Since each integer is the quotient of itself divided by 1, it is a rational number. We shall restate (*), call it the *division property* and use it to characterize Q.

The Division Property

For each of the integers a, b ≠ 0, there is a rational number p, such that
$a \div b = p$ *if and only if* $p \cdot b = a$.

Example: $2 \div 3$ is the rational number $\dfrac{2}{3}$ and $\dfrac{2}{3} \cdot 3 = 2$.

$81 \div 27$ is the rational number $\dfrac{81}{27}$ and $\dfrac{81}{27} \cdot 27 = 81$.

Consider the statement "$\dfrac{52}{13} = 4$." This is equivalent to

$$4 \cdot 13 = 52$$

by the division property. If we replace "52" in the first statement by its equivalent "$4 \cdot 13$," we have

$$\frac{4 \cdot 13}{13} = 4$$

Similarly, if we replace "4" in the second statement by its equivalent "$\dfrac{52}{13}$," we have

$$\frac{52}{13} \cdot 13 = 52$$

Therefore we shall restate the division property as:

For each of the integers, a, b ≠ 0, $\dfrac{a}{b} \cdot b = a$ and $\dfrac{a \cdot b}{b} = a$.

Example: Find the solution set for each of the following sentences $(n \in J)$.

(a) $\dfrac{6 \cdot n}{5} = 6$ (b) $\dfrac{17}{n} \cdot 29 = 17$ (c) $\dfrac{n \cdot 15}{15} = n$

Solution:

(a) Since $\dfrac{6 \cdot 5}{5} = 6$, the solution set is $\{5\}$.

(b) Since $\dfrac{17}{29} \cdot 29 = 17$, the solution set is $\{29\}$.

(c) Since $\dfrac{n \cdot 15}{15} = n$ becomes a true statement for any integer replacement of n, the solution set is J.

If in the division property we replace a by 1, we obtain as a special case, that: For each integer $b \neq 0$, $\frac{1}{b} \cdot b = 1$, and $\frac{1 \cdot b}{b} = 1$. We call $\frac{1}{b}$ the *reciprocal* of b. Hence each nonzero number has a reciprocal.

From the division property we note that $\frac{17}{5} \cdot 5 = 17$, so

$$\left(\frac{17}{5} \cdot 5\right) \cdot \frac{1}{5} = 17 \cdot \frac{1}{5} \qquad \text{[multiplication property]}$$

$$\left(\frac{17}{5}\right) \cdot \left(5 \cdot \frac{1}{5}\right) = 17 \cdot \frac{1}{5} \qquad \text{[regrouping]}$$

$$\frac{17}{5} \cdot 1 = 17 \cdot \frac{1}{5} \qquad \left[a \cdot \frac{1}{a} = 1 \right]$$

$$\frac{17}{5} = 17 \cdot \frac{1}{5} \qquad \text{[identity for multiplication]}$$

In general, we have

The Reciprocal Property

For each of the integers a, $b \neq 0$, $\frac{a}{b} = a \cdot \frac{1}{b}$.

Example:

$$\frac{3}{5} = 3 \cdot \frac{1}{5}$$

$$\frac{2}{3} = 2 \cdot \frac{1}{3}$$

$$\frac{4}{1} = 4 \cdot \frac{1}{1} = 4 \cdot 1 = 4$$

This property tells us that division of a first integer, a, by a second non-zero integer, b, can be performed by multiplying a by the reciprocal of b.

We shall discuss in subsequent sections how to add, subtract, multiply, and divide rational numbers. We assume now, however, that these operations can be performed and have all the properties in the rationals that they have in the integers. This is essential if we intend to add and multiply rational numbers in a way that is consistent with the way these operations are performed in the set of integers. For this reason we list here the properties of addition and multiplication in the set of rational numbers.

Let p, s, t, and u denote the rational numbers $\dfrac{a}{b}$, $\dfrac{c}{d}$, $\dfrac{e}{f}$, $\dfrac{g}{h}$, respectively, where $a, b, \ldots, h$ are integers.

For each of the rational numbers p, s, t, $u \neq 0$,

1. $p + s$ is a rational number	[closure property for addition]
2. $p \cdot s$ is a rational number	[closure property for multiplication]
3. $(p + s) + t = p + (s + t)$	[associative property for addition]
4. $(p \cdot s) \cdot t = p \cdot (s \cdot t)$	[associative property for multiplication]
5. $p + s = s + p$	[commutative property for addition]
6. $p \cdot s = s \cdot p$	[commutative property for multiplication]
7. $p + 0 = p$	[identity property for addition]
8. $p \cdot 1 = p$	[identity property for multiplication]
9. $p + {}^-p = 0$	[additive inverse property]
10. $p \div u = t$ if and only if $t \cdot u = p$	[division property]
11. $p \cdot (s + t) = (p \cdot s) + (p \cdot t)$ and $(p + s) \cdot t = (p \cdot t) + (s \cdot t)$	[distributive property for multiplication over addition]
12. $p - s = p + {}^-s$	[definition of subtraction]
13. If $p = s$, then $p \cdot t = s \cdot t$	[multiplication property]
14. If $p = s$, then $p + t = s + t$	[addition property]

Exercises 6.1

Each of the following sentences is a consequence of one of the properties 1 through 14 on this page, or one of the other properties of this section. For each sentence, identify the property by using either a name or a pattern sentence.

1. $\dfrac{2}{3} + \dfrac{3}{4} = \dfrac{3}{4} + \dfrac{2}{3}$. The answer for this sentence is either "the commutative property of addition" or "$p + s = s + p$."

2. $\left(\dfrac{5}{9} + \dfrac{^-8}{7}\right) + \dfrac{6}{8} = \dfrac{5}{9} + \left(\dfrac{^-8}{7} + \dfrac{6}{8}\right)$

3. $\left(\dfrac{3}{4} + \dfrac{1}{2}\right) \in Q$

4. $\dfrac{16}{2} = 8$ if and only if $8 \cdot 2 = 16$

5. $\dfrac{4}{9} \cdot 9 = 4$

6. $\dfrac{3}{4} + {}^-\!\left(\dfrac{3}{4}\right) = 0$

7. $\left(\dfrac{6}{7} + \dfrac{4}{-9}\right) \cdot \dfrac{2}{3} = \left(\dfrac{6}{7} \cdot \dfrac{2}{3}\right) + \left(\dfrac{4}{-9} \cdot \dfrac{2}{3}\right)$

8. $\dfrac{1}{8} \cdot 8 = 1$

9. $\dfrac{^-2}{3} \cdot 3 = {}^-2$

10. $\dfrac{^-5}{8} = {}^-5 \cdot \dfrac{1}{8}$

11. $\dfrac{3}{5} - \dfrac{2}{3} = \dfrac{3}{5} + {}^-\!\left(\dfrac{2}{3}\right)$

12. $\dfrac{7}{10} + \dfrac{17}{100} \in Q$

13. $\dfrac{243}{1000} + \left(\dfrac{57}{1000} + \dfrac{11}{1000}\right) = \left(\dfrac{243}{1000} + \dfrac{57}{1000}\right) + \dfrac{11}{1000}$

14. $\dfrac{3}{5} \cdot \dfrac{^-2}{7} = \dfrac{^-2}{7} \cdot \dfrac{3}{5}$

15. $\left(\dfrac{4}{9} \cdot \dfrac{8}{5}\right) \cdot 1 = \dfrac{4}{9} \cdot \dfrac{8}{5}$

16. $\left(\dfrac{2}{7} + \dfrac{4}{11}\right) \cdot \left(\dfrac{3}{8} + \dfrac{6}{13}\right) = \left(\dfrac{3}{8} + \dfrac{6}{13}\right) \cdot \left(\dfrac{2}{7} + \dfrac{4}{11}\right)$

17. $\left(\frac{2}{7}+\frac{4}{11}\right)\cdot\left(\frac{3}{8}+\frac{-6}{13}\right)=\left(\frac{2}{7}+\frac{4}{11}\right)\cdot\left(\frac{-6}{13}+\frac{3}{8}\right)$

18. $\left(\frac{2}{7}+\frac{4}{11}\right)\cdot\left(\frac{3}{8}+\frac{6}{13}\right)=\left(\frac{2}{7}+\frac{4}{11}\right)\cdot\frac{3}{8}+\left(\frac{2}{7}+\frac{4}{11}\right)\cdot\frac{6}{13}$

19. $\left(\frac{2}{7}+\frac{4}{11}\right)\cdot\left(\frac{3}{8}-\frac{6}{13}\right)=\left(\frac{2}{7}+\frac{4}{11}\right)\cdot\left(\frac{3}{8}+\left(\frac{-6}{13}\right)\right)$

20. $\left(\frac{-4}{9}\cdot\frac{8}{5}\right)\cdot 1=\frac{-4}{9}\left(\frac{8}{5}\cdot 1\right)$

21. $\frac{7}{10}\cdot\frac{3}{100}+\frac{7}{10}\cdot\frac{47}{100}=\frac{7}{10}\cdot\left(\frac{3}{100}+\frac{47}{100}\right)$

22. $\frac{-63}{100}\cdot 100=-63$ **23.** $\left(\frac{3}{5}+0\right)\cdot\frac{2}{3}=\frac{3}{5}\cdot\frac{2}{3}$

24. $\frac{-3}{8}\cdot\frac{2}{7}\in Q$ **25.** $\frac{53}{100}=53\cdot\frac{1}{100}$

26. $\frac{17}{10}-\frac{17}{100}=\frac{17}{10}+\left(\frac{-17}{100}\right)$ **27.** $\frac{3\cdot 6}{4\cdot 8}=(3\cdot 6)\cdot\frac{1}{(8\cdot 4)}$

28. $\left(\frac{4}{8}+\frac{3}{5}\right)+0=\frac{4}{8}+\frac{3}{5}$ **29.** $17\cdot\frac{1}{12}=\frac{17}{12}$

30. $\frac{3}{10}\cdot\frac{1}{10}=\frac{\frac{3}{10}}{10}$ **31.** $\frac{30}{6}=5$ if and only if $5\cdot 6=30$

32. $\frac{-3}{5}-\frac{19}{8}=\frac{-3}{5}+\left(\frac{-19}{8}\right)$

True or false?

33. Each integer is a rational number.

34. The product of each two rational numbers is a rational number.

35. The quotient of each two rational numbers is a rational number.

36. Each rational number has an opposite.

37. Each rational number is an integer.

38. Each rational number can be expressed as the quotient of two integers.

39. There is a rational number which is nonnegative.

40. The square of each rational number is not a rational number.

Use the division property to find a rational-number replacement for each p.

41. $\dfrac{6}{8} \cdot p = 6$ **42.** $\dfrac{5}{\frac{3}{8}} \cdot p = 5$

43. $\dfrac{p}{3} \cdot 3 = 5$ **44.** $\dfrac{p}{\frac{1}{4}} \cdot \dfrac{1}{4} = \dfrac{2}{5}$

45. $\dfrac{5 \cdot p}{7} = 5$ **46.** $\dfrac{p \cdot \frac{3}{4}}{\frac{3}{4}} = 11$

Rename each of the following rational numbers as a product of two rational-number factors.

47. $\dfrac{1}{5}$ **48.** $\dfrac{3}{8}$

49. $\dfrac{28}{3}$ **50.** $\dfrac{106}{54}$

6.2 Renaming Rational Numbers

Consider the following:

Example: "$\dfrac{2}{5} = \dfrac{14}{35}$" is equivalent to "$\dfrac{2}{5}(5 \cdot 35) = \dfrac{14}{35}(5 \cdot 35)$" by the multiplication property. By the commutative and associative properties for multiplication, this last sentence is equivalent to "$\left(\dfrac{2}{5} \cdot 5\right) \cdot 35 = 5 \cdot \left(\dfrac{14}{35} \cdot 35\right)$." But this is equivalent to "$2 \cdot 35 = 5 \cdot 14$." It is possible to reverse our steps to show that if $2 \cdot 35 = 5 \cdot 14$, then $\dfrac{2}{5} = \dfrac{14}{35}$. Hence $\dfrac{2}{5} = \dfrac{14}{35}$ if and only if $2 \cdot 35 = 5 \cdot 14$. This result is generalized as the

Equivalence Property for Rational Numbers

For each of the integers, $a,b \neq 0$, $c,d \neq 0$, $\dfrac{a}{b} = \dfrac{c}{d}$ if and only if $ad = bc$.

Example: $\dfrac{5}{8}$ and $\dfrac{625}{1000}$ name the same rational number, since $5 \cdot 1000 = 8 \cdot 625$.

Example: $\dfrac{5}{8}$ and $\dfrac{25}{64}$ name different rational numbers, since $5 \cdot 64 \neq 8 \cdot 25$.

Is $\dfrac{4}{9} = \dfrac{4 \cdot 7}{9 \cdot 7}$? Since $4 \cdot (9 \cdot 7) = 9 \cdot (4 \cdot 7)$ by the commutative and associative properties of multiplication, it follows by the *equivalence property* that $\dfrac{4}{9} = \dfrac{4 \cdot 7}{9 \cdot 7}$. Generalizing we obtain:

For each of the integers, $a, b \neq 0$, $c \neq 0$, $\dfrac{a}{b} = \dfrac{ac}{bc}$.

Example:

$$\frac{5}{9} = \frac{5 \cdot 5}{9 \cdot 5} = \frac{25}{45}$$

$$\frac{7}{18} = \frac{7 \cdot 3}{18 \cdot 3} = \frac{21}{54}$$

We can use this property to write different names for the same rational number. For instance, $\dfrac{3}{4}, \dfrac{6}{8}, \dfrac{9}{12}, \dfrac{12}{16}, \dfrac{15}{20}, \dfrac{18}{24}$, and $\dfrac{21}{28}$ are all names for the same rational number. Each of these numerals is called a *fraction*. We call the upper and lower numerals of a fraction the *numerator* and *denominator*, respectively.

Example: 3 is the numerator and 4 is the denominator of the fraction $\dfrac{3}{4}$.

Example: Rename each of the rational numbers $\dfrac{1}{3}, \dfrac{3}{4}$, and $\dfrac{5}{8}$, using fractions with the same denominator.

Solution: For the fractions $\dfrac{1}{3}, \dfrac{3}{4}, \dfrac{5}{8}$, the denominators are 3, 4, and 8, respectively. To rename each rational number we must multiply the numerator number and the denominator number by the same rational number. What we seek, then, is a number which is a multiple of 3, 4, and 8; in particular, the least common multiple of 3, 4, and 8. Since 3 is prime, $4 = 2^2$, and $8 = 2^3$, the least common multiple of 3, 4, and 8 is $2^3 \cdot 3 = 24$.

Then we have

$$\frac{1}{3} = \frac{1 \cdot 8}{3 \cdot 8} = \frac{8}{24}$$

$$\frac{3}{4} = \frac{3 \cdot 6}{4 \cdot 6} = \frac{18}{24}$$

$$\frac{5}{8} = \frac{5 \cdot 3}{8 \cdot 3} = \frac{15}{24}$$

Example: Rename each of the rational numbers $\frac{5}{6}$, $\frac{4}{15}$, and $\frac{3}{10}$, using fractions having the same denominator.

Solution: The least common multiple of the denominator numbers 6, 15, and 10 is 30 ($6 = 2 \cdot 3$, $15 = 3 \cdot 5$, $10 = 2 \cdot 5$, $30 = 2 \cdot 3 \cdot 5$). Hence

$$\frac{5}{6} = \frac{5 \cdot 5}{6 \cdot 5} = \frac{25}{30}$$

$$\frac{4}{15} = \frac{4 \cdot 2}{15 \cdot 2} = \frac{8}{30}$$

$$\frac{3}{10} = \frac{3 \cdot 3}{10 \cdot 3} = \frac{9}{30}$$

Exercises 6.2

Use the equivalence property for rational numbers to determine which of the following statements is true.

1. $\frac{3}{4} = \frac{12}{16}$ 2. $\frac{5}{9} = \frac{25}{45}$

3. $\frac{-3}{7} = \frac{9}{-13}$ 4. $\frac{15}{17} = \frac{45}{51}$

5. $\frac{4}{5} = \frac{16}{25}$ 6. $\frac{-2}{3} = \frac{-8}{27}$

7. $\frac{13}{-52} = \frac{-125}{500}$ 8. $\frac{98}{47} = \frac{100}{50}$

9. $\frac{600}{915} = \frac{200}{315}$ 10. $\frac{-51}{-72} = \frac{17}{24}$

11. $\dfrac{400}{-500} = \dfrac{500}{-600}$

12. $\dfrac{24}{47} = \dfrac{27}{50}$

13. $\dfrac{-81}{243} = \dfrac{-243}{729}$

14. $\dfrac{81}{243} = \dfrac{729}{2187}$

15. $\dfrac{7}{91} = \dfrac{-77}{-1001}$

16. $\dfrac{36}{100} = \dfrac{3060}{10,000}$

17. $\dfrac{52}{1000} = \dfrac{5200}{100,000}$

18. $\dfrac{478}{10} = \dfrac{4780}{100}$

19. $\dfrac{374}{100} = \dfrac{474}{200}$

20. $\dfrac{1234}{5678} = \dfrac{96,252}{442,984}$

Express each of the following rational numbers in the form $\dfrac{a}{b}$ or $\dfrac{^-a}{b}$, where a and b are positive integers with no common factors other than 1 or $^-1$.

21. $\dfrac{25}{45}$. Since $\dfrac{25}{45} = \dfrac{5 \cdot 5}{9 \cdot 5}$, we can rename it $\dfrac{5}{9}$.

22. $\dfrac{19}{57}$

23. $\dfrac{16}{36}$

24. $\dfrac{20}{35}$

25. $\dfrac{-24}{36}$

26. $\dfrac{-8}{20}$

27. $\dfrac{-100}{250}$

28. $\dfrac{-81}{27}$

29. $\dfrac{16}{-12}$

30. $\dfrac{30}{-45}$

31. $\dfrac{48}{-72}$

32. $\dfrac{63}{-27}$

33. $\dfrac{-24}{-36}$

34. $\dfrac{-108}{-48}$

35. $\dfrac{-144}{-288}$

36. $\dfrac{-45}{-270}$

Find a rational-number replacement for the variable a in each of the following sentences to make true statements ($a \neq 0$).

37. $\dfrac{3}{7} = \dfrac{a}{21}$ 38. $\dfrac{4}{36} = \dfrac{a}{72}$

39. $\dfrac{4}{36} = \dfrac{a}{18}$ 40. $\dfrac{2}{15} = \dfrac{a}{45}$

41. $\dfrac{a}{36} = \dfrac{1}{4}$ 42. $\dfrac{a}{48} = \dfrac{1}{4}$

43. $\dfrac{a}{-12} \doteq 1$ 44. $\dfrac{4}{a} = \dfrac{-1}{9}$

45. $\dfrac{16}{a} = \dfrac{-2}{5}$ 46. $\dfrac{3}{a} = \dfrac{a}{12}$

47. $\dfrac{a}{-2} = \dfrac{-5}{10}$ 48. $\dfrac{-a}{3} = \dfrac{-12}{42}$

49. $\dfrac{-a}{3} = \dfrac{12}{42}$ 50. $\dfrac{-a}{3} = \dfrac{42}{12}$

Complete each of the following sentences to make true statements.

51. A numeral used to name a rational number is called a(n) _____.

52. The upper numeral in a fraction is called the _____ of the fraction.

53. The lower numeral in a fraction is called the _____ of the fraction.

54. For two rational numbers $\dfrac{a}{b}$ and $\dfrac{c}{d}$, $\dfrac{a}{b} = \dfrac{c}{d}$ if and only if _____.

55. A property for rational numbers states that $\dfrac{ac}{bc}$ is equal to _____, for each of the integers $a, b \neq 0$, $c \neq 0$.

Supply the correct reason for each step in the following arguments, assuming that the properties of this section hold whenever the word "integers" is replaced by "rational numbers."

56. $\dfrac{4}{-5} = \dfrac{4(-1)}{-5(-1)}$

(a) _____

$= \dfrac{-4}{5}$

(b) _____

57. $\dfrac{\frac{7}{8}}{\frac{1}{8}} = \dfrac{\frac{7}{8} \cdot 8}{\frac{1}{8} \cdot 8}$

(a) _____

$= \dfrac{7}{1}$

(b) _____

$= 7$

(c) _____

58. $\dfrac{\frac{3}{4}}{\frac{5}{4}} = \dfrac{3 \cdot \frac{1}{4}}{5 \cdot \frac{1}{4}}$

(a) _____

$= \dfrac{3}{5}$

(b) _____

6.3 Addition and Subtraction

We are now ready to add rational numbers.   Consider the sum $\dfrac{3}{11} + \dfrac{7}{11}$.

$$\dfrac{3}{11} + \dfrac{7}{11} = 3 \cdot \dfrac{1}{11} + 7 \cdot \dfrac{1}{11} \qquad \left[\dfrac{a}{b} = a \cdot \dfrac{1}{b}\right]$$

$$= (3 + 7) \cdot \dfrac{1}{11} \qquad \text{[distributive property]}$$

$$= \dfrac{3 + 7}{11} \qquad \left[a \cdot \dfrac{1}{b} = \dfrac{a}{b}\right]$$

$$= \dfrac{10}{11} \qquad \text{[addition fact: } 3 + 7 = 10]$$

This illustration should suggest a way to compute sums of rational numbers named by fractions with the same denominator.

For each of the integers, $a, b, c \neq 0$, $\dfrac{a}{c} + \dfrac{b}{c} = \dfrac{a+b}{c}$

Example: Compute each of the following sums:

$$\text{(a)} \ \frac{3}{4} + \frac{7}{4} \qquad \text{(b)} \ \frac{2}{15} + \frac{8}{15} \qquad \text{(c)} \ \frac{7}{8} + \frac{5}{8}$$

Solution:

$$\text{(a)} \ \frac{3}{4} + \frac{7}{4} = \frac{3+7}{4} = \frac{10}{4} = \frac{5 \cdot 2}{2 \cdot 2} = \frac{5}{2}$$

$$\text{(b)} \ \frac{2}{15} + \frac{8}{15} = \frac{2+8}{15} = \frac{10}{15} = \frac{2 \cdot 5}{3 \cdot 5} = \frac{2}{3}$$

$$\text{(c)} \ \frac{7}{8} + \frac{5}{8} = \frac{7+5}{8} = \frac{12}{8} = \frac{3 \cdot 4}{2 \cdot 4} = \frac{3}{2}$$

To compute the sum of two rational numbers whose fractions do not have the same denominators, first rename them appropriately and then compute the sum.

Example: Compute each of the following sums:

$$\text{(a)} \ \frac{2}{3} + \frac{1}{4} \qquad \text{(b)} \ \frac{5}{7} + \frac{1}{9} \qquad \text{(c)} \ \frac{3}{8} + \frac{3}{16}$$

Solution:

$$\text{(a)} \ \frac{2}{3} + \frac{1}{4} = \frac{2 \cdot 4}{3 \cdot 4} + \frac{1 \cdot 3}{4 \cdot 3} = \frac{8}{12} + \frac{3}{12} = \frac{8+3}{12} = \frac{11}{12}$$

$$\text{(b)} \ \frac{5}{7} + \frac{1}{9} = \frac{5 \cdot 9}{7 \cdot 9} + \frac{1 \cdot 7}{9 \cdot 7} = \frac{45}{63} + \frac{7}{63} = \frac{45+7}{63} = \frac{52}{63}$$

$$\text{(c)} \ \frac{3}{8} + \frac{3}{16} = \frac{3 \cdot 2}{8 \cdot 2} + \frac{3}{16} = \frac{6}{16} + \frac{3}{16} = \frac{6+3}{16} = \frac{9}{16}$$

Now consider the sentence $\dfrac{^-2}{3} = {}^-\left(\dfrac{2}{3}\right)$. Since $\dfrac{2}{3} + \dfrac{^-2}{3} = \dfrac{2 + {}^-2}{3} = 0$,

$\dfrac{^-2}{3}$ is the opposite of $\dfrac{2}{3}$. Also $\dfrac{^-2}{3} = \dfrac{^-2(^-1)}{3(^-1)} = \dfrac{2}{^-3}$. Hence we have

For each of the integers, $a, b \neq 0$, $\dfrac{^-a}{b} = {}^-\left(\dfrac{a}{b}\right) = \dfrac{a}{^-b}$

Example: Compute $\dfrac{8}{9} - \dfrac{7}{9}$.

Solution:

$$\frac{8}{9} - \frac{7}{9} = \frac{8}{9} + \frac{^-7}{9}\right) \qquad [p - s = p + {}^-s]$$

$$= \frac{8}{9} + \frac{^-7}{9} \qquad \left[{}^-\!\left(\frac{a}{b}\right) = \frac{^-a}{b}\right]$$

$$= \frac{8 + {}^-7}{9} \qquad \left[\frac{a}{c} + \frac{b}{c} = \frac{a + b}{c}\right]$$

$$= \frac{1}{9} \qquad [\text{addition fact}: 8 + {}^-7 = 1]$$

This example suggests that

For each of the integers, $a,b,c \neq 0,$ $\dfrac{a}{c} - \dfrac{b}{c} = \dfrac{a - b}{c}$

Example: Compute each of the following differences:

$$\text{(a)} \ \frac{4}{5} - \frac{1}{5} \qquad \text{(b)} \ \frac{16}{19} - \frac{9}{19} \qquad \text{(c)} \ \frac{8}{9} - \frac{5}{9}$$

Solution:

(a) $\dfrac{4}{5} - \dfrac{1}{5} = \dfrac{4 - 1}{5} = \dfrac{3}{5}$

(b) $\dfrac{16}{19} - \dfrac{9}{19} = \dfrac{16 - 9}{19} = \dfrac{7}{19}$

(c) $\dfrac{8}{9} - \dfrac{5}{9} = \dfrac{8 - 5}{9} = \dfrac{3}{9} = \dfrac{1 \cdot 3}{3 \cdot 3} = \dfrac{1}{3}$

If the rational numbers whose difference is to be computed are not named with fractions having the same denominator, renaming them first will enable you to perform the subtraction.

Example: Compute each of the following differences:

$$\text{(a)} \ \frac{2}{7} - \frac{1}{4} \qquad \text{(b)} \ \frac{3}{5} - \frac{2}{15} \qquad \text{(c)} \ \frac{7}{16} - \frac{3}{4}$$

Solution:

(a) $\dfrac{2}{7} - \dfrac{1}{4} = \dfrac{2 \cdot 4}{7 \cdot 4} - \dfrac{1 \cdot 7}{4 \cdot 7} = \dfrac{8}{28} - \dfrac{7}{28} = \dfrac{8-7}{28} = \dfrac{1}{28}$

(b) $\dfrac{3}{5} - \dfrac{2}{15} = \dfrac{3 \cdot 3}{5 \cdot 3} - \dfrac{2}{15} = \dfrac{9}{15} - \dfrac{2}{15} = \dfrac{9-2}{15} = \dfrac{7}{15}$

(c) $\dfrac{7}{16} - \dfrac{3}{4} = \dfrac{7}{16} - \dfrac{3 \cdot 4}{4 \cdot 4} = \dfrac{7}{16} - \dfrac{12}{16} = \dfrac{7-12}{16} = \dfrac{^-5}{16}$

Exercises 6.3

Each of the following sentences is a consequence of one of the properties of rational numbers discussed so far. For each sentence, identify the property, either with a name or a pattern sentence.

1. $\dfrac{3}{5} + \dfrac{4}{5} = \dfrac{3+5}{5}$

2. $\dfrac{3}{5} - \dfrac{4}{5} = \dfrac{3-4}{25}$

3. $\dfrac{3}{5} = \dfrac{3 \cdot 2}{5 \cdot 2}$

4. $\dfrac{^-3}{5} = \dfrac{3}{^-5}$

5. $^-\left(\dfrac{4}{7}\right) = \dfrac{4}{^-7}$

6. $^-\left(\dfrac{3}{5}\right) = \dfrac{^-3}{5}$

7. $\dfrac{3}{5} + \dfrac{4}{25} = \dfrac{3 \cdot 5}{5 \cdot 5} + \dfrac{4}{25}$

8. $\dfrac{3 \cdot 5}{5 \cdot 5} + \dfrac{4}{25} = \dfrac{3 \cdot 5 + 4}{25}$

9. $^-\left(\dfrac{2}{3}\right) + \dfrac{4}{7} = \dfrac{^-2}{3} + \dfrac{4}{7}$

10. $\dfrac{^-2}{3} + \dfrac{4}{7} = \dfrac{^-2 \cdot 7}{3 \cdot 7} + \dfrac{4 \cdot 3}{7 \cdot 3}$

Compute each of the following sums or differences writing the results in the form $\dfrac{a}{b}$ or $\dfrac{^-a}{b}$, where a and b are positive integers with no common factors other than 1 or $^-1$.

11. $\dfrac{3}{7} + \dfrac{5}{7}$

12. $\dfrac{17}{24} + \dfrac{5}{24}$

13. $\dfrac{19}{100} + \dfrac{81}{100}$

14. $\dfrac{543}{1000} + \dfrac{157}{1000}$

15. $\dfrac{6}{110} - \dfrac{3}{110}$

16. $\dfrac{54}{100} - \dfrac{54}{1000}$

17. $\dfrac{3}{5} + \dfrac{2}{7}$

18. $\dfrac{5}{8} + \dfrac{1}{16}$

19. $\dfrac{6}{7} - \dfrac{2}{3}$ **20.** $\dfrac{2}{5} - \dfrac{1}{3}$

21. $\dfrac{1}{7} + \dfrac{1}{8}$ **22.** $\dfrac{1}{7} - \dfrac{2}{15}$

23. $\dfrac{2}{3} - \dfrac{3}{4}$ **24.** $\dfrac{^-3}{4} - \dfrac{1}{5}$

25. $\left(\dfrac{^-1}{2} + \dfrac{3}{4}\right) + \dfrac{1}{5}$ **26.** $\dfrac{^-1}{2} + \left(\dfrac{3}{4} + \dfrac{1}{5}\right)$

27. $\dfrac{6}{7} - \dfrac{3}{8}$ **28.** $\dfrac{3}{8} - \dfrac{6}{7}$

29. $\dfrac{9}{4} + \dfrac{2}{9}$ **30.** $\dfrac{2}{9} + \dfrac{9}{4}$

31. $\dfrac{47}{100} - \dfrac{347}{1000}$ **32.** $\dfrac{54}{1000} - \dfrac{54}{100}$

33. $\dfrac{323}{1000} + \dfrac{677}{1000}$ **34.** $\dfrac{323}{1000} - \dfrac{677}{1000}$

35. $\dfrac{^-323}{1000} + \dfrac{677}{1000}$ **36.** $\dfrac{^-323}{1000} - \dfrac{^-677}{1000}$

37. $\dfrac{3}{4} + \dfrac{9}{25}$ **38.** $\dfrac{3}{40} + \dfrac{9}{25}$

39. $\dfrac{3}{8} + \dfrac{9}{125}$ **40.** $\dfrac{3}{8} - \dfrac{9}{125}$

True or false ?

41. $\dfrac{3}{8} + \dfrac{1}{8} = \dfrac{1}{2}$ **42.** $\dfrac{16}{48} + \dfrac{60}{90} = 1$

43. $\dfrac{9}{25} + \dfrac{4}{9} = \dfrac{5}{8}$ **44.** $\dfrac{16}{100} + \dfrac{184}{100} = \dfrac{32}{16}$

45. $\dfrac{7}{10} + \dfrac{4}{50} = \dfrac{52}{50} - \dfrac{13}{50}$ **46.** $\dfrac{^-36}{1000} + \dfrac{^-172}{1000} = \dfrac{500}{1000} - \dfrac{708}{1000}$

47. $\left(\dfrac{3}{4} + \dfrac{2}{3}\right) + \dfrac{5}{9} = \dfrac{6}{9} + \left(\dfrac{20}{36} + \dfrac{27}{36}\right)$

48. $\dfrac{3}{7} + \dfrac{^-3}{17} = \dfrac{0}{119}$ **49.** $\dfrac{^-3}{25} = {}^-\left(\dfrac{3}{-25}\right)$ **50.** $\dfrac{^-3}{25} = {}^-\left(\dfrac{^-3}{25}\right)$

Solve each of the following sentences ($a \in Q$).

51. $\dfrac{3}{4} + \dfrac{a}{4} = \dfrac{19}{4}$

52. $\dfrac{67}{100} - \dfrac{a}{100} = \dfrac{23}{100}$

53. $\dfrac{2}{5} - \dfrac{a}{25} = \dfrac{4}{25}$

54. $\dfrac{9}{36} - \dfrac{a}{9} = \dfrac{5}{36}$

55. $\dfrac{a}{12} + \dfrac{1}{6} = \dfrac{1}{2}$

56. $\dfrac{a}{24} - \dfrac{1}{4} = 0$

57. $\dfrac{a}{100} + \dfrac{^{-}42}{100} = \dfrac{^{-}72}{100}$

58. $\dfrac{a}{10} + \dfrac{12}{25} = \dfrac{^{-}13}{25}$

59. $\dfrac{^{-}4}{a} + \dfrac{14}{a} = 1 \; (a \neq 0)$

60. $\dfrac{2}{a} + \dfrac{a}{2} = \dfrac{10}{3} \; (a \neq 0)$

61. Use some property of rational numbers to show that $\dfrac{^{-}3}{^{-}5} = \dfrac{3}{5}$.

62. The results of problem 61 suggest a general property for rational numbers. What is it?

Solve each of the following problems.

Example: One morning a clerk sold the following lengths of ribbon to her first three customers: $6\dfrac{3}{4}$ yards, $1\dfrac{1}{2}$ yards, and $1\dfrac{1}{3}$ yards. How much ribbon did she sell?

Solution 1:

$$6\dfrac{3}{4} = 6 + \dfrac{3}{4} = \dfrac{6}{1} + \dfrac{3}{4} = \dfrac{24}{4} + \dfrac{3}{4} = \dfrac{27}{4}$$

$$1\dfrac{1}{2} = 1 + \dfrac{1}{2} = \dfrac{1}{1} + \dfrac{1}{2} = \dfrac{2}{2} + \dfrac{1}{2} = \dfrac{3}{2}$$

$$1\dfrac{1}{3} = 1 + \dfrac{1}{3} = \dfrac{1}{1} + \dfrac{1}{3} = \dfrac{3}{3} + \dfrac{1}{3} = \dfrac{4}{3}$$

Since the least common multiple of 2,3, and 4 is 12, we have

$$6\frac{3}{4} + 1\frac{1}{2} + 1\frac{1}{3} = \frac{27}{4} + \frac{3}{2} + \frac{4}{3}$$

$$= \frac{27 \cdot 3}{4 \cdot 3} + \frac{3 \cdot 6}{2 \cdot 6} + \frac{4 \cdot 4}{3 \cdot 4}$$

$$= \frac{81}{12} + \frac{18}{12} + \frac{16}{12}$$

$$= \frac{81 + 18 + 16}{12}$$

$$= \frac{115}{12}$$

$$= \frac{108 + 7}{12}$$

$$= \frac{108}{12} + \frac{7}{12}$$

$$= 9 + \frac{7}{12}$$

$$= 9\frac{7}{12}$$

So she sold $9\frac{7}{12}$ yards of ribbon.

Solution 2:

$$6\frac{3}{4} + 1\frac{1}{2} + 1\frac{1}{3} = \left(6 + \frac{3}{4}\right) + \left(1 + \frac{1}{2}\right) + \left(1 + \frac{1}{3}\right)$$

$$= \left(6 + 1 + 1\right) + \left(\frac{3}{4} + \frac{1}{2} + \frac{1}{3}\right)$$

$$= 8 + \left(\frac{9}{12} + \frac{6}{12} + \frac{4}{12}\right)$$

$$= 8 + \left(\frac{9 + 6 + 4}{12}\right)$$

$$= 8 + \frac{19}{12}$$

$$= 8 + \left(\frac{12 + 7}{12}\right)$$

$$= 8 + \left(\frac{12}{12} + \frac{7}{12}\right)$$

$$= (8 + 1) + \frac{7}{12}$$

$$= 9\frac{7}{12}$$

63. If the clerk cut the ribbon from a 50-yard roll, how much ribbon is left on the roll?

64. The next four customers purchased the following lengths of ribbon: $\frac{2}{3}$ yard, $1\frac{2}{3}$ yards, $2\frac{1}{2}$ yards, and $1\frac{3}{4}$ yards. How much ribbon did these four customers purchase?

65. If each of the purchases of problem 64 are also taken from the 50-yard roll of problem 63, how much ribbon remains on the roll?

66. Sam wishes to purchase a board from his local lumber yard from which he can cut the following lengths: $6\frac{1}{3}$ feet, $4\frac{1}{4}$ feet, $3\frac{1}{3}$ feet. If the board only comes in lengths which are multiples of 2 feet, what is the shortest board Sam can buy?

67. If Sam buys the shortest board in problem 66, how much waste will he have?

68. Fred wishes to buy a molding strip to run around the walls of his living room and dining area at the ceiling. If the dimensions are those shown in the figure, compute the length of molding he needs.

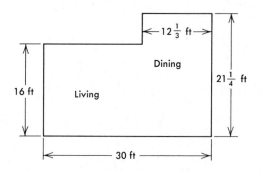

69. If the molding strip comes in lengths which are multiples of 2 feet, and Fred wishes to have no seams except at the corners, what is the least amount of material he can buy? How much waste would he have?

6.4 Multiplication

We have stated in Section 6.1 the basic properties of multiplication, but we need to have some techniques for finding simple numerals for products of rational numbers. Consider the product $\frac{1}{3} \cdot \frac{1}{2}$. Since

$$\left(\frac{1}{3} \cdot \frac{1}{2}\right) \cdot (3 \cdot 2) = \left(\frac{1}{3} \cdot 3\right) \cdot \left(\frac{1}{2} \cdot 2\right)$$

[associative and commutative properties for multiplication]

$$= 1 \cdot 1 \qquad\qquad \left[\frac{a}{b} \cdot b = a\right]$$

$$= 1 \qquad\qquad$$ [identity property for multiplication]

it follows that $\dfrac{1}{3} \cdot \dfrac{1}{2}$ must be the reciprocal of $3 \cdot 2$ because their product

is 1.   That is, $\dfrac{1}{3} \cdot \dfrac{1}{2} = \dfrac{1}{3 \cdot 2}$ Generalizing we have:

For each of the integers, $a \neq 0$, $b \neq 0$,

$$\frac{1}{a} \cdot \frac{1}{b} = \frac{1}{a \cdot b}$$

Example:

$$\frac{1}{4} \cdot \frac{1}{5} = \frac{1}{4 \cdot 5} = \frac{1}{20}$$

$$\frac{1}{7} \cdot \frac{1}{9} = \frac{1}{7 \cdot 9} = \frac{1}{63}$$

$$\frac{1}{2} \cdot \frac{1}{4} = \frac{1}{2 \cdot 4} = \frac{1}{8}$$

Suppose we wish to find a simple numeral for the product $\dfrac{3}{5} \cdot \dfrac{4}{7}$.

$$\frac{3}{5} \cdot \frac{4}{7} = \left(3 \cdot \frac{1}{5}\right) \cdot \left(4 \cdot \frac{1}{7}\right) \qquad \left[\frac{a}{b} = a \cdot \frac{1}{b}\right]$$

$$= (3 \cdot 4) \cdot \left(\frac{1}{5} \cdot \frac{1}{7}\right) \qquad$$ [commutative and associative properties for multiplication]

$$= (3 \cdot 4) \cdot \frac{1}{(5 \cdot 7)} \qquad \left[\frac{1}{a} \cdot \frac{1}{b} = \frac{1}{a \cdot b}\right]$$

$$= \frac{3 \cdot 4}{5 \cdot 7} \qquad\qquad \left[a \cdot \frac{1}{b} = \frac{a}{b}\right]$$

Hence we have found a way to compute products of rational numbers.

For each of the integers, $a,b \neq 0$, $c,d \neq 0$,

$$\frac{a}{b} \cdot \frac{c}{d} = \frac{ac}{bd}$$

Example:

$$\frac{2}{3} \cdot \frac{5}{6} = \frac{2 \cdot 5}{3 \cdot 6} = \frac{10}{18}$$

$$\frac{5}{8} \cdot \frac{3}{5} = \frac{5 \cdot 3}{8 \cdot 5} = \frac{3 \cdot 5}{8 \cdot 5} = \frac{3}{8}$$

$$\frac{6}{7} \cdot \frac{3}{10} = \frac{6 \cdot 3}{7 \cdot 10} = \frac{18}{70} = \frac{9 \cdot 2}{35 \cdot 2} = \frac{9}{35}$$

We can use this property for products of rational numbers together with the properties of exponents discussed in Chapter Five to rename expressions like $\left(\frac{1}{10}\right)^2 \cdot \left(\frac{1}{10}\right)^3$. You might wish to review those properties before reading on.

Example: Express each of the following in the form $\frac{a}{b}$ or $\frac{^-a}{b}$, where a and b are positive integers with no common factors other than 1 and $^-1$.

(a) $\left(\frac{1}{10}\right)^2 \cdot \left(\frac{1}{10}\right)^3$ (b) $\frac{1}{10^2} \cdot \frac{1}{10^3}$

(c) $\frac{3}{10^2} \cdot \frac{2}{10^4}$ (d) $\left(\frac{2}{3}\right)^2 \cdot \left(\frac{3}{4}\right)^3$

Solution:

(a) $\left(\frac{1}{10}\right)^2 \cdot \left(\frac{1}{10}\right)^3 = \left(\frac{1}{10}\right)^5$

$$= \frac{1}{10} \cdot \frac{1}{10} \cdot \frac{1}{10} \cdot \frac{1}{10} \cdot \frac{1}{10}$$

$$= \frac{1^5}{10^5}$$

$$= \frac{1}{100,000}$$

(b) $\dfrac{1}{10^2} \cdot \dfrac{1}{10^3} = \dfrac{1^2}{10^2 \cdot 10^3}$

$\phantom{\dfrac{1}{10^2} \cdot \dfrac{1}{10^3}} = \dfrac{1}{10^5}$

$\phantom{\dfrac{1}{10^2} \cdot \dfrac{1}{10^3}} = \dfrac{1}{100,000}$

(c) $\dfrac{3}{10^2} \cdot \dfrac{2}{10^4} = \dfrac{3 \cdot 2}{10^2 \cdot 10^4}$

$\phantom{\dfrac{3}{10^2} \cdot \dfrac{2}{10^4}} = \dfrac{6}{10^6}$

$\phantom{\dfrac{3}{10^2} \cdot \dfrac{2}{10^4}} = \dfrac{6}{1,000,000}$

(d) $\left(\dfrac{2}{3}\right)^2 \cdot \left(\dfrac{3}{4}\right)^3 = \dfrac{2^2}{3^2} \cdot \dfrac{3^3}{4^3}$ $\qquad$ or $\qquad$ $\left(\dfrac{2}{3}\right)^2 \cdot \left(\dfrac{3}{4}\right)^3 = \dfrac{2}{3} \cdot \dfrac{2}{3} \cdot \dfrac{3}{4} \cdot \dfrac{3}{4} \cdot \dfrac{3}{4}$

$\qquad\qquad\qquad\quad = \dfrac{2^2 \cdot 3^3}{3^2 \cdot 4^3}$ $\qquad\qquad\qquad\qquad\qquad\qquad = \dfrac{2 \cdot 2 \cdot 3 \cdot 3 \cdot 3}{3 \cdot 3 \cdot 4 \cdot 4 \cdot 4}$

$\qquad\qquad\qquad\quad = \dfrac{4 \cdot 3 \cdot 3^2}{4^3 \cdot 3^2}$ $\qquad\qquad\qquad\qquad\qquad\qquad = \dfrac{3 \cdot 4 \cdot 3 \cdot 3}{4 \cdot 4 \cdot 4 \cdot 3 \cdot 3}$

$\qquad\qquad\qquad\quad = \dfrac{4 \cdot 3}{4^3}$ $\qquad\qquad\qquad\qquad\qquad\qquad\quad = \dfrac{3}{4 \cdot 4}$

$\qquad\qquad\qquad\quad = \dfrac{3 \cdot 4}{4^2 \cdot 4}$ $\qquad\qquad\qquad\qquad\qquad\qquad\quad = \dfrac{3}{16}$

$\qquad\qquad\qquad\quad = \dfrac{3}{4^2}$

$\qquad\qquad\qquad\quad = \dfrac{3}{16}$

$\qquad\qquad$ or $\qquad$ $\left(\dfrac{2}{3}\right)^2 \cdot \left(\dfrac{3}{4}\right)^3 = \dfrac{2^2}{3^2} \cdot \dfrac{3^3}{4^3}$

$\qquad\qquad\qquad\qquad\qquad\qquad = \dfrac{2^2 \cdot 3^3}{3^2 \cdot 4^3}$

$\qquad\qquad\qquad\qquad\qquad\qquad = \dfrac{2^2 \cdot 3^3}{4^3 \cdot 3^2}$

$\qquad\qquad\qquad\qquad\qquad\qquad = \dfrac{4}{4^3} \cdot \dfrac{3^3}{3^2}$

$\qquad\qquad\qquad\qquad\qquad\qquad = \dfrac{1}{4^2} \cdot \dfrac{3}{1}$

$\qquad\qquad\qquad\qquad\qquad\qquad = \dfrac{1 \cdot 3}{4^2 \cdot 1}$

$\qquad\qquad\qquad\qquad\qquad\qquad\quad = \dfrac{3}{16}$

Consider the following pattern:

$$\frac{10^4}{10^1} = 10^{4-1} = 10^3 = 1000$$

$$\frac{10^3}{10^1} = 10^{3-1} = 10^2 = 100$$

$$\frac{10^2}{10^1} = 10^{2-1} = 10^1 = 10$$

$$\frac{10^1}{10^1} = 10^{1-1} = 10^0 = 1$$

$$\frac{10^0}{10^1} = ?$$

If we wish the pattern to continue, we shall have to assign a meaning to 10^{0-1} or 10^{-1}. Since $\frac{10}{10^1} = \frac{1}{10}$, 10^{-1} shall be defined as $\frac{1}{10}$. If we wish $\frac{10^{-1}}{10^1}$ to equal $10^{-1-1} = 10^{-2}$, then since $\frac{10^{-1}}{10^1} = \frac{\frac{1}{10}}{10} = \frac{\left(\frac{1}{10}\right) \cdot 10}{10 \cdot 10} = \frac{1}{10^2}$, 10^{-2} shall be defined as $\frac{1}{10^2}$ or $\frac{1}{100}$. In general we have the following definition.

For each rational number $p \neq 0$ and each integer n, $p^{-n} = \dfrac{1}{p^n}$

Example: Express each of the following in the form $\dfrac{a}{b}$ or $\dfrac{-a}{b}$, where a and b are positive integers and have no common factors other than 1 or -1.

(a) 10^{-5} (b) $\left(\dfrac{1}{10}\right)^{-4}$ (c) $\left(\dfrac{-2}{3}\right)^{-3}$ (d) $\left(\dfrac{3}{2}\right)^{-2}\left(\dfrac{3}{2}\right)^5$

Solution:

(a) $10^{-5} = \dfrac{1}{10^5}$

$\phantom{(a) 10^{-5}} = \dfrac{1}{100,000}$

(b) $\left(\dfrac{1}{10}\right)^{-4} = \dfrac{1}{\left(\dfrac{1}{10}\right)^4}$

$\qquad\qquad = \dfrac{1}{\dfrac{1}{10^4}}$

$\qquad\qquad = \dfrac{1 \cdot 10^4}{\dfrac{1}{10^4} \cdot 10^4}$

$\qquad\qquad = \dfrac{10^4}{1}$

$\qquad\qquad = 10,000$

(c) $\left(\dfrac{-2}{3}\right)^{-3} = \dfrac{1}{\left(\dfrac{-2}{3}\right)^3}$

$\qquad\qquad = \dfrac{1}{\dfrac{(-2)^3}{3^3}}$

$\qquad\qquad = \dfrac{1 \cdot 3^3}{\dfrac{(-2)^3}{3^3} \cdot 3^3}$

$\qquad\qquad = \dfrac{3^3}{(-2)^3} = \dfrac{27}{-8} = \dfrac{-27}{8}$

(d) $\left(\dfrac{3}{2}\right)^{-3} \cdot \left(\dfrac{3}{2}\right)^5 = \left(\dfrac{3}{2}\right)^{-3+5}$

$\qquad\qquad\qquad = \left(\dfrac{3}{2}\right)^2$

$\qquad\qquad\qquad = \dfrac{3^2}{2^2}$

$\qquad\qquad\qquad = \dfrac{9}{4}$

Exercises 6.4

Express each of the following in the form $\dfrac{a}{b}$ or $\dfrac{^-a}{b}$, where a and b are positive integers with no common factors other than 1 and $^-1$.

1. $\dfrac{1}{3} \cdot \dfrac{1}{4}$

2. $\dfrac{1}{7} \cdot \dfrac{1}{9}$

3. $\dfrac{1}{2} \cdot \dfrac{3}{4}$

4. $\dfrac{3}{7} \cdot \dfrac{2}{9}$

5. $\dfrac{^-3}{4} \cdot \dfrac{4}{5}$

6. $\dfrac{^-5}{8} \cdot \dfrac{1}{2}$

7. $\dfrac{2}{3} \cdot \dfrac{^-6}{5}$

8. $\dfrac{4}{9} \cdot \dfrac{^-45}{20}$

9. $\dfrac{^-2}{3} \cdot \dfrac{^-3}{4}$

10. $\dfrac{^-4}{5} \cdot \dfrac{^-15}{36}$

11. $\dfrac{13}{^-16} \cdot \dfrac{32}{39}$

12. $\dfrac{^-7}{8} \cdot \dfrac{^-13}{91}$

13. $\left(\dfrac{3}{4} + \dfrac{2}{3}\right) \cdot \dfrac{17}{12}$

14. $\left(\dfrac{5}{6} - \dfrac{2}{3}\right) \cdot \dfrac{6}{7}$

15. $\left(\dfrac{^-5}{8} + \dfrac{3}{4}\right) \cdot 4$

16. $\left(\dfrac{5}{6} + \dfrac{5}{6}\right) \cdot \dfrac{6}{5}$

17. $\left(\dfrac{2}{3} - \dfrac{1}{2}\right) \cdot \left(\dfrac{1}{2} - \dfrac{2}{3}\right)$

18. $\left(\dfrac{3}{4} \cdot \dfrac{^-1}{3}\right) \cdot \dfrac{5}{6}$

19. $\dfrac{3}{4} \cdot \left(\dfrac{^-1}{3} \cdot \dfrac{5}{6}\right)$

20. $\left(\dfrac{3}{7} + \dfrac{11}{7}\right) \cdot \left(\dfrac{14}{5} - \dfrac{9}{5}\right)$

21. $\dfrac{3}{7} \cdot \dfrac{2}{3} \cdot \dfrac{8}{5} \cdot \dfrac{15}{56}$

22. $\dfrac{1}{2} \cdot \dfrac{2}{3} \cdot \dfrac{3}{4} \cdot \dfrac{4}{5} \cdot \dfrac{5}{6}$

23. $\left(\dfrac{1}{10}\right)^2 \left(\dfrac{1}{10}\right)^3$

24. $10^{-2} \cdot 10^{-3}$

25. $\left(\dfrac{3}{4}\right)^6 \cdot \left(\dfrac{3}{4}\right)^{-4}$

26. $3^6 \cdot 3^{-4}$

27. $10^7 \cdot 10^{-3}$

28. $10^{-5} \cdot 10^2$

29. $3^{-2} \cdot 2^{-3}$

30. $\left(\dfrac{1}{3}\right)^2 \cdot 3^2$

31. $\left(\dfrac{5}{7} \cdot 7\right)^{2}$

32. $\left(\dfrac{7}{8} \cdot 8\right)^{-2}$

33. $\left(\dfrac{3}{4}\right)^{-1}$

34. $\left(\dfrac{4}{3}\right)^{-1}$

35. $\left(\dfrac{5}{8}\right)^{-1}$

36. $\left(\dfrac{8}{5}\right)^{-1}$

37. $\left(\dfrac{3}{5}\right)^{2} \cdot \left(\dfrac{5}{3}\right)^{2}$

38. $\left(\dfrac{3}{5}\right)^{-2}\left(\dfrac{5}{3}\right)^{-2}$

39. $10^{-12} \cdot 10^{6} \cdot 10^{8}$

40. $10^{-5} \cdot 10^{8} \cdot 10^{4} \cdot \left(\dfrac{1}{10}\right)^{-7}$

Solve each of the following sentences ($a \in Q$, $a \neq 0$).

41. $\dfrac{a}{7} \cdot \dfrac{3}{4} = \dfrac{-9}{28}$

42. $\dfrac{a}{7} \cdot \dfrac{3}{4} = \dfrac{3}{7}$

43. $\dfrac{6a}{7} \cdot \dfrac{2a}{3} = \dfrac{16}{7}$

44. $\dfrac{3}{a} \cdot \dfrac{a}{4} = \dfrac{3}{4}$

45. $\left(\dfrac{a}{2}\right)^{3} = \dfrac{27}{8}$

46. $\left(\dfrac{4}{5}\right)^{2} = 1 - \dfrac{a}{25}$

47. $a^{-2} = 10^{4}$

48. $a^{3} = 10^{-3}$

49. $a^{3} = \dfrac{1}{27}$

50. $\left(\dfrac{3}{a}\right)^{2} = \left(\dfrac{a}{3}\right)^{2}$

Supply the missing reasons.

51.
$$\dfrac{\dfrac{1}{3}}{\dfrac{3}{4}} = \dfrac{1 \cdot \dfrac{4}{3}}{\dfrac{3}{4} \cdot \dfrac{4}{3}}$$

(a) _____

$$= \dfrac{\dfrac{4}{3}}{1}$$

(b) _____

$$= \dfrac{4}{3}$$

(c) _____

Solve each of the following problems.

52. Henry bought 50 feet of TV antenna cable. If the store charged 12 cents for each 3 feet, how much did Henry pay?

53. How much must Marge pay for $9\frac{7}{12}$ yards of ribbon at 18 cents per yard?

54. 1- by 8-inch white pine boards cost 25 cents per foot. Determine the cost of 26 feet of board in dollars.

55. Of those enrolled at Clever College, $\frac{1}{3}$ are freshmen, $\frac{1}{4}$ are sopho-

mores, $\frac{1}{5}$ are juniors, and the rest are seniors. If 3720 are enrolled

at Clever College, how many are there in each class?

56. Three fourths of $184 is _____.

57. At the Restful Realty Agency, Pete, the broker, has made the following arrangement with his employer. On each sale, the agency

gets $\frac{3}{50}$ of the selling price and Pete earns $\frac{2}{3}$ of this amount. If Pete

sells a house for $30,000, how much will he earn?

6.5 Division

The division property guarantees that each integer can be divided by a nonzero integer to yield a rational number. In particular we used the property in Section 6.1 to develop the idea of a reciprocal of an integer. We showed there that any nonzero integer b had a reciprocal $\frac{1}{b}$ such that

$b \cdot \frac{1}{b} = 1$. We wish to extend the reciprocal idea to rational numbers.

We shall say that the reciprocal of any rational number $\frac{a}{b}$ is another rational

number $\frac{c}{d}$, such that $\frac{a}{b} \cdot \frac{c}{d} = 1$. How do we find $\frac{c}{d}$?

Consider the quotient $1 \div \frac{4}{5} = p$. By the division property p is a ra-

tional number such that $p \cdot \frac{4}{5} = 1$. Thus p is the reciprocal of $\frac{4}{5}$. Since

$\frac{5}{4} \cdot \frac{4}{5} = 1, p = \frac{5}{4}$. So that we might be consistent with our idea of recip-

rocal in Section 6.1 we shall interpret the reciprocal of $\frac{4}{5}$ as $\dfrac{1}{\frac{4}{5}}$. Therefore $p = 1 \div \dfrac{4}{5} = \dfrac{1}{\frac{4}{5}}$.   Also since the reciprocal of $\dfrac{4}{5}$ is $\dfrac{5}{4}$ we conclude

that $\dfrac{1}{\frac{4}{5}} = \dfrac{5}{4}$.   In general:

For the integers $a \neq 0$, $b \neq 0$,

$$1 \div \frac{a}{b} = \frac{1}{\frac{a}{b}} = \frac{b}{a} \quad and \quad \frac{a}{b} \cdot \frac{b}{a} = 1.$$

Example:

$$1 \div \frac{2}{3} = \frac{1}{\frac{2}{3}} = \frac{3}{2} \qquad \frac{2}{3} \cdot \frac{3}{2} = \frac{2 \cdot 3}{3 \cdot 2} = \frac{6}{6} = 1$$

$$1 \div \frac{5}{9} = \frac{1}{\frac{5}{9}} = \frac{9}{5} \qquad \frac{5}{9} \cdot \frac{9}{5} = \frac{5 \cdot 9}{9 \cdot 5} = \frac{45}{45} = 1$$

$$1 \div \frac{15}{3} = \frac{1}{\frac{15}{3}} = \frac{3}{15} \qquad \frac{15}{3} \cdot \frac{3}{15} = \frac{15 \cdot 3}{3 \cdot 15} = \frac{45}{45} = 1$$

Now we can find a simple numeral for the quotient $\dfrac{2}{3} \div \dfrac{4}{5} = p.$

$$p \cdot \frac{4}{5} = \frac{2}{3} \qquad\qquad \text{[division property]}$$

$$\left(p \cdot \frac{4}{5} \right) \cdot \frac{5}{4} = \frac{2}{3} \cdot \frac{5}{4} \qquad \text{[multiplication property]}$$

$$p\left(\frac{4}{5} \cdot \frac{5}{4} \right) = \frac{2}{3} \cdot \frac{5}{4} \qquad \text{[regrouping]}$$

$$p = \frac{2}{3} \cdot \frac{5}{4} \qquad\qquad \left[\frac{a}{b} \cdot \frac{b}{a} = 1, \text{ which is the} \right.$$

$$\left. \text{multiplicative identity} \right]$$

This generalizes as:

For each of the integers, a, $b \neq 0$, $c \neq 0$, $d \neq 0$,

$$\frac{a}{b} \div \frac{c}{d} = \frac{a}{b} \cdot \frac{d}{c}$$

Example:

$$\frac{3}{5} \div \frac{3}{4} = \frac{3 \cdot 4}{5 \cdot 3} = \frac{4 \cdot 3}{5 \cdot 3} = \frac{4}{5}$$

$$\frac{6}{7} \div \frac{1}{2} = \frac{6 \cdot 2}{7 \cdot 1} = \frac{12}{7}$$

Note: If the numerator or denominator of a fraction is a fraction, or if both numerator and denominator are fractions, the fraction is called a

complex fraction. $\dfrac{\frac{2}{3}}{\frac{3}{8}}$, $\dfrac{\frac{1}{2}}{5}$, and $\dfrac{3}{\frac{4}{6}}$ are examples of complex fractions.
$\dfrac{3}{\frac{4}{\frac{6}{5}}}$

We shall interpret $\dfrac{\frac{a}{b}}{\frac{c}{d}}$ as $\dfrac{a}{b} \div \dfrac{c}{d}$ for the integers $a, b \neq 0, c \neq 0, d \neq 0$.

Example: Express $\dfrac{\frac{1}{2}}{\frac{1}{3}}$ and $\dfrac{\frac{3}{4}}{\frac{9}{8}}$ in the form $\dfrac{a}{b}$, where a and b are positive

integers with no common factor other than 1.

Solution:

$$\frac{\frac{1}{2}}{\frac{1}{3}} = \frac{1}{2} \div \frac{1}{3} = \frac{1 \cdot 3}{2 \cdot 1} = \frac{3}{2}$$

$$\frac{\frac{3}{4}}{\frac{9}{8}} = \frac{3}{4} \div \frac{9}{8} = \frac{3 \cdot 8}{4 \cdot 9} = \frac{3 \cdot 2 \cdot 4}{4 \cdot 3 \cdot 3} = \frac{2(3 \cdot 4)}{3(3 \cdot 4)} = \frac{2}{3}$$

Now consider the division patterns below.

I	II

$$a = b \cdot q + r$$

(1) $\dfrac{8}{3} = 8 \div 3$

(1) $8 = 3 \cdot 2 + 2$

$$\begin{array}{r} 2 \\ 3\overline{)8} \\ 6 \\ \hline 2 \end{array}$$

(2) $\dfrac{17}{4} = 17 \div 4$

(2) $17 = 4 \cdot 4 + 1$

$$\begin{array}{r} 4 \\ 4\overline{)17} \\ 16 \\ \hline 1 \end{array}$$

(3) $\dfrac{46}{13} = 46 \div 13$

(3) $46 = 13 \cdot 3 + 7$

$$\begin{array}{r} 3 \\ 13\overline{)46} \\ 39 \\ \hline 7 \end{array}$$

(4) $\dfrac{157}{19} = 157 \div 19$

(4) $157 = 19 \cdot 8 + 5$

$$\begin{array}{r} 8 \\ 19\overline{)157} \\ 152 \\ \hline 5 \end{array}$$

(5) $\dfrac{2034}{30} = 2034 \div 30$

(5) $2034 = 30 \cdot 67 + 24$

$$\begin{array}{r} 67 \\ 30\overline{)2034} \\ 180 \\ \hline 234 \\ 210 \\ \hline 24 \end{array}$$

Do you see any connection between patterns I and II? They suggest, since any rational number $\dfrac{a}{b}$, where $a,b \neq 0$ are integers, can be interpreted as the quotient of the numerator number a and the denominator number b, that $a = b \cdot q + r$. The integers q, called the *quotient*, and r, called the *remainder*, are obtained from the division algorithm. Note that $0 \leq r < b$. (Why?) The left half of pattern II is called division with a remainder.

Example: Represent $\dfrac{2034}{30}$ as the sum of an integer and a rational number.

Solution: The fifth sentence of patterns I and II above gives us $2034 = 30 \cdot 67 + 24$ as a result of division with a remainder. Now:

$$\frac{2034}{30} = 2034 \cdot \frac{1}{30} \qquad\qquad \text{[reciprocal property]}$$

$$2034 \cdot \frac{1}{30} = (30 \cdot 67 + 24)\,\frac{1}{30} \qquad\qquad \text{[renaming 2034]}$$

$$\frac{2034}{30} = \frac{30 \cdot 67}{30} + \frac{24}{30} \qquad\qquad \left[\text{distributive property and}\ a \cdot \frac{1}{b} = \frac{a}{b}\right]$$

$$\frac{2034}{30} = 67 + \frac{4}{5} \qquad\qquad \left[\text{renaming } \frac{30 \cdot 67}{30} \text{ and } \frac{24}{30}\right]$$

We can in general say that *for each of the integers* a, $b \neq 0$, $\dfrac{a}{b} = q + \dfrac{r}{b}$. *q and r are integers obtained from the division algorithm and* $0 \leq r < b$.

Example: Represent $\dfrac{8346}{53}$ as the sum of an integer and a rational number.

Solution:

$$
\begin{array}{r}
157 \\
53\overline{)8346} \\
53\ \\
\hline
304 \\
265 \\
\hline
396 \\
371 \\
\hline
25
\end{array}
$$

$$\frac{8346}{53} = 157 + \frac{25}{53}$$

The results of the last two examples, $67 + \dfrac{4}{5}$ and $157 + \dfrac{25}{53}$, are called *mixed numerals* and are usually written $67\dfrac{4}{5}$ and $157\dfrac{25}{53}$, respectively.

Exercises 6.5

Express each of the following in the form $\dfrac{a}{b}$ or $\dfrac{-a}{b}$, where a and b are positive integers with no common factors other than 1 or -1.

1. $\dfrac{2}{3} \div \dfrac{1}{3}$

2. $\dfrac{3}{4} \div \dfrac{5}{4}$

3. $\dfrac{2}{7} \div 1$

4. $\dfrac{5}{8} \div \dfrac{4}{5}$

5. $\dfrac{8}{5} \div \dfrac{4}{5}$

6. $\dfrac{1}{2} \div \dfrac{1}{4}$

7. $\dfrac{13}{16} \div \dfrac{3}{4}$

8. $1 \div \dfrac{5}{9}$

9. $\dfrac{-3}{7} \div \dfrac{2}{5}$

10. $\dfrac{-7}{8} \div \dfrac{-5}{12}$

11. $\dfrac{-13}{27} \div \dfrac{-52}{81}$

12. $\dfrac{16}{25} \div \dfrac{-4}{5}$

13. $\left(\dfrac{3}{8} + \dfrac{2}{5}\right) \div \dfrac{16}{25}$

14. $\left(\dfrac{5}{9} - \dfrac{2}{3}\right) \div \dfrac{-1}{18}$

15. $\left(\dfrac{-6}{7} + \dfrac{13}{14}\right) \div \dfrac{1}{2}$

16. $\dfrac{2}{3} \div \left(\dfrac{3}{4} - \dfrac{1}{3}\right)$

17. $\dfrac{5}{8} \div 2$

18. $16 \div \dfrac{-3}{4}$

19. $\dfrac{-2}{5} \div -2$

20. $-20 \div \dfrac{4}{5}$

21. $\dfrac{3}{5} \div \dfrac{3}{10}$

22. $\dfrac{3}{10} \div \dfrac{-3}{100}$

23. $\dfrac{3}{1000} \div \dfrac{3}{100}$

24. $\dfrac{17}{100} \div \left(\dfrac{17}{100}\right)^{-1}$

25. $\dfrac{\dfrac{54}{1000}}{\dfrac{-27}{100}}$

26. $\dfrac{\dfrac{-243}{1000}}{\dfrac{9}{10}}$

27. $3 \div \dfrac{3}{10}$

28. $48 \div \dfrac{-2}{3}$

29. $-36 \div 52$

30. $(-12)^3 \div (15)^2$

Use division with a remainder to rename each of the following as a mixed numeral.

31. $\dfrac{18}{5}$ **32.** $\dfrac{^-24}{7}$ **33.** $\dfrac{112}{15}$

34. $\dfrac{268}{11}$ **35.** $\dfrac{594}{^-36}$ **36.** $\dfrac{^-204}{^-16}$

37. $\dfrac{1532}{48}$ **38.** $\dfrac{2006}{124}$ **39.** $\dfrac{^-5832}{40}$

40. $\dfrac{^-1246}{^-32}$

Determine which of the following generalizations are true and which are false.

41. The sum of two positive rational numbers is a positive rational number.

42. Each rational number is either positive or negative.

43. The quotient of two negative integers is a positive rational number.

44. Each rational number has an opposite.

45. The product of any rational number with zero is a rational number.

46. The sum of any two rational numbers is a nonzero rational number.

47. Each rational number has a reciprocal.

48. Division of rational numbers is a closed operation.

49. For each first rational number there is a second rational number such that the product of the two is the first rational number.

50. The result of multiplying a nonnegative rational number by a non-positive rational number is a negative rational number.

Solve each of the following sentences, $(x,y \in Q, \; y \neq 0)$.

51. $\dfrac{x}{3} = 7$ **52.** $6x - 3 = 3$

53. $2x + 7 = 8$ **54.** $3x - 2 = 7$

55. $5x - 4 = 21$ **56.** $7x - 5 = 6 \cdot 5$

57. $\dfrac{3x}{2} = 6$ **58.** $\dfrac{4x}{9} = \dfrac{16}{9}$

59. $\dfrac{3x}{2} = \dfrac{15}{8}$ **60.** $\dfrac{x + x}{2} = 1$

61. $\dfrac{x + x}{2} = x$ **62.** $\dfrac{3}{y} = \dfrac{7}{9}$

63. $\dfrac{5}{6} = \dfrac{x}{12}$ **64.** $\dfrac{2}{y} = \dfrac{18}{9y}$

Solve each of the following problems.

65. $12 is $\frac{2}{3}$ of _____ dollars.

66. Bill bought 5 loaves of bread, or $\frac{1}{7}$ of the amount the grocer had in stock.   How many loaves remain ?

67. If a real estate broker earns $1200 by selling a $25,000 house, what fractional part of the selling price is his commission ?

68. If Grace selects $\frac{3}{8}$, or 24, of the items on a bargain basement sale table, how many items were for sale ?

69. If $\frac{1}{2}$ of $\frac{3}{4}$ of a number is $\frac{1}{3}$, what is the number ?

70. Three fifths of 75 is equal to three fourths of _____.

Express the following complex fractions in the form $\frac{a}{b}$ or $\frac{-a}{b}$, where a and b are positive integers having only 1 or -1 as common factors.

71. $\dfrac{\frac{16}{5}}{\frac{22}{15}}$

72. $\dfrac{\frac{2}{3}+1}{\frac{1}{2}-\frac{1}{8}}$

73. $\dfrac{\frac{-3}{4}}{1-\frac{2}{\frac{1}{5}}}$

74. $\dfrac{2+\frac{3}{\frac{1}{8}}}{4-\frac{2}{\frac{3}{\frac{4}{9}}}}$

75. $\dfrac{\frac{1}{4}}{\frac{1}{2}} - \dfrac{\frac{-3}{8}}{\frac{3}{24}}}{\frac{7}{2}}$

6.6 Order in the Rationals

The order relation in the integers was established in the following way:

(1) *For each of the integers a and b, b > a if and only if the graph of b is to the right of the graph of a on the number line.*

Since integers are also rational numbers we ask: Can we extend the order relation in the integers to the set of rational numbers? We first restate the order relation as follows:

(2) *For each of the integers a and b, b > a if and only if b = a + c, where c is a positive integer.*

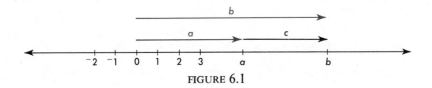

FIGURE 6.1

We see in Figure 6.1 that if $b > a$, the graph of b is to the right of the graph of a, by **(1)**. Hence there is a vector representing the positive number c such that $b = a + c$.

Similarly, if the graph of b is to the right of the graph of a on the number line, there is a vector representing c such that $b = a + c$ and, by **(1)**, $b > a$.

Thus **(1)** can be restated as **(2)**, which shall be used to establish the order relation in the rational numbers.

Definition of Order

For each of the rational numbers p and s, s > p if and only if s = p + t, where t is a positive rational number.

Example: Determine the larger of $\dfrac{2}{3}$ and $\dfrac{19}{29}$.

Solution: We rename each of these numbers.

$$\frac{2}{3} = \frac{2 \cdot 29}{3 \cdot 29} = \frac{58}{87} \quad \text{and} \quad \frac{19}{29} = \frac{19 \cdot 3}{29 \cdot 3} = \frac{57}{87}$$

Since $\dfrac{58}{87} = \dfrac{57}{87} + \dfrac{1}{87}$ and $\dfrac{1}{87}$ is positive, it follows that $\dfrac{58}{87} > \dfrac{57}{87}$.

That is,

$$\frac{2}{3} > \frac{19}{29}$$

Example: Order the members of set A from least to greatest.

$$A = \left\{ \frac{1}{2}, \frac{^{-}2}{3}, \frac{^{-}4}{5}, \frac{4}{5}, \frac{^{-}5}{6}, 0, \frac{3}{7}, \frac{^{-}2}{7} \right\}$$

Solution: The members of A can be renamed. The least common multiple of 2, 3, 5, 6, and 7 is 210. Hence

$$\frac{1}{2} = \frac{105}{210}, \; \frac{^{-}2}{3} = \frac{^{-}140}{210}, \; \frac{^{-}4}{5} = \frac{^{-}168}{210}, \; \frac{4}{5} = \frac{168}{210},$$

$$\frac{^{-}5}{6} = \frac{^{-}185}{210}, \; 0 = \frac{0}{210}, \; \frac{3}{7} = \frac{90}{210}, \; \frac{^{-}2}{7} = \frac{^{-}60}{210}.$$

Since $^{-}185 < {}^{-}168 < {}^{-}140 < {}^{-}60 < 0 < 90 < 105 < 168$, it follows that

$$\frac{^{-}185}{210} < \frac{^{-}168}{210} < \frac{^{-}140}{210} < \frac{^{-}60}{210} < \frac{0}{210} < \frac{90}{210} < \frac{105}{210} < \frac{168}{210}$$

Therefore, ordering the members of set A from least to greatest we have

$$A = \left\{ \frac{^{-}5}{6}, \frac{^{-}4}{5}, \frac{^{-}2}{3}, \frac{^{-}2}{7}, 0, \frac{3}{7}, \frac{1}{2}, \frac{4}{5} \right\}$$

Now how are rational numbers graphed?

Example: Graph $\dfrac{1}{3}$.

Solution: We can interpret $\dfrac{1}{3}$ as "one part in three." If we divide the segment between the graphs of 0 and 1 into three equal segments, $\dfrac{1}{3}$ is associated with the first point of subdivision and $\dfrac{2}{3}$ with the next subdivision point.

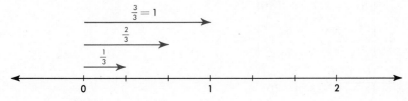

Example: Graph $\frac{7}{5}$.

Solution 1: Since $\frac{7}{5} = 7 \cdot \frac{1}{5}$, we obtain the following graph:

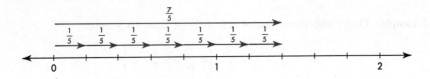

Solution 2: $\frac{7}{5} = \frac{5}{5} + \frac{2}{5} = 1 + \frac{2}{5}$.   The graph then is

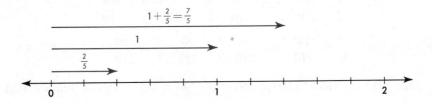

Since each rational number is the quotient, $\frac{a}{b}$, of two integers, a and $b \neq 0$, the techniques illustrated above may be used to obtain the graph of any rational number.   Therefore, we can associate each rational number with a point on the number line.

Exercises 6.6

Graph each of the following sets.

1. $\left\{ 0, \frac{1}{8}, \frac{1}{4}, \frac{3}{8}, \frac{1}{2}, \frac{5}{8}, \frac{3}{4}, \frac{7}{8}, 1 \right\}$

2. $\left\{ \frac{-5}{9}, \frac{-3}{5}, \frac{-1}{5}, \frac{2}{3}, \frac{4}{9} \right\}$

3. $\left\{ \frac{13}{6}, \frac{15}{4}, \frac{12}{7}, \frac{19}{8}, \frac{21}{10} \right\}$

4. $\left\{ \frac{-5}{4}, \frac{-5}{5}, \frac{-5}{6}, \frac{-5}{7}, \frac{-5}{8} \right\}$

5. $\left\{ \frac{6}{5}, \frac{6}{6}, \frac{6}{7}, \frac{6}{8}, \frac{6}{9}, \frac{6}{10} \right\}$

6. $\left\{\dfrac{101}{10}, \dfrac{110}{10}, \dfrac{101}{100}, \dfrac{110}{100}\right\}$

7. $\left\{\dfrac{-16}{7}, \dfrac{-23}{9}, \dfrac{-43}{8}, \dfrac{-25}{6}, \dfrac{-35}{7}\right\}$

8. $\left\{\dfrac{1}{3}, \dfrac{2}{6}, \dfrac{3}{9}, \dfrac{4}{12}, \dfrac{5}{15}, \dfrac{6}{18}, \dfrac{7}{21}, \dfrac{8}{24}, \dfrac{9}{27}, \dfrac{10}{30}\right\}$

9. $\left\{\dfrac{a}{3}, a \in J: {}^{-}6 \leq a \leq 6\right\}$

10. $\left\{\dfrac{4}{a}, a \in J: 1 \leq a \leq 16\right\}$

11. $\left\{\dfrac{a}{b}, a \in J, b \in J, b \neq 0: a = 2b\right\}$

Order the members of each of the following sets from least to greatest.

12. $\left\{\dfrac{4}{5}, \dfrac{3}{4}, \dfrac{2}{3}\right\}$ 13. $\left\{\dfrac{-3}{8}, \dfrac{-4}{7}, \dfrac{-5}{10}\right\}$

14. $\left\{\dfrac{3}{20}, \dfrac{5}{28}, \dfrac{6}{35}\right\}$ 15. $\left\{\dfrac{-12}{10}, \dfrac{-123}{100}, \dfrac{-1205}{1000}, \dfrac{-26}{50}\right\}$

16. Why does the graph of the set in problem 8 consist of a single point?

One of the consequences of our definition of order and the properties of rational numbers is:

For each of the integers $a, b > 0, c, d > 0, \dfrac{a}{b} > \dfrac{c}{d}$ if and only if $ad > bc$.

Use this property to find the greater of the two rational numbers in each of the following pairs.

17. $\left(\dfrac{1}{2}, \dfrac{2}{3}\right)$ 18. $\left(\dfrac{3}{8}, \dfrac{4}{7}\right)$

19. $\left(\dfrac{5}{6}, \dfrac{3}{4}\right)$ 20. $\left(\dfrac{-5}{12}, \dfrac{-7}{16}\right)$

21. $\left(\dfrac{-11}{5}, \dfrac{-18}{7}\right)$ 22. $\left(\dfrac{-3}{5}, \dfrac{1}{3}\right)$

23. $\left(\dfrac{-5}{8}, \dfrac{2}{-3}\right)$ 24. $\left(\dfrac{25}{4}, \dfrac{38}{6}\right)$

25. We know that $\frac{2}{3} < \frac{3}{4}$ since $\frac{2}{3} = \frac{8}{12} < \frac{9}{12} = \frac{3}{4}$ or since $2 \cdot 4 < 3 \cdot 3$.

Why is it then that although $\frac{3}{-4} < \frac{2}{3}$, it does not follow that $3 \cdot 3 <$

$-4 \cdot 2$? What do you observe if $\frac{3}{-4}$ is renamed $\frac{-3}{4}$?

For each of the following pairs of rational numbers, find a rational number larger than the smaller one and smaller than the larger one.

Example: $\left(\frac{2}{3}, \frac{5}{6}\right)$.

Solution: $\frac{2}{3} = \frac{4}{6} = \frac{8}{12}$ and $\frac{5}{6} = \frac{10}{12}$. Since $\frac{9}{12} > \frac{8}{12}$ and $\frac{9}{12} < \frac{10}{12}$ and

$\frac{9}{12} = \frac{3}{4}$ we have $\frac{2}{3} < \frac{3}{4} < \frac{5}{6}$. So $\frac{3}{4}$ is a rational number larger than $\frac{2}{3}$ and

smaller than $\frac{5}{6}$.

26. $\left(\frac{5}{8}, \frac{7}{8}\right)$ **27.** $\left(\frac{1}{3}, \frac{2}{3}\right)$

28. $\left(\frac{4}{7}, \frac{5}{7}\right)$ **29.** $\left(\frac{1}{4}, \frac{1}{5}\right)$

30. $\left(\frac{2}{7}, \frac{3}{4}\right)$ **31.** $\left(\frac{3}{8}, \frac{1}{3}\right)$

32. $\left(\frac{5}{12}, \frac{4}{7}\right)$ **33.** $\left(\frac{3}{10}, \frac{31}{100}\right)$

Problems 26 through 33 suggest that, for each two rational numbers p and s, where $p < s$, there is at least one rational number t such that $p < t < s$. A set of numbers that has this property is said to be *dense*.

34. Is the set of natural numbers a dense set?
35. Is the set of whole numbers a dense set?
36. Is the set of integers a dense set?
37. Is the set of positive rationals a dense set?

6.7 Interpretations of Rational Numbers

We have shown that the invention of rational numbers grew out of the need to solve division problems. Consequently, the fraction $\frac{2}{3}$ denotes the quotient $2 \div 3$. There are, however, other useful interpretations of fractions. In this section we shall consider some of them.

Denoting A Quotient

Consider the following problem:

If 16 dollars is to be equally shared by some boys, each receiving 4 dollars, how many boys are there?

To solve this problem, we need to find a number n such that $4 \cdot n = 16$. Such a number is $\frac{16}{4}$. But $\frac{16}{4} = 4$. Hence there are four boys.

Denoting A Fractional Part

Two pies are to be split into three equal portions (see Figure 6.2). What (fractional) part of a pie is each portion?

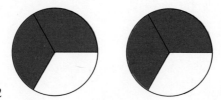

FIGURE 6.2

Separate each pie into three portions, calling each portion $\frac{1}{3}$ of a pie. The denominator 3 names the number of parts in each pie, Since each pie contains three parts or $\frac{3}{3}$, two pies contain $2 \cdot \frac{3}{3} = \frac{6}{3} = 6 \cdot \frac{1}{3}$. Six one-thirds can easily be separated into three equal portions of two one-thirds each. Hence each portion is $\frac{2}{3}$ of a pie. Note that $\frac{2}{3}$ is also the quotient $2 \div 3$.

As another illustration, suppose we wish to find $\frac{2}{3}$ of 15 (see Figure 6.3).

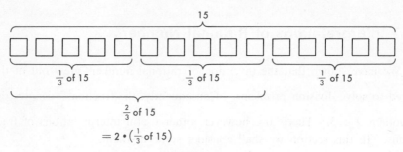

$$= 2 \cdot \left(\tfrac{1}{3} \text{ of } 15 \right)$$

FIGURE 6.3

Finding $\frac{1}{3}$ of 15 is equivalent to asking how large is each of three equal parts of 15. Since

$$3 \cdot 5 = 15, \quad 15 \div 3 = 5, \quad \text{or } \frac{1}{3} \cdot 15 = 5$$

But

$$\frac{2}{3} \text{ is } 2 \cdot \frac{1}{3}, \quad \text{so } \frac{2}{3} \text{ of } 15 \text{ is } 2 \cdot \left(\frac{1}{3} \text{ of } 15 \right) \quad \text{or } 2(5) \text{ or } 10$$

Note that

$$\frac{2}{3} \cdot 15 = \frac{2}{3} \cdot \frac{15}{1} = \frac{30}{3} = 10$$

Hence we can find a fractional part of a number by ordinary multiplication of rational numbers.

Example: Find $\frac{2}{3}$ of $\frac{3}{4}$.

Solution: $\frac{2}{3}$ of $\frac{3}{4}$ can be written

$$\frac{2}{3} \cdot \frac{3}{4} = \frac{2 \cdot 3}{3 \cdot 4} = \frac{6}{12} = \frac{1}{2}$$

Hence $\frac{2}{3}$ of $\frac{3}{4}$ is $\frac{1}{2}$. For a graphic interpretation, see Figure 6.4.

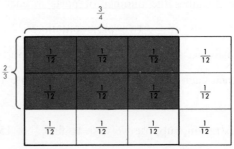

FIGURE 6.4

Denoting A Ratio

Occasionally we wish to compare the magnitudes of two quantities. If one item costs twice as much as another, we say that the ratio of their costs is 2 to 1, written 2:1 or $\frac{2}{1}$. If the age of a first person is 18 and that of a second person is 21, the ratio of their ages is $\frac{18}{21}$. But $\frac{18}{21} = \frac{6}{7}$, so we might also say that the ratio of their ages is $\frac{6}{7}$.

Example: If the contents of two boxes of canned goods are in the ratio $\frac{3}{4}$ and the smaller carton contains 36 cans, how many cans does the larger contain?

Solution: Suppose the large carton contains n cans. Then the ratio of the contents is $\frac{36}{n}$. But $\frac{36}{n} = \frac{3}{4}$. Therefore $36 \cdot 4 = n \cdot 3$ or $144 = n \cdot 3$. By the division property $n = \frac{144}{3} = 48$. Hence the large carton contains 48 cans.

Denoting A Rate Pair

If 3 pencils cost 10 cents, what is the cost of 12 pencils?

If 3 pencils cost 10 cents, then $2 \cdot 3$ or 6 pencils cost $2 \cdot 10$ or 20 cents, $3 \cdot 3$ or 9 pencils cost $3 \cdot 10$ or 30 cents, and $4 \cdot 3$ or 12 pencils cost $4 \cdot 10$ or 40 cents. This suggests, since $\frac{3}{10} = \frac{3 \cdot 4}{10 \cdot 4} = \frac{12}{40}$, that we denote the rate pair, 3 for 10, by the fraction $\frac{3}{10}$.

Example: If an automobile travels 135 miles in 3 hours, how far does it travel in 5 hours at the same rate?

Solution: Suppose it travels n miles in 5 hours. Form the rate pairs $\frac{n}{5}$ and $\frac{135}{3}$. Then $\frac{n}{5} = \frac{135}{3}$. Hence $3n = 5 \cdot 135 = 675$. By the division property $n = \frac{675}{3} = 225$. Therefore, the automobile will travel 225 miles in 5 hours.

Denoting A Percent

This interpretation will be discussed in Chapter 7.

Exercises 6.7

1. Give an example of each interpretation of the use of rational numbers, different from any in the text.

2. If potatoes cost 48 cents for 10 pounds, then
   (a) 72 cents would buy _____ pounds.
   (b) 16 pounds would cost _____ cents.

3. What is the ratio of 1 foot to 1 yard?

4. How much will John earn if he works $24\frac{3}{5}$ hours at $2 per hour?

5. If Mary plans to serve equal portions of two pies to 10 people, what portion of a pie does each person receive?

6. A recipe to serve 25 people requires $2\frac{1}{2}$ cups of flour. If the recipe is changed to serve 10 people, how many cups of flour does it now require?

7. Harry Meyers bought a set of tools at a "$\frac{1}{4}$ off" sale. If the usual price was $128, how much did he save? How much did he pay?

8. A mixture of nuts contains $1\frac{3}{4}$ pounds of peanuts for each $\frac{5}{8}$ pounds of cashews. What is the ratio of peanuts to cashews?

9. At the Korner Kandy Kitchen, Karen sells $\frac{7}{8}$ pounds of candy for each $1\frac{1}{4}$ pounds of candy that Kathy sells. What is the ratio of candy sold by Karen to candy sold by Kathy?

10. Anton is $2\frac{1}{3}$ times as far from Bankville as Canton is. It is 7 miles from Canton to Bankville. How far is it from Anton to Bankville?

11. The Coastal Comets scored 288 points in 12 games. What was the average number of points scored per game?

12. How long will it take Paul to drive 327 miles if he averages 33 miles per hour?

13. On a 5-day hiking trip, Bill and Bob traveled $5\frac{3}{4}$ miles the first day, $10\frac{1}{3}$ miles the second day, $2\frac{1}{2}$ miles the third day, $5\frac{3}{8}$ miles the fourth day, and $6\frac{3}{4}$ miles the fifth day. What was their average rate per day?

14. If Mr. Burns earns $1200 for selling a $20,000 house, how much will he earn by selling a $30,000 house?

15. How tall is a flagpole that casts a 12-foot shadow at the same time that a 6-foot man casts a 4-foot shadow?

16. If orange juice is on sale at 20 cents for 3 cans, how much would a case of two dozen cans cost?

17. A plane can fly 400 miles in 45 minutes. How far will it travel in 75 minutes?

18. A 3-gallon salt solution contains $1\frac{3}{4}$ pounds of salt. How many pounds of salt are there in a 1-gallon solution?

19. A cough syrup is $\frac{8}{9}$ water. If a bottle contains 8 ounces of cough syrup, how much is water?

20. Three men enter into a business agreement in which the first man receives half as much as the second man and the third man receives twice as much as the first. If, on a particular transaction, the total profit is $2500, how much does each man receive?

21. 27 units on a Fahrenheit thermometer measure the same change in temperature as 15 units on a centigrade thermometer. 1 centigrade unit, then, is equivalent to how many Fahrenheit units?

22. If truck A can carry $\frac{3}{4}$ ton and make five 8-mile trips per day while truck B can carry $1\frac{1}{4}$ tons and make three 9-mile trips per day, what is the ratio of their ton-mile carrying capacities?

23. Truck C carries $2\frac{1}{4}$ tons per load and makes three 12-mile trips per day. What is the carrying capacity of truck D if it can carry the daily load of truck C in two 12-mile trips?

6.8 Summary

A rational number was defined as a number of the form $\frac{a}{b}$, where a and b are integers and $b \neq 0$. $\frac{a}{b}$ was interpreted as $a \div b$. Consequently when $b = 1$, $\frac{a}{b}$ can be considered the integer a. The operations of addition, multiplication, subtraction, and division were carried into the set of rationals with the same properties they had in the integers. We were then able to develop methods for performing computations in the rationals. Those methods are described in the next example.

Example: Compute

$$\text{(a) } \frac{2}{3} + \frac{3}{4} \qquad \text{(b) } \frac{2}{3} - \frac{3}{4}$$

$$\text{(c) } \frac{2}{3} \cdot \frac{3}{4} \qquad \text{(d) } \frac{2}{3} \div \frac{3}{4}$$

Solution:

(a) 12 is the least common multiple of 3 and 4,

$$\frac{2}{3} = \frac{2 \cdot 4}{3 \cdot 4} = \frac{8}{12} \text{ and } \frac{3}{4} = \frac{3 \cdot 3}{4 \cdot 3} = \frac{9}{12}$$

Therefore $\frac{2}{3} + \frac{3}{4} = \frac{8}{12} + \frac{9}{12} = \frac{8+9}{12} = \frac{17}{12}$

(b) The first two steps are exactly the same as those for the addition problem. Therefore $\frac{2}{3} - \frac{3}{4} = \frac{8}{12} - \frac{9}{12} = \frac{8-9}{12} = \frac{-1}{12}$

(c) $\frac{2}{3} \cdot \frac{3}{4} = \frac{2 \cdot 3}{3 \cdot 4} = \frac{6}{12}$ or $\frac{2}{3} \cdot \frac{3}{4} = \frac{2 \cdot 3}{3 \cdot 4} = \frac{2 \cdot 3}{4 \cdot 3} = \frac{2}{4}$ by the renaming property for rational numbers. $\frac{6}{12}$ is equivalent to $\frac{2}{4}$ because $6 \cdot 4 = 2 \cdot 12$. Both fractions are equivalent to $\frac{1}{2}$.

(d) $\frac{2}{3} \div \frac{3}{4} = \dfrac{\dfrac{2}{3}}{\dfrac{3}{4}} = \frac{2}{3} \cdot \frac{4}{3} = \frac{2 \cdot 4}{3 \cdot 3} = \frac{8}{9}$

The ordering in the integers was then extended to the rationals. We said the rational number p is greater than the rational number s if and only if there is a positive rational number t such that $p = s + t$.

The chapter ended with a discussion of the various interpretations of the symbol $\frac{a}{b}$. It is possible to interpret $\frac{2}{3}$ as

1. 2 divided by 3.
2. 2 parts of a total of 3 parts.
3. A comparison or ratio. The sentence, "The first house had two-thirds the floor space of the second house," makes such a comparison.
4. A rate pair. For example: 2 ties for $3.
5. Percentage. We show in Chapter Seven that $\frac{2}{3}$ is equivalent to $66\frac{2}{3}$ percent.

Exercises 6.8—Review

Complete the sentences.

1. The set of rational numbers contains the set of integers as a(n) _____.
2. Many fractions can represent the same _____.
3. If two fractions represent the same rational number they are _____.
4. $\frac{1}{b}$ is called the _____ of b if $b \neq 0$.
5. The first step in adding two rational numbers is to find the _____ of their denominators.
6. If either the numerator or denominator of a fraction is a fraction, the fraction is called a(n) _____ fraction.
7. The phrase "three pairs for eight dollars" can be symbolized by the rational number _____.
8. b^{-1} is another way of writing _____.

9. A comparison of two rational numbers p and s, symbolized as $\frac{p}{s}$, is often called a(n) _____.

10. Because $\frac{5}{6} = \frac{1}{2} + \frac{1}{3}$, we can conclude that $\frac{5}{6}$ is _____ $\frac{1}{3}$.

Rename each product in simpler form.

11. $\frac{3}{5} \cdot 5$ 12. $7 \cdot \frac{1}{3}$ 13. $\frac{^-6 \cdot 2}{2}$

Find the reciprocal of each of the following.

14. 2   **15.** $\dfrac{1}{2}$ **16.** $\dfrac{3}{5}$

17. $\dfrac{-8}{7}$ **18.** $\dfrac{4}{25}$ **19.** $\dfrac{1}{-16}$

Replace the comma by the $=$ sign for those pairs of rational numbers that are equivalent.

20. $\dfrac{3}{4},\dfrac{9}{12}$ **21.** $\dfrac{4}{5},\dfrac{15}{20}$ **22.** $\dfrac{2}{-3},\dfrac{4}{6}$

23. $\dfrac{-7}{2},\dfrac{21}{-6}$ **24.** $\dfrac{21}{32},\dfrac{168}{256}$

Find the least common multiple for the denominators of each set of rational numbers and rename the rational numbers so that they have the least common multiple as a common denominator.

25. $\left\{\dfrac{1}{2},\dfrac{2}{3}\right\}$ **26.** $\left\{\dfrac{2}{5},\dfrac{1}{4},\dfrac{3}{8}\right\}$ **27.** $\left\{\dfrac{-4}{3},\dfrac{10}{7},\dfrac{5}{-9}\right\}$

Perform the following computations.

28. $\dfrac{1}{2}-\dfrac{2}{3}$ **29.** $\dfrac{2}{5}+\dfrac{1}{4}+\dfrac{3}{8}$ **30.** $\dfrac{-4}{3}+\dfrac{10}{7}+\dfrac{5}{-9}$

31. $\dfrac{6}{8}\cdot\dfrac{9}{4}$ **32.** $\dfrac{2}{3}\cdot\dfrac{3}{2}$ **33.** $\dfrac{2}{3}\div\dfrac{3}{2}$

34. $\dfrac{-5}{8}\cdot\dfrac{6}{-10}$ **35.** $\dfrac{-3}{4}\div\dfrac{1}{8}$ **36.** $\left(4+\dfrac{2}{3}\right)\div\dfrac{7}{6}$

37. $\left(1-\dfrac{7}{2}\right)\cdot\dfrac{2}{5}$ **38.** $\left(\dfrac{3}{8}-\dfrac{1}{4}-\dfrac{6}{16}+\dfrac{2}{8}\right)\cdot\dfrac{1}{3}$

39. $10^{-3}\cdot10^{4}$ **40.** $10^{-2}\cdot10^{-7}$ **41.** $\left(\dfrac{3}{4}\right)^{-1}$

42. $\left(\dfrac{2}{5}\right)^{-2}$ **43.** $10^{-1}\div10^{-3}$ **44.** $10^{-2}\cdot10^{4}\cdot\left(\dfrac{1}{10}\right)^{-3}$

45. $\left(\dfrac{2}{3}-\dfrac{1}{4}\right)\cdot\left(\dfrac{1}{2}+\dfrac{3}{8}\right)$ **46.** $\left(\dfrac{2}{3}-\dfrac{1}{4}\right)\div\left(\dfrac{1}{2}+\dfrac{3}{8}\right)$

Write the following numerals (**a**) as a mixed numeral, (**b**) in the form $a = b \cdot q + r$.

Example: $\dfrac{8}{5}$

Solution: (**a**) $\dfrac{8}{5} = 1\dfrac{3}{5}$ (**b**) $8 = 5 \cdot 1 + 3$

47. $\dfrac{11}{3}$ **48.** $\dfrac{29}{5}$ **49.** $\dfrac{376}{15}$

Order the following sets of rational numbers from smallest to largest.

50. $\left\{ \dfrac{3}{8}, \dfrac{2}{3}, \dfrac{-1}{2} \right\}$ **51.** $\left\{ \dfrac{11}{8}, \dfrac{5}{6}, \dfrac{4}{3}, \dfrac{3}{2} \right\}$

52. $\left\{ -6, -2, \dfrac{-7}{3}, \dfrac{-15}{2}, \dfrac{-1}{4} \right\}$ **53.** $\left\{ 2, \dfrac{21}{3}, \dfrac{15}{6}, \dfrac{100}{14}, 8\dfrac{1}{4} \right\}$

54. The jet flew 2000 miles in $3\dfrac{1}{2}$ hours. How much longer would it take to complete the flight of 3000 miles?

55. An alcohol mixture contains $1\dfrac{1}{2}$ parts alcohol to $2\dfrac{1}{2}$ parts water. What ratio of the total mixture is alcohol?

56. Four partners divided the profits of a stock speculation evenly. If the speculation netted the partnership a profit that amounted to $\dfrac{3}{5}$ of the original investment, how much of the original investment did each partner realize?

chapter seven

NUMERATION AND DECIMAL NOTATION

7.0 Introduction

Now that we have discussed the set of rational numbers and the algorithms we used with them for computing, we need to note that there are other ways to name rational numbers. In particular, we shall, in this chapter, extend the meaning of our place-value principal for base-ten, or decimal, notation so that we can write numerals for rational numbers in a manner similar to the way we write numerals for whole numbers. We shall also discuss how the algorithms apply to these numerals. We then note that this form of numeral leads us to conclude that there are still some numbers that we have not accounted for; that is, there are some numbers that are *not* rational. Consideration of these numbers leads to a larger set of numbers, called the set of *real numbers*.

(*Note:* To avoid confusing the multiplication symbol " · " with the decimal point, we shall use, wherever necessary, the symbol "×" to indicate multiplication.)

7.1 Numeration, Exponents, and Decimal Notation

The base-ten numeration system was discussed in Section 1.3. We shall return to this discussion and use exponential notation to clarify the place-value principle.

Example 1:

$$8436 = 8000 + 400 + 30 + 6$$
$$= 8 \times 1000 + 4 \times 100 + 3 \times 10 + 6 \times 1$$
$$= 8 \times 10^3 + 4 \times 10^2 + 3 \times 10^1 + 6 \times 10^0$$

172

The "8", by virtue of the place-value position for base-ten numeration, represents eight thousand or 8×10^3.   For any natural number it is possible to represent the place value of a digit by an integral power of 10.   The exponent is equal to the number of zeros to the right of the digit.

Example 2: $7,000,000 = 7 \times 10^6$.

Example 3: $386 \frac{2}{10} = 3 \times 10^2 + 8 \times 10^1 + 6 \times 10^0 + 2 \times 10^{-1}$.

Here we use the facts that $\frac{2}{10} = 2 \times \frac{1}{10}$ and $\frac{1}{10} = 10^{-1}$.

Examples 1 and 3 together strongly suggest that a numeral for $386 \frac{2}{10}$ might be written without a common fraction, such as $\frac{2}{10}$, if we could somehow convey that the numeral 2 has place value, tenths.   This is done by placing a *decimal point* to the right of the numeral in the ones position. We interpret 386.2 as $386 \frac{2}{10}$.

Example 4: Write a base-ten numeral for $5806 \frac{78}{100}$.

Solution:

$$5806 \frac{78}{100} = 5 \times 10^3 + 8 \times 10^2 + 0 \times 10^1 + 6 \times 10^0 + 7 \times 10^{-1} +$$
$$8 \times 10^{-2}$$
$$= 5806.78$$

Note: $7 \times 10^{-1} + 8 \times 10^{-2} = \frac{7}{10} + \frac{8}{100} = \frac{70}{100} + \frac{8}{100} = \frac{78}{100}$.

Examples 3 and 4 indicate that each digit of a numeral written in decimal notation holds a position that represents an integral power of 10.   The first digit to the right of the decimal point holds the 10^{-1}, or tenths, position.   The second digit to the right of the decimal point holds the 10^{-2}, or hundredths, position; and so on.   We can therefore write $\frac{7}{10}$ as .7 and $\frac{8}{100}$ as .08.

Example 5: Write a base-ten numeral for $230 \frac{1}{2}$.

Solution: The first question that comes to mind is what to do with $\frac{1}{2}$. Can

we represent $\frac{1}{2}$ as a fraction having some power of 10 in the denominator ?

Since $\frac{1}{2} = \frac{5}{10} = 5 \times 10^{-1}$, we have

$$230 \frac{1}{2} = 230 + \frac{1}{2}$$
$$= 230 + 5 \times 10^{-1}$$
$$= 230.5$$

Exercises 7.1

Write each of the following numerals first as a mixed numeral and then in English.

Example: 8.32.

Solution:

$8 \frac{32}{100}$ is the mixed numeral form of 8.32

Eight and thirty-two hundredths

1. 20.05	**2.** 284.106
3. 56.037	**4.** 1000.7852
5. 10,000.0001	

Write each of the following numerals in English.

6. 0.12	**7.** 10.063
8. 846.5	**9.** 28.3365
10. 400.05	**11.** 326.80321
12. 8.6020	**13.** 99.993046
14. 4.00003	**15.** 12.0080500

16. Extend Figure 1.4 (page 13) to the right to indicate place values for tenths, hundredths, and so on to place value billionths.

Write a base-ten numeral for each of the following:

17. Eight and three-tenths

18. Two hundred fifty-six and forty-eight thousandths

19. Nine ten-thousandths

20. Eleven and five hundred eight hundred-thousandths

21. Six million and seven thousand two millionths

22. $8 \frac{3}{10}$ **23.** $520 \frac{36}{1000}$

24. $29 \frac{45}{100}$ **25.** $79,003 \frac{89,216}{100,000}$

26. $4 \frac{2}{100,000}$ **27.** $11 \frac{6}{20}$

28. $48 \frac{3}{4}$ **29.** $17 \frac{8}{125}$.

Write a fraction or mixed numeral for each of the following numbers.

30. 5.5   **31.** 0.38

32. 11.013   **33.** 529.001

34. 7843.1006   **35.** 0.00107

36. 111.30   **37.** 817.064

Write a base-ten numeral for each of the following.

Example:

$$15 \times 10^{-2} = 15 \times \frac{1}{100} = \frac{15}{100} = .15$$

38. 6×10^{-2} **39.** 8×10^{-3}

40. 23×10^{-3} **41.** 42×10^{-5}

42. 806×10^{-3} **43.** 253×10^{-4}

44. $70,095 \times 10^{-7}$ **45.** 25×10^{-1}

46. 890×10^{-2}

For each of the following write a numeral of the form $a \times 10^{b^-}$, where a and b are to be replaced by whole numbers.

Example:

$$.83 = \frac{83}{100} = 83 \times \frac{1}{100} = 83 \times 10^{-2}$$

47. .3   **48.** .04

49. .206   **50.** .0532

51. .10906   **52.** .00032

53. .005007   **54.** .000080

55. Why do you think newspapers prefer to print numerals in decimal form rather than in fractional or mixed-numeral form?

7.2 Addition and Subtraction

Having introduced decimal notation we now consider the use of our algorithms for computing sums and differences of rational numbers written as base-ten numerals.

Example: Compute $6.37 + 4.65$.

Solution:

$$6.37 + 4.65 = \left(6 + \frac{3}{10} + \frac{7}{100}\right)$$
$$+ \left(4 + \frac{6}{10} + \frac{5}{100}\right)$$

[the numbers 6.37 and 4.65 are renamed in expanded notation]

$$= (6 + 4) + \left(\frac{3}{10} + \frac{6}{10}\right)$$
$$+ \left(\frac{7}{100} + \frac{5}{100}\right)$$

[the commutative and associative properties of addition allow us to regroup the numbers]

$$= 10 + \frac{9}{10} + \frac{12}{100}$$

[basic addition facts for rational numbers]

$$= 10 + \frac{9}{10} + \left(\frac{10}{100} + \frac{2}{100}\right)$$

[renaming numbers]

$$= 10 + \left(\frac{9}{10} + \frac{10}{100}\right) + \frac{2}{100}$$

[regrouping by commutative and associative properties of addition]

$$= 10 + 1 + \frac{2}{100}$$

[basic addition facts for rational numbers]

$$= 11.02$$

[renaming in decimal notation]

A shorthand description of the use of the addition algorithm in the above example follows.

$$\begin{array}{r} 6.37 \\ 4.65 \\ \hline \end{array}$$

(7 + 5) hundredths ────────────→ 12
(3 + 6) tenths ──────────────→ 9 $\begin{array}{r} 6.37 \\ 4.65 \\ \hline 11.02 \end{array}$
(6 + 4) ones ──────────→ 10
$\qquad\qquad\qquad\qquad\qquad \begin{array}{r} \hline 11.02 \end{array}$

Example: Compute $353.1 + 76.988$.

Solution: Since $353.1 = 353.100$, we have

$$\begin{array}{r} 353.100 \\ 76.988 \\ \hline 431.088 \end{array}$$

The zeros in the hundredths and thousandths places of 353.100 are *place-holders*. Using zeros this way when adding numbers written in decimal-notation form helps to prevent computation errors.

The next two examples illustrate the use of the subtraction algorithm in computing differences of rational numbers written as base-ten numerals.

Example: Compute $86.75 - 39.68$.

Solution:

$$86.75 - 39.68 = \left(80 + 6 + \frac{7}{10} + \frac{5}{100}\right)$$

[renaming the numbers 86.75 and 39.68]

$$- \left(30 + 9 + \frac{6}{10} + \frac{8}{100}\right)$$

$$= (80 - 30) + (6 - 9)$$

[regrouping]

$$+ \left(\frac{7}{10} - \frac{6}{10}\right)$$

$$+ \left(\frac{5}{100} - \frac{8}{100}\right)$$

$$= (70 - 30) + (16 - 9)$$

$\left[\text{renaming} \left(80 + 6 + \dfrac{7}{10}\right. \right.$

$$+ \left(\frac{6}{10} - \frac{6}{10}\right)$$

$\left. + \dfrac{5}{100}\right) \text{ as } \left(70 + 16\right.$

$$+ \left(\frac{15}{100} - \frac{8}{100}\right)$$

$\left. \left. + \dfrac{6}{10} + \dfrac{15}{100}\right) \right]$

$$= 40 + 7 + 0 + \frac{7}{100}$$

[basic subtraction facts for integers and fractions]

$$= 47.07$$

[renaming

$\left.\left(40 + 7 + 0 + \dfrac{7}{100}\right)\right]$

The algorithm applied directly to $86.75 - 39.68$ is

$$
\begin{array}{r}
86.75 \\
-39.68 \\
\hline
47.07
\end{array}
$$

Example: Compute $760 - 325.104$.

Solution: Since $760 = 760.000$, we have

$$760.000 = \left(700 + 50 + 9 + \frac{9}{10} + \frac{9}{100} + \frac{10}{1000}\right)$$

$$- 325.104 = \left(300 + 20 + 5 + \frac{1}{10} + \frac{0}{100} + \frac{4}{1000}\right)$$

$$\overline{434.896} = \left(400 + 30 + 4 + \frac{8}{10} + \frac{9}{100} + \frac{6}{1000}\right)$$

Zeros are used as placeholders to simplify the subtraction operation.

Exercises 7.2

Use the step-by-step procedure of the first example in this section to compute each of the indicated sums.

1. $8.65 + 3.42$ 2. $26.93 + 45.08$
3. $851.007 + 68.346$ 4. $539.517 + 267.3$
5. $896.04 + 755.079$

Solve each of the following sentences directly. $n \in Q$.

6. $5.36 + 7.75 = n$ 7. $22.94 + 37.07 = n$
8. $482.0061 + 29.307 = n$ 9. $658.304 + 924.7106 = n$
10. $1129 + 856.003 = n$ 11. $6829.4216 + 5437.079 = n$
12. $84.18563 + 17.820075 = n$

Use the step-by-step procedure of the third example of this section to compute each of the following differences.

13. $8.57 - 5.32$ 14. $7.36 - 4.28$
15. $10.04 - 3.26$ 16. $21 - 17.54$
17. $82.49 - 15.5$

Solve each of the following sentences directly. $n \in Q$.

18. $6.98 - 4.35 = n$ **19.** $12.53 - 5.76 = n$
20. $58.3 - 26.512 = n$ **21.** $125.0082 - 16.5036 = n$
22. $250 - 76.1452 = n$ **23.** $76.3005 - 17.16 = n$
24. $100.0003 - 58.2576 = n$

25. Review the procedure followed in the first example of this section. Explain how the associative and commutative properties of addition are used for regrouping.

Compute the following.

26. $8.12 + 5.006 + 26.74$
27. $26.583 + 84.27 + 125.069 + 200.4$
28. $25.18 + {}^-18.69 + 56.03$ **29.** $42.07 - 86.385$
30. 648.035   **31.**   154.531
        27.02 $^-749.91$
        86.8431
       110.153
        62.2572

32. $^-16.34 + {}^-84.056 + {}^-29.333 + {}^-184.37$
33. $^-58.3 + 186.25 + {}^-749.834 + 547.861$
34.   1000.   **35.**   1000.
            18.65 -18.316
           250.048
        65072.1542
           714.3
            86.104
           909.2

36. John Quincy wrote checks in the following amounts during the month of May: $125.00, $85.17, $25.63, $14.81, $50.00, $182.63, and $36.75. He deposited the following amounts to his account during May: $268.36, $59.12, and $101.55. Determine whether Mr. Quincy's checking account balance was larger or smaller at the end of May than it was at the beginning of May and by how much.

37. Cow College, an agricultural school, is built on 528.42 acres. Academic buildings and surrounding grounds use 86.43 acres. Athletic fields consume 110.36 acres. Walks and drives use 3.74 acres, and parking lots utilize 12.59 acres. How much acreage remains for agricultural pursuits?

38. Find the total boundary length of the piece of property shown.

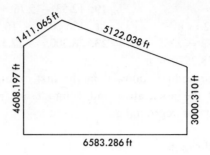

39. Find dimensions *A*, *B*, *C*, and *D* in the diagram.

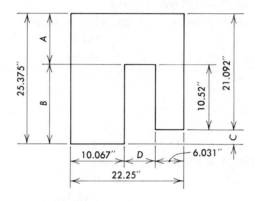

7.3 Multiplication and Scientific Notation

Consider the sentence "12.8 × 1000 = *n*." "To solve for *n*" means "to compute a numeral for 12.8 × 1000, then find the solution set."

$$12.8 \times 1000 = (1 \times 10 + 2 \times 1 \qquad \text{[renaming]}$$
$$+ 8 \times 10^{-1}) \times 10^3$$
$$= (1 \times 10 \times 10^3) + (2 \times 1 \qquad \text{[distributive property]}$$
$$\times 10^3) + (8 \times 10^{-1} \times 10^3)$$
$$= 1 \times 10^4 + 2 \times 10^3 \qquad \text{[associative property and}$$
$$+ 8 \times 10^2 \qquad\qquad \text{properties of exponents]}$$
$$= 12,800 \qquad\qquad\qquad \text{[renaming]}$$

12,800 is a base-ten numeral for 12.8 × 1000. {12,800} is the solution set.

Example: Solve the sentence "26.45 × 10,000 = *n*."   *n* ∈ *Q*.

Solution:

$$26.45 \times 10,000 = [(2 \times 10) + (6 \times 1) + (4 \times 10^{-1}) + (5 \times 10^{-2})] \times 10^4$$
$$= (2 \times 10 \times 10^4) + (6 \times 1 \times 10^4) + (4 \times 10^{-1} \times 10^4)$$
$$+ (5 \times 10^{-2} \times 10^4)$$
$$= (2 \times 10^5) + (6 \times 10^4) + (4 \times 10^3) + (5 \times 10^2)$$
$$= 264,500$$

Answer: $\{264,500\}$

The problems discussed above suggest a shortcut: *The product of a base-ten numeral and 10^b, b a positive integer, is obtained by moving the decimal point b places to the right.*

Now consider the product 2.84×10^{-2}.

$$2.84 \times 10^{-2} = [(2 \times 1) + (8 \times 10^{-1}) \qquad \text{[renaming]}$$
$$+ (4 \times 10^{-2})] \times 10^{-2}$$
$$= (2 \times 1 \times 10^{-2}) + (8 \times 10^{-1} \qquad \text{[distributive property]}$$
$$\times 10^{-2}) + (4 \times 10^{-2} \times 10^{-2})$$
$$= (2 \times 10^{-2}) + (8 \times 10^{-3}) \qquad \text{[property of exponents]}$$
$$+ (4 \times 10^{-4})$$
$$= .0284 \qquad \text{[renaming]}$$

Example: Solve the sentence "$8.13 \times 10^{-3} = n$." $\quad n \in Q$.

Solution:

$$8.13 \times 10^{-3} = [8 \times 1 + 1 \times 10^{-1} + 3 \times 10^{-2}] \times 10^{-3}$$
$$= [8 \times 1 \times 10^{-3} + 1 \times 10^{-1} \times 10^{-3} + 3 \times 10^{-2} \times 10^{-3}]$$
$$= 8 \times 10^{-3} + 1 \times 10^{-4} + 3 \times 10^{-5}$$
$$= .00813$$

So $\{.00813\}$ is the solution set.

Example: Express 48.325 as the product of a whole number and an integral power of 10.

Solution:

$$48.325 = 4 \times 10 + 8 \times 1 + 3 \times 10^{-1} + 2 \times 10^{-2} + 5 \times 10^{-3}$$
$$= (4 \times 10^4 \times 10^{-3}) + (8 \times 10^3 \times 10^{-3}) + (3 \times 10^2 \times 10^{-3})$$
$$+ (2 \times 10^1 \times 10^{-3}) + (5 \times 1 \times 10^{-3})$$
$$= [(4 \times 10^4) + (8 \times 10^3) + (3 \times 10^2) + (2 \times 10^1) + (5 \times 1)]$$
$$\times 10^{-3}$$
$$= 48,325 \times 10^{-3}$$

Note that the "5" in "48.325" is in the thousandths, or 10^{-3}, place.

Find a shortcut for working the last two examples.

Now consider a product where neither factor is an integer power of 10, such as 7.01×32.36.

$$
\begin{aligned}
7.01 \times 32.36 &= (701 \times 10^{-2}) \times (3236 \times 10^{-2}) && \text{[renaming]} \\
&= (701 \times 3236) \times (10^{-2} \times 10^{-2}) && \text{[commutative and} \\
&&& \text{associative properties]} \\
&= 2{,}268{,}436 \times 10^{-4} && \text{[multiplication algorithm} \\
&&& \text{and properties of} \\
&&& \text{exponent]} \\
&= 226.8436 && \text{[renaming]}
\end{aligned}
$$

So 7.01 $\times$ 32.36 $=$ 226.8436

$\uparrow$ $\uparrow$ $\uparrow$

hundredths   hundredths   ten-thousandths

10^{-2} $\times$ 10^{-2} $=$ 10^{-4}

Example: Solve the sentence "$n = .007 \times .13$." $n \in Q$.

Solution:

$$
\begin{aligned}
n &= .007 \times .13 \\
&= (7 \times 10^{-3}) \times (13 \times 10^{-2}) \\
&= (7 \times 13) \times (10^{-3} \times 10^{-2}) \\
&= 91 \times 10^{-5} \\
&= .00091
\end{aligned}
$$

So $n = .00091 = .007 \times .13$

$\uparrow$ $\uparrow$ $\uparrow$

$10^{-5} = 10^{-3} \times 10^{-2}$

$\{.00091\}$ is the solution set.

Observe that in the computations in the last two examples discussed we have

1. Expressed each factor as the product of a whole number and an integral power of 10.
2. Found the product of the whole numbers using the multiplication algorithm for whole numbers.
3. Used the properties of exponents to find the place value of the ones digit of the product of the whole numbers.
4. Written the result in base ten notation.

Engineers and scientists often work with very large or very small numbers. They find it convenient to express these numbers as a product of a number between 1 and 10 and some integral power of 10. This method of numeration is called *scientific notation*.

Example: Write each of the following numerals in scientific notation.

(a)	186,000	(b)	250,000,000
(c)	.00005	(d)	.00000832
(e)	781.646	(f)	.004385

Solution:

(a)	1.86×10^5	(b)	2.5×10^8
(c)	5×10^{-5}	(d)	8.32×10^{-6}
(e)	7.81646×10^2	(f)	4.385×10^{-3}

Example: Compute $250,000,000 \times .00005$.

Solution:

$$2.5 \times 10^8 \times 5 \times 10^{-5} = 2.5 \times 5 \times 10^8 \times 10^{-5}$$
$$= 12.5 \times 10^3$$
$$= 12,500$$

Exercises 7.3

Compute the following.

1. 8×10^2
2. 52×10^3
3. 68×10^{-2}
4. $10^{-3} \times 10^4$
5. $10^{-5} \times 10^2$
6. 18×10^{-1}
7. $10^{-5} \times 10^{-2} \times 10^4$
8. 370×10^{-2}
9. $5462 \times 10^{-1} \times 10^{-2}$
10. $263 \times 10^{-3} \times 10^2$

Use a step-by-step procedure, as was done on page 181 to solve the following sentences. $n \in Q$.

11. $5.3 \times 10^3 = n$
12. $836.78 \times 10^{-2} = n$
13. $.25 \times 10^4 = n$
14. $28.364 \times 10^2 = n$
15. $8.5 \times 10^{-3} = n$

Solve each of the following sentences. $n \in Q$.

16. $950 \times 10^3 = n$ 17. $26.423 \times 10^2 = n$
18. $37.31 \times 10^{-3} = n$ 19. $865.1 \times 10^{-2} = n$
20. $1000.21 \times 10^{-5} = n$ 21. $78.3621 \times 10^3 = n$
22. $1 \times 10^3 = n$ 23. $1 \times 10^6 = n$
24. $1 \times 10^9 = n$ 25. $100 \times 10^4 = n$

26. The right-hand multiplier in problem 16 is one thousand and in problem 19 it is one hundredth. Name the right-hand multipliers for each of the sentences in problems 16 through 25.

Express each of the following as the product of a whole number and an integral power of 10.

27. 36.1   28. 4.72
29. 4.121   30. .6041
31. 58.213   32. .00481
33. .219   34. 613.613
35. 60.072   36. .0000481
37. 304.1   38. 257.4831
39. 71.171   40. 6.13×10^5

Use the four-step procedure discussed on page 182 to solve each of the following sentences. $n \in Q$.

41. $5.81 \times 53.064 = n$ 42. $63.822 \times 18.4 = n$
43. $125.26 \times 87.02 = n$ 44. $9.37 \times .0056 = n$
45. $.123 \times .0987 = n$ 46. $822 \times .063 = n$

47. The step-by-step procedure used in problems 41 through 46 suggest a general rule for multiplication in decimal notation. State such a rule.

Compute the following.

48. 108.3×76.2 49. 34.51×112.67
50. 4.98×26 51. $6025.1 \times .08$
52. $.036 \times .24$ 53. $374.26 \times .1$
54. $374.26 \times .01$ 55. $374.26 \times .001$
56. $374.26 \times .00001$ 57. $8.3 \times 50 \times .2$
58. $26.7 \times 15.41 \times 1.03$ 59. $100.5 \times .01 \times 56.83$
60. $13.9 \times 6.342 \times 451.68 \times 7$ 61. $82.7 \times 54.51 \times .003 \times 1000.24$

62. Martin worked as a lab assistant for $1.63 per hour. How much was he paid last week if he worked 24.5 hours?

63. Martin's less experienced co-worker, Ted, receives $1.55 per hour as a lab assistant. Ted worked 27.6 hours last week   How much more (or less) was Ted paid than Martin?

64. The Freeway Construction Company received a contract to build 12.4 miles of freeway. The average cost of construction was 1.16 million dollars for each mile of freeway. Compute the company's profit if it received as payment for its work an amount equal to 1.15 times the cost of the job.

65. What do we mean when we say a numeral is written in scientific notation?

Use scientific notation to represent the quantities in each of the following sentences.

66. The distance from the earth to the moon is approximately 240,000 miles.

67. The distance from the earth to the sun is approximately 93,000,000 miles.

68. The diameter of the Milky Way is approximately 3,000,000,000,000,-000,000,000 miles.

69. A copper bar 1 foot long will expand .0000093 foot for an increase of 1 degree in temperature.

70. The radius of an electron is approximately .000000000078 inch.

Perform the following multiplications using scientific notation.

71. $82,000,000 \times 20,000$ **72.** $.00007 \times .0004$
73. $435,000,000,000 \times .0000061$ **74.** $.000000058 \times 900,000$
75. $15,000 \times .000003 \times 742,000$

76. Except for our sun, the star nearest the earth is approximately 4 light-years from earth. Approximately how many miles from earth is this star? (1 light-year is the distance traveled by a beam of light in 1 year. Light travels 186,000 miles per second.)

77. How many feet will 5000 feet of copper transmission wire expand under a temperature increase of 50 degrees? (See problem 69.)

7.4 Division

Since division and multiplication are inverse operations, we can use some of the properties of multiplication to compute quotients. For instance, consider the quotient $2.4 \div 8$ which has no integer solution. However, we can rename 2.4 as 24 tenths, or $\frac{24}{10}$. Then we have

$$2.4 \div 8 = \frac{24}{10} \div 8 \qquad \text{[renaming]}$$

$$= \frac{24}{10} \times \frac{1}{8} \qquad \begin{array}{l}\text{[dividing is multiplying} \\ \text{by the reciprocal]}\end{array}$$

$$= \frac{24 \times 1}{10 \times 8} \qquad \left[\frac{a}{b} \cdot \frac{c}{d} = \frac{a \cdot c}{b \cdot d}\right]$$

$$= \frac{24 \times 1}{8 \times 10} \qquad \begin{array}{l}\text{[commutative property} \\ \text{for multiplication]}\end{array}$$

$$= \frac{24}{8} \times \frac{1}{10} \qquad \left[\frac{a}{b} \cdot \frac{c}{d} = \frac{a \cdot c}{b \cdot d}\right]$$

$$= 3 \times \frac{1}{10} \qquad \left[\text{renaming } \frac{24}{8}\right]$$

$$= .3 \qquad \begin{array}{l}\text{[renaming in decimal} \\ \text{numeration]}\end{array}$$

That is, by using the properties of our operations, we have converted the problem to one we can solve.

An alternative approach for finding the solution of $2.4 \div 8 = n$ is to find a solution for $n \times 8 = 2.4$. Since $3 \times 8 = 24$ and $2.4 = 24 \times .1$, it follows that $n = 3 \times .1 = .3$.

The number line also affords a method of solution. If we interpret "$2.4 \div 8 = n$" as meaning "How large is each of 8 equal parts of 2.4?," we can consider the segment from the graph of 0 to the graph of 2.4 separated into eight equal segments as in Figure 7.1. The length of each of these segments is .3, since $.3 \times 8 = 2.4$.

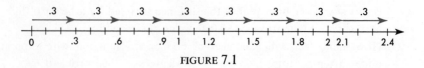

FIGURE 7.1

Example: Compute (a) $.56 \div 8$, (b) $.04 \div 8$.

Solution:

(a) Since $.56 = 56 \times \dfrac{1}{100}$ and $56 \div 8 = 7$, it follows that $.56 \div 8 =$

$7 \times \dfrac{1}{100} = .07$

Note: $.07 \times 8 = .56$.

(b) $.04 = .040 = 40 \times \dfrac{1}{1000}$ and $40 \div 8 = 5$, so

$.04 \div 8 = 5 \times \dfrac{1}{1000} = .005$

Example: Express $\dfrac{3}{8}$ in base-ten notation.

Solution:

$$\frac{3}{8} = \frac{3000}{8000} = \frac{3000}{8} \times \frac{1}{1000}$$

We can use the division algorithm to compute $\dfrac{3000}{8}$.

$$
\begin{array}{r}
375 \\
8)\overline{3000} \\
24 \\
\hline
60 \\
56 \\
\hline
40 \\
40 \\
\hline
0
\end{array}
$$

So $\dfrac{3}{8} = \dfrac{3000}{8} \times \dfrac{1}{1000} = 375 \times \dfrac{1}{1000} = .375$

Note: Since $8 = 2^3$, 8 is a factor of $2^3 \times 5^3 = (2 \times 5)^3 = 1000$.

Example: Express $\dfrac{5}{32}$ in base-ten notation.

Solution:

$32 = 2^5$, so 32 is a factor of $2^5 \times 5^5 = (2 \times 5)^5 = 10^5 = 100,000$.   Hence

$$\frac{5}{32} = \frac{5 \times 100,000}{32 \times 100,000}$$

$$= \frac{500,000}{32} \times \frac{1}{100,000}$$

$$= 15625 \times 10^{-5}$$

$$= .15625$$

```
        15625
   32)500000
        32
        180
        160
         200
         192
          80
          64
         160
         160
           0
```

The preceding examples suggest a shortcut for locating the position of the decimal point in the computed quotient.   What is it ?

Each of the decimal-numeral representations obtained in the examples are called *terminating decimals* because at some point in the division algorithm there is a zero *remainder*.   There are, however, infinitely many rational numbers whose decimal-numeral representations are non-terminating.

Example: Express $\frac{1}{3}$ in base-ten notation.

Solution:

```
        .333
   3)1.000
       9
      10
       9
      10
       9
      10
```

The division algorithm never yields a zero remainder and so it appears that $\frac{1}{3} = .333 \ldots$.   We will show in Section 7.6 that $\frac{1}{3}$ does equal $.333 \ldots$.

Now consider an indicated quotient such as $2.5 \div .05$, where the divisor is expressed as a decimal numeral. The same basic technique for computing quotients can still be used.

$$2.5 \div .05 = \frac{25}{10} \div \frac{5}{100}$$

$$= \frac{25}{10} \times \frac{100}{5}$$

$$= \frac{25}{5} \times \frac{100}{10}$$

$$= 5 \times 10$$

$$= 50$$

Alternatively,

$$2.5 \div .05 = (25 \times 10^{-1}) \div (5 \times 10^{-2})$$

$$= \frac{25 \times 10^{-1}}{5 \times 10^{-2}}$$

$$= \frac{25 \times 10^{-1} \times 10^2}{5 \times 10^{-2} \times 10^2}$$

$$= \frac{25 \times 10^1}{5}$$

$$= 5 \times 10$$

$$= 50$$

Note that, since 2.5 is equivalent to 2.50, or 250 hundredths, and .05 is 5 hundredths, the indicated quotient $2.5 \div .05$ is equivalent to $250 \div 5$. Here is a third solution:

$$2.5 \div .05 = \frac{2.5}{.05}$$

$$= \frac{2.5 \times 100}{.05 \times 100}$$

$$= \frac{250}{5}$$

$$= 50$$

Example: Compute $136.92 \div .0326$.

Solution:

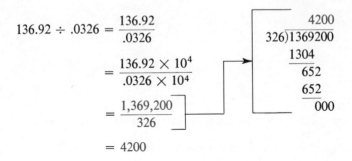

$$136.92 \div .0326 = \frac{136.92}{.0326}$$

$$= \frac{136.92 \times 10^4}{.0326 \times 10^4}$$

$$= \frac{1,369,200}{326}$$

$$= 4200$$

Exercises 7.4

Solve each of the following sentences. $n \in Q$.

1. $1978 \div 23 = n$ **2.** $225 \div 25 = n$

3. $11{,}024 \div 106 = n$ **4.** $87 \div 15 = n$

5. $576 \div 24 = n$ **6.** $76{,}467 \div 284 = n$

7. $3 \div 10^{-2} = n$ **8.** $10^3 \div 10^{-2} = n$

9. $10^{-3} \div 10^{-2} = n$ **10.** $25 \times 10^{-2} \div 5 \times 10^{-3} = n$

Using Figure 7 1 as a guide, illustrate each of the following divisions.

11. $.6 \div 3$ **12.** $1.6 \div 8$ **13.** $.2 \div 5$

14. $12 \div 40$ **15.** $1.2 \div 4$

Follow the step-by-step procedures of the examples of this section to express each of the following rational numbers as decimal numerals.

16. $\dfrac{1}{8}$ **17.** $\dfrac{2}{5}$ **18.** $\dfrac{3}{4}$ **19.** $\dfrac{5}{16}$ **20.** $\dfrac{8}{25}$

Use a shortcut to express each of the following rational numbers as decimal numerals.

21. $\dfrac{5}{8}$ **22.** $\dfrac{3}{5}$ **23.** $\dfrac{1}{4}$ **24.** $\dfrac{3}{16}$ **25.** $\dfrac{4}{25}$

26. $\dfrac{11}{15}$ **27.** $\dfrac{41}{32}$ **28.** $28\dfrac{3}{20}$ **29.** $\dfrac{35}{8}$ **30.** $186\dfrac{13}{45}$

Express each of the following rational numbers as common fractions.

31. .25   **32.** .5
33. .875   **34.** .284
35. .05   **36.** .032
37. .0045   **38.** 100.3
39. 6.42   **40.** 12.015625

41. $\frac{1}{3}$ has a nonterminating repeating decimal-numeral representation. Name five other common fractions which also have nonterminating repeating decimal-numeral representations.

Determine, mentally, solutions to the following sentences. $n \in Q$.

42. $.8 \div .2 = n$ **43.** $.2 \div .8 = n$
44. $10 \div .1 = n$ **45.** $.1 \div 10 = n$
46. $5 \div .02 = n$ **47.** $.02 \div 5 = n$
48. $.3 \div .02 = n$ **49.** $.02 \div .4 = n$

Use scientific notation to perform the following computations. First try to make the computations mentally and then check your results with written computations.

50. $\dfrac{8000 \times 40,000}{.005}$ **51.** $\dfrac{39,000 \times 200,000}{3000}$

52. $\dfrac{.0025 \times 16,000,000}{.04}$ **53.** $\dfrac{.0032 \times .0007}{.014 \times .000016}$

54. $\dfrac{78,000,000}{1300 \times 12,000}$

55. Average velocity is expressed by the formula $v = \dfrac{s}{t}$, where v represents velocity, s distance, and t time. Find the average velocity of a car that travels 438.6 miles in 7.29 hours.

56. A floor is to be covered by vinyl tiles. Each tile is .54 square foot. The floor to be covered is 323.88 square feet. How many whole tiles must be purchased to cover the floor? What is the cost of the vinyl-tile floor covering if each tile costs 41 cents?

57. A certain fabricating process requires aluminum stripping .23 foot long. How many of these strips can be cut from a 6-foot strip? If 1500 of the .23-foot strips are required for the fabricating process, determine the number of 6-foot strips required and the waste that results.

The following fractions have nonterminating repeating decimal representations. Determine the representations of

58. $\frac{1}{6}$ **59.** $\frac{1}{7}$ **60.** $\frac{1}{13}$

61. Why must every nonterminating decimal representation of a common fraction have a repeating pattern? (*Hint:* Look at the results of problems 58 through 60 and refer back to division with a remainder discussed in Chapter Six.)

7.5 Percent Notation

Percent notation provides us with a convenient means of comparing a number to one hundred. The comparison 75 to a 100 can be expressed as the ratio $\frac{75}{100}$, or, using percent notation, as 75%. If a student has correctly solved 75 of 100 problems, his score is 75%. The symbol "%" should be thought of as "parts of a hundred." Thus "75%" is "seventy-five parts of a hundred."

Example: Interpret the statement, "Defense consumes forty-six percent of the nation's annual budget."

Solution: 46% is 46 parts of 100. We can therefore say that the Defense Department spends forty-six of every one hundred dollars in the nation's annual budget.

Percent notation allows us to write a fraction whose denominator is 100 using only the numerator of the fraction followed by the symbol %.

Example: Write each of the following rational numbers in percent notation: $\frac{5}{100}, \frac{650}{100}, \frac{1}{2}, \frac{7}{8}, \frac{27}{20}, \frac{1}{3}$.

Solution:

$$\frac{5}{100} = 5\% \qquad\qquad \frac{650}{100} = 650\%$$

$$\frac{1}{2} = \frac{50}{100} = 50\% \qquad \frac{7}{8} = \frac{875}{1000} = \frac{875 \times .1}{1000 \times .1} = \frac{87.5}{100} = 87\frac{1}{2}\%$$

$$\frac{27}{20} = \frac{135}{100} = 135\% \qquad \frac{1}{3} = \frac{33\frac{1}{3}}{100} = 33\frac{1}{3}\%$$

This example suggests that each rational number can be expressed in percent notation. The number must first be named as a fraction whose denominator is 100. The numerator of the fraction *followed* by the percent symbol, %, is the percent representation of the number. Since each rational number also has a decimal representation, it might be profitable to compare its decimal representation to its percent representation.

Example: Express $\dfrac{5}{100}, \dfrac{650}{100}, \dfrac{1}{2}, \dfrac{7}{8}, \dfrac{27}{20}, \dfrac{1}{3}$ in decimal notation and compare the results to those obtained in the preceding example.

Solution:

$$\frac{5}{100} = .05 \rightarrow 5\%$$

$$\frac{650}{100} = \frac{600}{100} + \frac{50}{100} = 6.5 \rightarrow 650\%$$

$$\frac{1}{2} = .5 \rightarrow 50\%$$

$$\frac{7}{8} = .875 \rightarrow 87\frac{1}{2}\%$$

$$\frac{27}{20} = 1.35 \rightarrow 135\%$$

$$\frac{1}{3} = .333\ldots \rightarrow 33\frac{1}{3}\%$$

The pattern established in this example indicates that any rational number expressed in base-ten notation can easily be expressed in percent notation. Formulate a rule for doing this.

The pattern established in the last example is reversible. If a rational number is expressed in percent notation, it is possible to write it in base-ten notation. Develop a rule for making the change from percent to base-ten notation.

The following examples illustrate the use of percent notation.

Example: The total cost of an automobile is $3800. If the cost for "extras" is $475, what percent of the total car cost is for extras?

Solution: This problem can be solved using proportions.

1. Compare the cost for extras to the total cost.

$$\frac{475}{3800}$$

2. Form a proportion between the ratio $\dfrac{475}{3800}$ and an equivalent ratio having 100 as denominator. (Why ?)

$$\frac{475}{3800} = \frac{P}{100}$$

3. Solve the proportion for P.

$$\frac{475 \times 100}{3800} = P$$

$$\frac{475}{38} = P$$

4.

$$
\begin{array}{r}
12.5 \\
38\overline{)475.0} \\
38 \\
\hline
95 \\
76 \\
\hline
190 \\
190 \\
\hline
\end{array}
$$

5. $P = 12.5$.   Since P is the numerator of a fraction whose denominator is 100, $\dfrac{12.5}{100} = 12.5\%$.

6. We conclude that $475 is 12.5\%$ of $3800

Example: The cost for tax and license amounts to 5 percent of the total car cost of $3800.   How much money is spent on tax and license ?

Solution: We again use proportions to solve the problem.

1. 5% is $\dfrac{5}{100}$ and this ratio is equal to the ratio formed by comparing the cost for tax and license, C, to the total car cost.

2. Thus $\dfrac{5}{100} = \dfrac{C}{3800}$.

3. $\dfrac{}{100} = C$

$$190 = C$$

4. Tax and license cost $= $190

Example: $650, the cost for tax, license, and extras on a certain car is 20 percent of the total cost of the car.   What is the cost of the car ?

Solution: Using proportions the problem is solved in the following way.

1. 20% is $\dfrac{20}{100}$. This ratio is equal to the ratio formed by comparing the cost of tax, license, and extras, T, to the total cost.

2. Thus $\dfrac{20}{100} = \dfrac{650}{T}$.

3. $20 \times T = 650 \times 100 = 65{,}000.$

4. By the inverse relationship between division and multiplication we get $T = 65{,}000 \div 20.$

5. $T = \$3250.$

Exercises 7.5

Interpret each of the following statements.

1. 30% of John's time is spent sleeping.
2. Bill won 80% of the games in which he was the starting pitcher.
3. Tom's lifetime batting average is .310.
4. If an investor can make a profit on 60% of his investments, he is doing well.
5. My house is worth 25% more than the price at which I bought it.
6. Frank's salary increased 200% over the last 3 years.
7. Complete the table.

Fraction	Decimal	Percent
$\frac{1}{2}$		
		15%
	.37	
	.25	
		100%
$\frac{1}{8}$		
$\frac{7}{5}$		
	2.2	
		160%

Estimate the percent of the total area that is shaded.

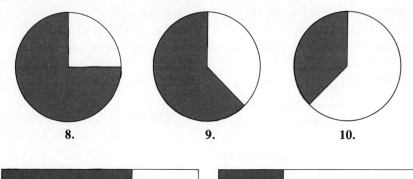

8. 9. 10.

11. 12.

Complete each of the following sentences.

13. 50% of 20 is _____.

14. 20 is 50% of _____.

15. 10 is _____ percent of 20.

16. 40 is $33\frac{1}{3}\%$ of _____.

17. $33\frac{1}{3}\%$ of 270 is _____.

18. 85 is 8% of _____.

19. 4% of 3600 is _____.

20. 18% of 4400 is _____.

21. 120% of 250 is _____.

22. 300 is 150% of _____.

23. 15 is _____ percent of 5.

24. 23% of Mr. Jones's annual income of $12,000 is spent on food. How much money does the Jones family spend on food annually?

25. The Smith family spends $1800 of its annual income of $8000 on food. Does the Smith family spend a greater percentage of its annual income on food than the Jones family?

26. The Friendly Loan Company lends money at 6% a year. What is the monthly interest rate?

27. Pete Boomer won the National League batting crown with these statistics: 378 hits in 1110 official times at bat. What was his winning batting average?

28. The average annual rainfall in Arid County is 10.86 inches. 8.12 inches of rain fell last year. What percent of the average annual rainfall was last year's rainfall?

29. A particular loan agency offers a financing rate for houses of 20% down and 7% of the unpaid balance per year. Mr. Brown finances a $25,000 house at this rate. His monthly payments are $130. How much of his *first* monthly payment is interest?

30. A bank offers two car-financing plans to its customers. They are: (1) 10% down and 6% per year on the remaining principal for a maximum of 3 years, and (2) $33\frac{1}{3}$% down and $4\frac{1}{2}$% per year on the remaining principal for a maximum of 30 months. Suppose Mr. Carl and Mr. Storm both wish to borrow $3300. Mr. Carl chooses plan 1 for the maximum 3-year period and Mr. Storm chooses plan 2 for the maximum 30-month period. Determine the total amount of interest paid by each gentleman and their monthly payments.

Write a problem for each of the following sentences.

      31. 20% of 500 = n **32.** P% of 200 = 160

      33. 1000 = 18% of n

34. The price of Savage, the economy car for college students, had a $7\frac{1}{2}$% price increase this year. If last year's model cost $2300, what is the price of the new model?

35. The Rank Radio Shop buys car radios for $28 and marks them up 30%. What is the selling price of the radios?

36. The "Soft Shoulder Men's Shoppe" cut the price of its $80 suits by 20%. Three months later it increased the price of these suits by 20%. What is the current price of the suits?

37. A certain copper alloy is 63.8% copper by weight. How many pounds of alloy can be made with 350 pounds of copper?

38. The cost of living rose 3.8% during each of the last 2 years. Mr. Jason's income rose 10.2% during that same period. What is the actual dollar difference between the $10,600 Mr. Jason earned 2 years ago and his current income?

39. Twenty-five years ago 48 of Lincoln High School's 420 graduates entered college. This year 260 of Lincoln's 630 graduates will go to college. Find the percent increase of Lincoln High School graduates over the last 25 years. Find also the percent increase of Lincoln High School graduates entering college.

7.6 Rational and Irrational Numbers

A rational number was defined in Chapter Six as a quotient of two integers. $\dfrac{3}{5}$, $\dfrac{-1}{2}$, $\dfrac{856}{21}$, and $\dfrac{68}{-534}$ are examples of rational numbers. In Section 7.4 we saw that the decimal-numeral representation of a rational number had one of two forms: terminating or nonterminating.

Example: Find the decimal-numeral representation of $\dfrac{23}{40}$.

Solution:

$$
\begin{array}{r}
.575 \\
40)\overline{23.000} \\
\underline{200} \\
300 \\
\underline{280} \\
200 \\
\underline{200} \\
0
\end{array}
$$

$$\frac{23}{40} = .575$$

The division algorithm terminates where a zero remainder is obtained.

Example: Find the decimal-numeral representation for $\dfrac{1}{7}$.

Solution:

$$
\begin{array}{r}
.142857142857 \\
7\overline{)1.000000000000} \\
\underline{7} \\
30 \\
\underline{28} \\
20 \\
\underline{14} \\
60 \\
\underline{56} \\
40 \\
\underline{35} \\
50 \\
\underline{49} \\
10 \\
\underline{7} \\
30 \\
\underline{28} \\
20 \\
\underline{14} \\
60 \\
\underline{56} \\
40 \\
\underline{35} \\
50 \\
\underline{49} \\
1
\end{array}
$$

The remainders 3, 2, 6, 4, 5, 1, 3, 2, 6, 4, 5, 1, etc., form a repeating pattern of six digits. Consequently the quotient must form a repeating pattern of six digits. The division algorithm does not terminate because a zero remainder is never obtained. We conclude that the decimal-numeral representation for $\frac{1}{7}$ is the nonterminating repeating decimal .142857142857 . . . .

We have seen from the discussion of division with a remainder in Section 6.5 that

For each two positive integers a and b, a = b · q + r, where q and r are integers and $0 \leq r < b$.

The relationship between the pattern sentence and the division algorithm is shown in the following examples.

Example:

$$a = b \cdot q + r$$
$$15 = 2 \cdot 7 + 1$$

$$
\begin{array}{r}
7 \\
2\overline{)15} \\
14 \\
\hline
1
\end{array}
$$

Example:

$$a = b \cdot q + r$$
$$100 = 26 \cdot 3 + 22$$

$$
\begin{array}{r}
3 \\
26\overline{)100} \\
78 \\
\hline
22
\end{array}
$$

The division of 1 by 7 can be interpreted as a repeated use of division with a remainder.

$$
\begin{array}{r}
.1 \\
7\overline{)1.0} \\
7 \\
\hline
3
\end{array}
\qquad
\begin{array}{l}
a = b \cdot q + r \\
1.0 = 7 \times .1 + .3
\end{array}
$$

$$
\begin{array}{r}
.14 \\
7\overline{)1.00} \\
7 \\
\hline
30 \\
28 \\
\hline
2
\end{array}
\qquad .30 = 7 \times .04 + .02
$$

$$
\begin{array}{r}
.142 \\
7\overline{)1.000} \\
7 \\
\hline
30 \\
28 \\
\hline
20 \\
14 \\
\hline
6
\end{array}
\qquad .020 = 7 \times .002 + .006
$$

Since the remainder r must always be less than 7 and greater than or equal to 0, there can be at most seven distinct remainders and *six* distinct nonzero remainders. As soon as a remainder is repeated, so is the q associated with it. If $r = 0$, the division algorithm terminates.

The above discussion can be applied to finding the decimal-numeral representation of any rational number and so: *The decimal-numeral representation of each rational number either terminates or is nonterminating and repeating.*

Now can we be sure that each terminating or nonterminating repeating decimal numeral represents a rational number ?

A terminating decimal numeral represents a rational number whose denominator is some power of 10.

Example:

$$.132 = 132 \times 10^{-3} = \frac{132}{1000}$$

$$.46582 = 46{,}582 \times 10^{-5} = \frac{46{,}582}{100{,}000}$$

A nonterminating repeating decimal numeral also represents a rational number. The following examples suggest this.

Example: Show that $.333\ldots = \frac{1}{3}$.

1. $.333\ldots = n$	[we assume $.333\ldots$ is some rational number n.]
2. $10 \times .333\ldots = 10 \times n$	[multiplication law]
3. $3.333 = 10n$	[multiplication by 10]
4. $3.333\ldots - .333\ldots = 10n - n$	[addition property]
5. $3 = 9n$	[performing subtractions]
6. $3 \div 9 = n$	[multiplication and division are inverse operations]
7. $\frac{1}{3} = n$	$\left[\text{renaming } 3 \div 9 \text{ as } \frac{3}{9} \text{ or } \frac{1}{3}\right]$

Example: Show that $.142857142857\ldots = \frac{1}{7}$.

Solution:

1. $.142857142857 \ldots = n$
2. $10^6 \times .142857142857 \ldots = 10^6 \times n$
3. $142,857.142857142857 \ldots - .142857142857 \ldots = 1,000,000n - n$
4. $142,857 = 999,999n$
5. $142,857 \div 999,999 = n$
6. $\dfrac{142,857}{999,999} = \dfrac{1 \times 142,857}{7 \times 142,857} = \dfrac{1}{7} = n$

Example: What rational number is represented by '.00323232 . . .'?

Solution:

1. $.00323232 \ldots = n$
2. $10^2 \times .00323232 \ldots = 10^2 \times n$
3. $.323232 \ldots - .00323232 \ldots = 100n - n$
4. $.32 = 99n$
5. $.32 \div 99 = n$
6. $\dfrac{32}{100} \times \dfrac{1}{99} = \dfrac{32}{9900} = \dfrac{8}{2475} = n$

The above discussion and examples permit us now to state:

Each rational number has a decimal-numeral representation and each terminating and nonterminating repeating decimal numeral represents a rational number.

Can one construct a decimal numeral that is nonterminating *and* nonrepeating? Imagine a roulette wheel having only the 10 digits on its face. Spin the wheel and record the digit in which the black ball sits after the wheel comes to rest. If this process could be continued indefinitely, the set of digits recorded in order and preceded by a decimal point would form a nonterminating and nonrepeating decimal numeral.

Infinitely many nonterminating, nonrepeating decimal numerals exist. But what numbers do they represent? Certainly not rational numbers. (Why?)

A nonterminating, nonrepeating decimal numeral represents an *irrational number*. Such a numeral characterizes an irrational number.

If we form the union of the infinitely large set of irrational numbers, *I*, and the infinitely large set of rational numbers, *Q*, we obtain the set of *real numbers, R*. The Venn diagram of Figure 7.2 illustrates the relationship between the sets of numbers that have been discussed in this text.

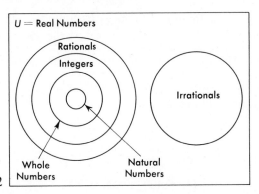

FIGURE 7.2

Our number system has again been extended. Can we add, multiply, divide, and subtract real numbers in a way that is consistent with the manner in which we performed these operations in the set of rational numbers? The answer is yes, because we require that the same properties for addition and multiplication hold in the set of real numbers as held in the set of rationals (see page 205).

Exercises 7.6

Complete the following sentences.

1. A terminating decimal numeral represents a(n) _____ number.

2. A nonterminating decimal numeral having no repeating pattern represents a(n) _____ number.

3. The set of real numbers is the union of the set of rational numbers and _____.

4. The set of whole numbers is a proper subset of the real numbers. It is not, however, a subset of _____.

5. If a number is an element of the set of irrational numbers, it is not an element of _____.

6. A rational number can have a nonterminating _____ decimal representation.

7. There are _____ many irrational numbers.

A rational number is square if it is the product of two identical rational factors. $1 = 1 \times 1$, $4 = 2 \times 2$, $\frac{1}{4} = \frac{1}{2} \times \frac{1}{2}$, and $1.44 = 1.2 \times 1.2$ are examples of square rational numbers. The process of multiplying a number by itself is called *squaring*.

The inverse process, finding a nonnegative number which when multiplied by itself equals a given number, is called the *square root process* or square rooting. The square root of $\frac{1}{4}$ is $\frac{1}{2}$. The square root of 4 is 2. The symbol for the square-root process, "$\sqrt{}$," is called a *radical*. $\sqrt{4} = 2$. Compute the indicated square root:

8. $\sqrt{16}$ **9.** $\sqrt{25}$
10. $\sqrt{49}$ **11.** $\sqrt{81}$
12. $\sqrt{144}$ **13.** $\sqrt{225}$
14. $\sqrt{400}$ **15.** $\sqrt{900}$

A discussion similar to the one above might be developed for cubes and cube roots. The cube of 3 is 27; it is $3 \times 3 \times 3$. The cube root of 27, $\sqrt[3]{27}$, is one of the three equal factors of 27. $\sqrt[3]{27} = 3$ since $3 \cdot 3 \cdot 3 = 27$. Compute:

16. 2^3 **17.** 5^3
18. $\sqrt[3]{64}$ **19.** $\sqrt[3]{1}$
20. $\sqrt[3]{216}$ **21.** 7^3
22. $\sqrt[3]{1000}$ **23.** $\sqrt[3]{125}$
24. $\sqrt[3]{1728}$ **25.** 11^3

The roulette-wheel approach to forming irrational numbers (page 202) is not the only source of irrational numbers. The square root of a rational number which is not square is an irrational number. The cube root of a rational number which is not the cube of some rational number is an irrational number, and so on. Which of the following are irrational numbers?

26. $.31313\ldots$ **27.** $\sqrt{15}$
28. $\sqrt[3]{8}$ **29.** $\sqrt{2}$
30. $\dfrac{\sqrt{16}}{\sqrt{25}}$ **31.** $\sqrt{.01}$
32. $5 \times \sqrt[3]{64}$ **33.** π
34. $\sqrt[3]{100}$ **35.** $\sqrt[3]{1} \times \sqrt{121}$
36. $8 \times \sqrt{2}$

Which law(s) of addition or multiplication is (are) exhibited in each of the following sentences?

37. $\sqrt{2} + \sqrt{3} = \sqrt{3} + \sqrt{2}$
38. $\sqrt{2} + 0 = \sqrt{2}$
39. $\sqrt[3]{9} \times 1 = \sqrt[3]{9}$
40. $\sqrt{2} \times \sqrt{3} = \sqrt{3} \times \sqrt{2}$

41. $\sqrt{2} + \sqrt{2} + \sqrt{2} = \sqrt{2}(1 + 1 + 1) = \sqrt{2} \times 3 = 3\sqrt{2}$

42. $5 + \sqrt{2} + 4 = 5 + 4 + \sqrt{2} = 9 + \sqrt{2}$

43. $\sqrt{5} + \dfrac{3}{8} - \sqrt{5} = \sqrt{5} - \sqrt{5} + \dfrac{3}{8} = \dfrac{3}{8}$

44. $\sqrt{7} \cdot \dfrac{1}{\sqrt{7}} = 1$

45. $5 \cdot \sqrt{5} \cdot 3 = 5 \cdot 3 \cdot \sqrt{5} = 15\sqrt{5}$

46. $\sqrt{3} + 4\sqrt{3} = (1 + 4)\sqrt{3} = 5\sqrt{3}$

Why are each of the following sentences true?

47. $\sqrt{4} \cdot \sqrt{4} = 4$ **48.** $\sqrt{2} \cdot \sqrt{2} = 2$

49. $\sqrt[3]{27} \cdot \sqrt[3]{27} \cdot \sqrt[3]{27} = 27$ **50.** $\sqrt[3]{9} \cdot \sqrt[3]{9} \cdot \sqrt[3]{9} = 9$

Solve each of the following sentences. $n \in R$. $R = \{$real numbers$\}$.

51. $\sqrt{3} \cdot \sqrt{3} = n$ **52.** $\sqrt[3]{2} \cdot \sqrt[3]{2} \cdot \sqrt[3]{2} = n$

53. $\sqrt[3]{8} \cdot \sqrt[3]{9} = n$ **54.** $\sqrt{5} \cdot \sqrt{5} \cdot \sqrt[3]{4} \cdot \sqrt[3]{4} \cdot \sqrt[3]{4} = n$

55. Problems 37 through 54 are intended to support the last paragraph of this section (read it again). We can perform the arithmetic operations in the set of real numbers. It seems, however, that there are limitations. We cannot combine $\sqrt{2}$ and $\sqrt{3}$ in problem 37 and form a single numeral. Nor can we find a single numeral product for $3\sqrt{2}$ in problem 41. Why can we not combine the decimal-numeral representations of $\sqrt{2}$ and $\sqrt{3}$ to obtain the decimal-numeral representation of the sum $\sqrt{2} + \sqrt{3}$. (*Hint:* What kind of decimal-numeral representation does an irrational number have?)

56. An irrational number can be formed by adding a rational number to another irrational number. Why? (*Hint:* Think of the decimal representations of rational and irrational numbers.)

57. Form five irrational numbers by adding a rational number to $\sqrt{2}$.

58. Think of other ways, besides those indicated in problem 56 and in the discussion preceding problems 26 through 36, of forming irrational numbers. (*Hint:* Use the arithmetic operations.)

59. Form 10 irrational numbers based on your answer to problem 58.

What rational numbers are represented by the following nonterminating repeating decimals?

60. $.1111 \ldots$ **61.** $.9999 \ldots$

62. $.404040 \ldots$ **63.** $212212212 \ldots$

64. $.011111 \ldots$

Fill in the blank spaces in the sentences below.

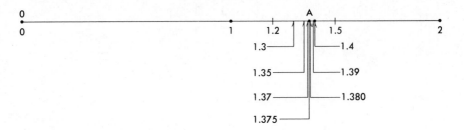

The length l, of the line segment between O and A cannot be measured exactly.   However, it is true that

$$1 < l < 2$$
$$1 < l < 1.5$$
$$1.3 < l < 1.5$$
$$1.3 < l < 1.4$$
$$1.35 < l < 1.39$$
$$1.37 < l < 1.38$$
$$1.375 < l < 1.380$$

We conclude that l must be represented by a terminating or nonterminating decimal numeral.   There are no other possibilities.   Therefore we can say that "To every point on the

65. number line there corresponds a _____ or an

66. _____."

67. It is also true that there is a _____ between the real numbers and the points on the number line.

7.7 Summary

Each rational number can be expressed in decimal-numeral notation by extending the place-value principle for base-ten numerals to the right of the ones place.   The algorithms for whole numbers can then be extended to apply to numerals of this type.

The notion of percent is used as an interpretation of a fractional part, that is, parts of one hundred.   Hence any rational number can be written in percent notation.   For example, .42, $\frac{1}{2}$, and $3\frac{1}{4}$ are 42%, 50%, and 325%, respectively.

Finally, consideration of decimal numerals leads to the conclusion that some numbers we use have not been included in the set of rationals. These numbers can be represented by nonrepeating, nonterminating decimal numerals and can be approximated to any degree of accuracy by a rational number. These irrational numbers will be discussed in more detail in Chapter Nine.

Exercises 7.7—Review

Complete each sentence:

1. The symbol "4" used in the symbol "10^4" is called a(n) _____ .
2. The term used to express parts per hundred is _____ .
3. Each rational number can be expressed as a decimal numeral by using the _____ principle.
4. Each terminating decimal numeral represents a(n) _____ number.
5. Each nonterminating repeating decimal numeral represents a(n) _____ number.
6. Each nonterminating, nonrepeating decimal numeral represents a(n) _____ number.
7. The set of real numbers is the union of the set of _____ numbers with the set of _____ numbers.
8. The sum of a rational number with an irrational number is a(n) _____ number.
9. The algorithms for computing with rational numbers expressed in decimal-numeral notation are based on the computing algorithms for _____ .
10. Expressing .00005 as 5×10^{-5} is an example of the use of _____ .

True or false ?

11. $10^{-7} < 10^{-8}$
12. $10^7 < 10^8$
13. 25% of 12 > .25% of 1200
14. Each real number can be written as a decimal numeral.
15. Each irrational number can be approximated as closely as desired by a rational number.
16. There are two irrational numbers whose sum is zero.
17. The sum of each two rational numbers is a rational number.

18. The product of each two rational numbers is a rational number.
19. The sum of each two irrational numbers is an irrational number.
20. The product of each two irrational numbers is an irrational number.

Compute the following.

21. $34.82 + 29.75 + 48.36 + 24.62$
22. $653.4 + 29.748 + 4.396 + 2.581$
23. $367.528 - 159.929$
24. $1000.0000 - 317.9823$
25. 37.48×4.36
26. $618.4 \times .0093$
27. $3.296 \div 1.03$
28. $65.8782 \div .0018$
29. $(6.47 \times 10^{-6}) \times (3.29 \times 10^{-2})$
30. $(4.8 \times 10^{-8}) \times (2.1 \times 10^{-10}) \div (1.4 \times 10^{-6})$
31. 64% of 293
32. $37\frac{1}{2}\%$ of 64
33. 175% of 96
34. 300% of 20
35. The balance in Tom's checking account on the first of the month is $283.47. Complete the entries in the statement.

Date	Withdrawals	Deposits	Balance
1			283.47
5	34.10 25.61		
7		38.59	
14	87.50	38.59	
15	10.00		
21	8.76	38.59	
28		38.59	
29	15.00		
31	2.81 11.98		

36. Gerri plans to use 15% more for clothes this month than last. If she spent $20 for clothes last month, how much will she spend this month?

37. Fred averaged 21.3 miles per gallon this month in his small car. Two years ago, when it was new, he averaged 24.6 miles per gallon. At what percent efficiency is he currently operating his car?

38. Paula designs and makes dresses for her friends as a side interest. Last month she spent $87.30 for materials and other costs, while receiving $112.50 for the goods she made. What is her percent of profit?

39. Find the cost of tiling a rectangular floor 12 feet by 18 feet with 9-inch tiles which cost $10.00 per gross but come only in boxes of 3 dozen each. (A gross is a dozen dozen.)

chapter eight

OTHER BASES

8.0 Introduction

The digits 1, 2, and 1 of the numeral 121 have position value 10^2, 10^1, and 10^0, respectively. $121 = 1 \cdot 10^2 + 2 \cdot 10^1 + 1 \cdot 10^0$. However, if we should choose a number other than ten as the base number of our numeration system, 121 would represent a number different than one hundred twenty-one. For example, if we choose three as our base, 121 represents $1 \cdot 3^2 + 2 \cdot 3^1 + 1 \cdot 3^0$, which is a numeral for sixteen. We see that, depending upon the base number chosen, a single numeral can represent many numbers.

In this chapter you will learn to represent numbers in bases different than ten. You will also add, multiply, subtract, and divide in bases other than ten. We hope that in having you perform the fundamental arithmetic operations in what might be considered other number languages you gain a better understanding of these operations.

In Section 8.3 we discuss techniques for quickly determining whether or not a number has 2, 3, 4, 5, 6, 8, or 9 as a factor. These techniques, which we call *divisibility tests*, then lead us directly to the method of casting out nines, which you can use to check your computations.

8.1 Notation in Bases Other Than Ten

The expanded form of the numeral 243, $2 \cdot 10^2 + 4 \cdot 10 + 3$, shows that each digit has been assigned a place value that is some integral power of ten. Ten is the base number in our numeration system, a fact that has little to do with any particular property of the number ten but is probably due to man's having ten fingers. Man probably began counting by comparing his set of ten fingers to the set of things he was counting (one-to-one correspondence). He learned to count in groups of ten. If, however, man had only five fingers he may have counted by fives instead of tens, using for his digit set $\{0, 1, 2, 3, 4\}$. Five is the base number in this counting system and the numerals for the numbers zero through fifteen are:

$$0, 1, 2, 3, 4, 10, 11, 12, 13, 14, 20, 21, 22, 23, 24, 30$$

Note that there is no single digit symbol to name five. Hence we regroup as 1 five and 0 ones, and 10 becomes the numeral for five. Similarly, 11 is 1 five and 1 one, or six; 12 is 1 five and 2 ones, or seven; and 30 is 3 fives and no ones, or fifteen.

We shall call this number-naming scheme *base-five notation*. To distinguish a base-five numeral from a base-ten numeral we shall use a subscript to denote the base.

Example:

$23_{(five)}$ names the same number as $13_{(ten)}$
$34_{(five)}$ names the same number as $19_{(ten)}$

Note: $34_{(five)}$ means $(3 \cdot 5 + 4)_{(ten)}$ or $(15 + 4)_{(ten)}$ or $19_{(ten)}$.

The place values in base-five notation are integer powers of five (see Figure 8.1).

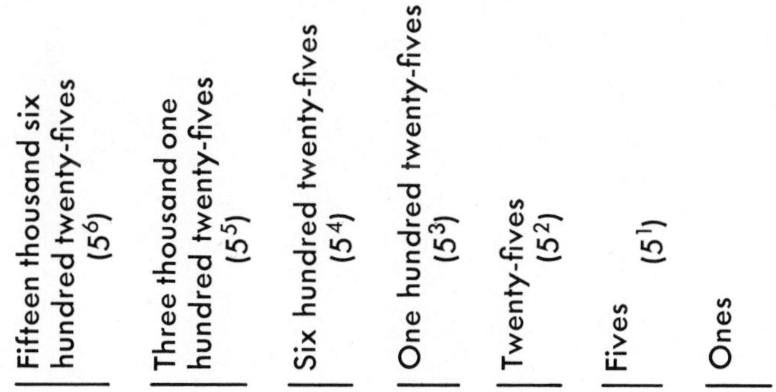

Fifteen thousand six hundred twenty-fives (5^6) | Three thousand one hundred twenty-fives (5^5) | Six hundred twenty-fives (5^4) | One hundred twenty-fives (5^3) | Twenty-fives (5^2) | Fives (5^1) | Ones

FIGURE 8.1

Example: Find a base-ten numeral for $342_{(ten)}$.

Solution:

$$342_{(five)} = (3 \cdot 5^2 + 4 \cdot 5 + 2)_{(ten)}$$
$$= (75 + 20 + 2)_{(ten)}$$
$$= 97_{(ten)}$$

To find a base-five numeral for any number, we must know what multiples of integral powers of five are contained in that number.

Example: Find a base-five numeral for $343_{(ten)}$.

Solution: First observe that the largest power of 5 less than 343 is $5^3 = 125$. Dividing 343 by 125 we have $343 = 2 \cdot 125 + 93$. The largest power of 5 less than 93 is $5^2 = 25$. Dividing 93 by 25 we have $93 = 3 \cdot 25 + 18$. The largest power of 5 less than 18 is $5^1 = 5$. Dividing 18 by 5 we have $18 = 3 \cdot 5 + 3$. Therefore

$$343 = 2 \cdot 125 + 93$$
$$= 2 \cdot 125 + 3 \cdot 25 + 18$$
$$= 2 \cdot 125 + 3 \cdot 25 + 3 \cdot 5 + 3$$

But $(2 \cdot 125 + 3 \cdot 25 + 3 \cdot 5 + 3)_{(ten)} = 2333_{(five)}$

We can shortcut this process as shown below.

$$
\begin{array}{r r l}
125) & 343 & (\ 2 \\
& \underline{250} & \\
25) & 93 & (\ 3 \\
& \underline{75} & \\
5) & 18 & (\ 3 \\
& \underline{15} & \\
1) & 3 & (\ 3 \\
& \underline{3} & \\
& 0 &
\end{array}
$$

Example: Find a base-five numeral for $976_{(ten)}$.

Solution:

$$
\begin{array}{r r l}
625) & 976 & (\ 1 \\
     & 625 & \\
\hline
125) & 351 & (\ 2 \\
     & 250 & \\
\hline
 25) & 101 & (\ 4 \\
     & 100 & \\
\hline
  5) & 1   & (\ 0 \\
     & 0   & \\
\hline
  1) & 1   & (\ 1 \\
     & 1   & \\
\hline
     & 0   & \\
\end{array}
$$

Hence $976_{(ten)} = 12401_{(five)}$. Note that all the division computations are performed with base-ten numerals.

The preceding discussion may suggest that we might choose any whole number greater than one as a base for a place-value system of numeration. This is indeed the case. We need only to select an appropriate set of digit symbols, and to assign to each numeral position a value equal to the appropriate integral power of the base.

Finding a numeral for a number in any base is done just as it was for base-five numerals.

Example: Find a base-six numeral, a base-eight numeral, and a base-twelve numeral for $200_{(ten)}$.

Solution:

(a) Base six:

$$
\begin{array}{r r l}
36) & 200 & (\ 5 \\
    & 180 & \\
\hline
 6) & 20 & (\ 3 \\
    & 18 & \\
\hline
 1) & 2   & (\ 2 \\
    & 2   & \\
\hline
    & 0   & \\
\end{array}
$$

So $200_{(ten)} = 532_{(six)}$

(**b**) Base eight:

$$64)\ \overline{200}\ \quad (\ \underline{3}$$
$$\underline{192}$$
$$8)\ \overline{8}\ \quad (\ \underline{1}$$
$$\underline{8}$$
$$1)\ \overline{0}\ \quad (\ \underline{0}$$
$$\underline{0}$$
$$0$$

So $200_{(ten)} = 310_{(eight)}$

(**c**) Base twelve:

$$144)\ \overline{200}\ \quad (\ \underline{1}$$
$$\underline{144}$$
$$12)\ \overline{56}\ \quad (\ \underline{4}$$
$$\underline{48}$$
$$1)\ \overline{8}\ \quad (\ \underline{8}$$
$$\underline{8}$$
$$0$$

So $200_{(ten)} = 148_{(twelve)}$

Example: The table of Figure 8.2 shows the numerals for the elements of $\{x \in W: 1 \le x \le 15_{(ten)}\}$ in several different base notations. (The digit set for base-twelve notation is $\{0, 1, 2, 3, 4, 5, 6, 7, 8, 9, T, E\}$. T is ten and E is eleven.)

Ten	Five	Six	Three	Eight	Two	Twelve
1	1	1	1	1	1	1
2	2	2	2	2	10	2
3	3	3	10	3	11	3
4	4	4	11	4	100	4
5	10	5	12	5	101	5
6	11	10	20	6	110	6
7	12	11	21	7	111	7
8	13	12	22	10	1000	8
9	14	13	100	11	1001	9
10	20	14	101	12	1010	T
11	21	15	102	13	1011	E
12	22	20	110	14	1100	10
13	23	21	111	15	1101	11
14	24	22	112	16	1110	12
15	30	23	120	17	1111	13

FIGURE 8.2

When base-ten notation is extended to the right to include negative powers of ten we are able to write rational numbers in decimal form.

Example:

$$\frac{1}{2} = .5$$

$$3\frac{1}{4} = 3.25$$

$$1\frac{7}{8} = 1.875$$

$$26\frac{41}{100} = 26.41$$

If base-five notation is extended to the right, Figure 8.1 becomes Figure 8.3, and we could now use base-five notation to write rational numbers.

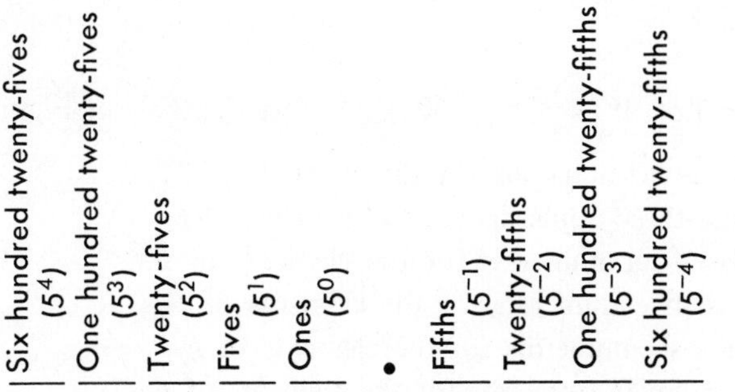

FIGURE 8.3

Example: Write the rational number $.22_{(five)}$ as a base-ten numeral.

Solution:

$$.22_{(five)} = \left(2 \cdot \frac{1}{5} + 2 \cdot \frac{1}{25}\right)_{(ten)}$$

$$= \left(2 \cdot \frac{2}{10} + 2 \cdot \frac{4}{100}\right)_{(ten)}$$

$$= \left(\frac{4}{10} + \frac{8}{100}\right)_{(ten)}$$

$$= .48_{(ten)}$$

Example: Change $.92_{(ten)}$ to a base-five numeral.

Solution:

1. We first try to determine the number of fifths in ninety-two hundredths.

$$\frac{92}{100} = \frac{80}{100} + \frac{12}{100} = \frac{4}{5} + \frac{12}{100}$$

2. Now we ask, "How many twenty-fifths in twelve hundredths?"

$$\frac{12}{100} = \frac{3}{25}$$

So $\dfrac{92}{100} = \dfrac{4}{5} + \dfrac{3}{25}$

or $.92_{(ten)} = .43_{(five)}$

Exercises 8.1

Suppose $F = \{x \in W: 1 \leq x \leq 50_{(ten)}\}$. Use the table of Figure 8.2 to:

1. Write base-two numerals for the elements of F.
2. Write base-three numerals for the elements of F.
3. Write base-four numerals for the elements of F.
4. Write base-five numerals for the elements of F.
5. Write base-six numerals for the elements of F.
6. Write base-seven numerals for the elements of F.
7. Write base-eight numerals for the elements of F.
8. Write base-nine numerals for the elements of F.
9. Write base-twelve numerals for the elements of F. (Use T to denote ten and E to denote eleven.)
10. Write base-twenty numerals for the elements of F. (Use a, b, c, $\ldots$, j to denote ten, eleven, $\ldots$, nineteen.)

Convert each of the following numerals to base ten.

11. $345_{(six)}$	**12.** $345_{(seven)}$
13. $345_{(eight)}$	**14.** $345_{(twelve)}$
15. $111{,}011_{(two)}$	**16.** $121_{(three)}$
17. $444_{(six)}$	**18.** $333_{(nine)}$
19. $202{,}021_{(three)}$	**20.** $TE98_{(twelve)}$ (see problem 9)

Example: Convert $56_{(eight)}$ to a base-five numeral.

Solution: $56_{(eight)} = (5 \cdot 8 + 6 \cdot 1)_{(ten)} = 46_{(ten)}$

$$
\begin{array}{r}
25)\overline{46}\quad (\underline{1}) \\
25 \\
\hline
5)\overline{21}\quad (\underline{4}) \\
20 \\
\hline
1)\overline{1}\quad (\underline{1}) \\
1 \\
\hline
0
\end{array}
$$

$$56_{(eight)} = 46_{(ten)} = 141_{(five)}$$

Convert each numeral to the indicated base.

21. $72_{(eight)} \rightarrow$ _____(five)

22. $301_{(ten)} \rightarrow$ _____(six)

23. $67_{(ten)} \rightarrow$ _____(two)

24. $90_{(ten)} \rightarrow$ _____(three)

25. $2150_{(ten)} \rightarrow$ _____(twelve)

26. $272_{(ten)} \rightarrow$ _____(four)

27. $352_{(ten)} \rightarrow$ _____(five)

28. $31{,}024_{(ten)} \rightarrow$ _____(twenty)

29. $1343_{(ten)} \rightarrow$ _____(seven)

30. $1296_{(ten)} \rightarrow$ _____(six)

31. $44_{(eight)} \rightarrow$ _____(four)

32. $53_{(six)} \rightarrow$ _____(three)

33. $1000_{(seven)} \rightarrow$ _____(ten)

34. $222_{(eight)} \rightarrow$ _____(two)

35. $110{,}110_{(two)} \rightarrow$ _____(eight)

36. $110{,}110_{(three)} \rightarrow$ _____(nine)

37. $15{,}108_{(ten)} \rightarrow$ _____(twelve)

38. $108_{(twelve)} \rightarrow$ _____(ten)

39. $246_{(seven)} \rightarrow$ _____(twelve)

40. $1246_{(twelve)} \rightarrow$ _____(twenty)

41. Suppose b is a digit symbol for any whole number two through nine. Explain the following statement: "$b_{(ten)}$ names the same number as $10_{(base\ b)}$."

42. On a trip to the planet Flaxn our spacemen discover that the Flaxnians used a place-value numeration system in which the digit symbols are, in order, $\sim$, $\triangle$, $\vdash$, $\bowtie$, and $\cap$. What Flaxnian numeral would be used to write the decimal numeral 2000?

43. How can you identify odd numbers that are represented in base-two notation ?

44. How can you identify an even number written in base-five notation ?

Refer to Figure 8.2 to do the following problems.

45. State as many relationships as you can find between the numerals in the base-ten and base-five columns.

46. If you have worked problem 45 carefully, you should be able to *predict* (not compute) the base-five numeral for fifty.

47. State as many relationships as you can find between the numerals in the base-six and base-three columns.

48. Your work on problem 47 should allow you to *predict* the base-six and base-three numerals for thirty-six.

Computer computations are performed by circuits that are either in an on or off state. These internal states can be modeled mathematically by assigning 1 to on and 0 to off. {0, 1} is the set of digits for base-two notation. It is not surprising, therefore, that base-two notation plays an extremely important role in computer design. Base-eight notation plays an important role in computer programming because of its special relationship to base-two notation. Observe the following pattern:

Base eight	Base two
4	$\underbrace{100}_{4}$
7	$\underbrace{111}_{7}$
14	$\underbrace{1}_{1}\underbrace{100}_{4}$
17	$\underbrace{1}_{1}\underbrace{111}_{7}$
54	$\underbrace{101}_{5}\underbrace{100}_{4}$
57	$\underbrace{101}_{5}\underbrace{111}_{7}$
134	$\underbrace{1}_{1}\underbrace{011}_{3}\underbrace{100}_{4}$
137	$\underbrace{1}_{1}\underbrace{011}_{3}\underbrace{111}_{7}$

49. Use the above pattern to convert $101100101_{(two)}$ to a base-eight numeral.

50. Use the above pattern to convert $256_{(eight)}$ to a base-two numeral.

Convert each numeral to a base-ten numeral.

51. $.1101_{(two)}$ **52.** $.024_{(six)}$

53. $.58_{(twelve)}$ **54.** $.37_{(nine)}$

55. $.021_{(three)}$ **56.** $.434_{(five)}$

Convert each base-ten numeral to the indicated base.

57. $.56 \rightarrow$ _____(five)   **58.** $.625 \rightarrow$ _____(two)

59. $.8125 \rightarrow$ _____(four)   **60.** $.8125 \rightarrow$ _____(two)

8.2 Arithmetic Using Other Base Notations

Expressing numbers in various bases does not change the properties of that set of numbers. A number is prime or composite in any base. A number is either odd or even, regardless of the choice of base. "Six is greater than four" is a true statement no matter what base we use to write numerals for six and four.

The properties of the arithmetic operations are likewise not altered by a change of notation. Addition and multiplication are commutative operations in the set of real numbers. *One* remains the multiplicative identity element, etc. We can, therefore, use the same addition, subtraction, multiplication, and division algorithms to compute with base-five numerals as we did using base-ten numerals. Only the form of the basic arithmetic facts are altered.

Example: A basic addition fact is "The sum of two and three is five." Express this fact using (a) base ten, (b) base twelve, (c) base five, (d) base three, (e) base two.

Solution:

(a) $2 + 3 = 5$, since 2, 3, and 5 are the base-ten symbols for two, three, and five, respectively.

(b) $2 + 3 = 5$, since 2, 3, and 5 are the base-twelve symbols for two, three, and five, respectively.

(c) $2 + 3 = 10$, since 2, 3, and 10 are the base-five symbols for two, three, and five, respectively.

(**d**) $2 + 10 = 12$, since 2, 10, and 12 are the base-three symbols for two, three, and five, respectively.

(**e**) $10 + 11 = 101$, since 10, 11, and 101 are the base-two symbols for two, three, and five, respectively.

If one is to add and multiply in base-five notation he must learn the basic addition and multiplication facts as he did for base-ten addition and multiplication. These facts are given in the colored portions of the tables.

+	0	1	2	3	4	10	11	12
0	0	1	2	3	4	10	11	12
1	1	2	3	4	10	11	12	13
2	2	3	4	10	11	12	13	14
3	3	4	10	11	12	13	14	20
4	4	10	11	12	13	14	20	21
10	10	11	12	13	14	20	21	22
11	11	12	13	14	20	21	22	23
12	12	13	14	20	21	22	23	24

•	0	1	2	3	4	10	11	12
0	0	0	0	0	0	0	0	0
1	0	1	2	3	4	10	11	12
2	0	2	4	11	13	20	22	24
3	0	3	11	14	22	30	33	41
4	0	4	13	22	31	40	44	53
10	0	10	20	30	40	100	110	120
11	0	11	22	33	44	110	121	132
12	0	12	24	41	53	120	132	144

FIGURE 8.4

Note that the entries in the addition table of Figure 8.4 may be obtained by counting in base five. The entries in the multiplication table of Figure 8.4 may be obtained as follows:

(a) For the 0 row, since $0 \cdot a = 0$, for any number a, all the entries are 0.
(b) For the 1 row, since $1 \cdot a = a$, for any number a, the entries are copies of the column headings.
(c) For the 2 row, begin with 0 and count by twos in base five.
(d) For the 3 row, begin with 0 and count by threes in base five.
(e) For the 4 row, begin with 0 and count by fours in base five.

You should be able to follow similar procedures and construct addition and multiplication facts for any base.

Now that we have the basic addition and multiplication results tabulated, we can use the properties of rational numbers and the basic algorithms to compute any sum or product, without renaming the numbers in base ten.

Example: Compute (a) $243_{(five)} + 121_{(five)}$, (b) $24_{(five)} \cdot 31_{(five)}$.

Solution:

(a) $243_{(five)} + 121_{(five)}$
$= [(2 \cdot 100 + 4 \cdot 10 + 3) + (1 \cdot 100 + 2 \cdot 10 + 1)]_{(five)}$
$= [(2 + 1) \cdot 100 + (4 + 2) \cdot 10 + (3 + 1)]_{(five)}$
$= [3 \cdot 100 + (11) \cdot 10 + 4]_{(five)}$
$= [3 \cdot 100 + (10 + 1) \cdot 10 + 4]_{(five)}$
$= [3 \cdot 100 + 10 \cdot 10 + 1 \cdot 10 + 4]_{(five)}$
$= [3 \cdot 100 + 1 \cdot 100 + 1 \cdot 10 + 4]_{(five)}$
$= [4 \cdot 100 + 1 \cdot 10 + 4]_{(five)}$
$= 414_{(five)}$

Supply a reason for each step in this development.

The above solution can be condensed to

$243_{(five)}$ $[3 + 1 = 4, 4 + 2 = 11, 2 + 1 + 1 = 4$ in base five]
$+121_{(five)}$
$\overline{414_{(five)}}$

(b) $24_{(five)} \cdot 31_{(five)}$

$24_{(five)}$
$\times 31_{(five)}$ Note that in base five
$\overline{4_{(five)}}$ $4 = 1 \cdot 4$
$20_{(five)}$ $20 = 1 \cdot 20$
$220_{(five)}$ $220 = 30 \cdot 4 = (3 \cdot 4) \cdot 10 = (22) \cdot 10$
$1100_{(five)}$ $1100 = 30 \cdot 20 = (3 \cdot 2) \cdot 100 = (11) \cdot 100$
$\overline{1344_{(five)}}$

If we remember that subtraction and division are the inverse operations for addition and multiplication, we can look upon the tables of Figure 8.4 as supplying basic subtraction and division facts.

Example: Solve the sentence $13_{(five)} - 4_{(five)} = n$.

Solution: Since $13_{(five)} - 4_{(five)} = n$ if and only if $n + 4_{(five)} = 13_{(five)}$, we can ask, "What number is to be added to $4_{(five)}$ to obtain a sum of $13_{(five)}$?" We find 4 in the left column of the addition table and trace along the 4 row until we find 13. 13 is in the 4 column. Hence the solution set is $\{4_{(five)}\}$. Can you simplify this process?

Example: Solve the sentence "$22_{(five)} \div 3_{(five)} = n$."

Solution: $22_{(five)} \div 3_{(five)} = n$ if and only if $n \cdot 3_{(five)} = 22_{(five)}$. From this point we proceed as we did above to find $n = 4_{(five)}$. Hence the solution set is $\{4_{(five)}\}$.

Example: Compute (a) $403_{(five)} - 212_{(five)}$ (b) $3001_{(five)} - 1422_{(five)}$ (c) $341_{(five)} \div 31_{(five)}$ (d) $101031_{(five)} \div 43_{(five)}$

Solution:

$$(\mathbf{a}) \quad
\begin{array}{r}
403 \\
-212 \\
\hline
141
\end{array}
\left[
\begin{array}{l}
= (3 \cdot 10^2 + 10 \cdot 10 + 3)_{(five)} \\
= (2 \cdot 10^2 + 1 \cdot 10 + 2)_{(five)} \\
= (1 \cdot 10^2 + 4 \cdot 10 + 1)_{(five)}
\end{array}
\right]
\qquad
(\mathbf{b}) \quad
\begin{array}{r}
3001 \\
-1442 \\
\hline
1004_{(five)}
\end{array}$$

$$(\mathbf{c}) \quad
\begin{array}{r}
11_{(five)} \\
31)\overline{341} \\
31 \\
\hline
31 \\
31 \\
\hline
0
\end{array}
\qquad
(\mathbf{d}) \quad
\begin{array}{r}
1032_{(five)} \\
43)\overline{101031} \\
43 \\
\hline
303 \\
234 \\
\hline
141 \\
141 \\
\hline
0
\end{array}$$

Exercises 8.2

1. Complete these base-eight addition and multiplication tables.

+	0	1	2	3	4	5	6	7
0				3				
1								10
2			4					
3	3							
4						11		
5							13	
6					12			
7		10						

•	0	1	2	3	4	5	6	7
0					0			
1						5		
2							14	
3								25
4				14				
5	0							
6		6						
7			16					

2. Construct addition and multiplication tables for base three.

3. Construct addition and multiplication tables for base two.

4. Construct addition and multiplication tables for base six

5. Construct addition and multiplication tables for base twelve.

For each of the following sentences, solve for n in the indicated base. $n \in W$.

6. $324_{(five)} + 1_{(five)} = n$

7. $344_{(five)} + n = 400_{(five)}$

8. $n + 1_{(five)} = 1000_{(five)}$

9. $110_{(two)} + n = 1000_{(two)}$

10. $T91_{(twelve)} - n = T00_{(twelve)}$

11. $n + 33_{(four)} = 100_{(four)}$

12. $n + n = 100_{(\text{two})}$ **13.** $3_{(\text{four})} \cdot 2_{(\text{four})} = n$

14. $2_{(\text{three})} \cdot n = 20_{(\text{three})}$ **15.** $n \cdot n = 100_{(\text{five})}$

Compute each of the following, expressing the result in the indicated base.

16. $342_{(\text{five})} + 243_{(\text{five})}$ **17.** $601_{(\text{seven})} + 166_{(\text{seven})}$

18. $8T9_{(\text{twelve})} + 9TE_{(\text{twelve})}$ **19.** $10,111_{(\text{two})} + 1,011,101_{(\text{two})}$

20. $344_{(\text{five})} - 123_{(\text{five})}$ **21.** $343_{(\text{six})} - 124_{(\text{six})}$

22. $209_{(\text{twelve})} - 9T_{(\text{twelve})}$ **23.** $3131_{(\text{four})} - 313_{(\text{four})}$

24. $33_{(\text{five})} \cdot 21_{(\text{five})}$ **25.** $111_{(\text{two})} \cdot 101_{(\text{two})}$

26. $TE_{(\text{twelve})} \cdot 90_{(\text{twelve})}$ **27.** $44_{(\text{six})} \cdot 33_{(\text{six})}$

28. $100_{(\text{four})} \div 10_{(\text{four})}$ **29.** $1100_{(\text{three})} \div 20_{(\text{three})}$

Each of the following sentences is true in some base. For each sentence, identify the base.

30. $3 + 5 = 10$ **31.** $2 + 6 = 11$

32. $4 + 4 = 13$ **33.** $9 + 8 = 15$

34. $10 + 10 = 100$ **35.** $100 + 100 = 1000$

36. $3 \cdot 4 = 20$ **37.** $10 \cdot 10 = 100$

38. In a table for an operation, the entries along a line from the upper left corner to the lower right corner constitute the *main diagonal*. The main diagonal separates each of the tables of problems 1 through 5 into two parts that are symmetric about the main diagonal. What property of the operations addition and multiplication does this illustrate?

39. How do the tables show the additive identity element?

40. How do the tables show the multiplicative identity?

41. Use the base-five multiplication table to show that $12_{(\text{five})}$ is a prime number.

42. Extend the base-eight multiplication table to show that $13_{(\text{eight})}$ is a prime number.

8.3 Tests for Divisibility

It is frequently convenient to know whether a number is divisible by another number without using the division algorithm. In this section we shall explore some ways for doing this.

Most of you have observed that even numbers, numbers divisible by 2, end in 0, 2, 4, 6, or 8 in base-ten notation. If we recall that the place values, from right to left, are ones, tens, hundreds, etc., and remember that $10 = 2 \cdot 5$, then each place value is divisible by 2, except the ones place.

Example: Under what conditions is the number whose base-ten numeral is $783d$ divisible by 2? d is any of the digits 0, 1, 2, 3, 4, 5, 6, 7, 8, and 9.

Solution:

$$783d = 7000 + 800 + 30 + d$$

Also $(7000 + 800 + 30 + d) \div 2 = \dfrac{7000}{2} + \dfrac{800}{2} + \dfrac{30}{2} + \dfrac{d}{2}$

$$3500 + 400 + 15 + \frac{d}{2} = 3915 + \frac{d}{2}$$

Thus $783d$ is divisible by 2 if and only if d is divisible by 2.

Example: Under what conditions is the number whose base-ten numeral is $abcd$, where a, b, c, and d are digits, divisible by 2?

Solution:

$$abcd = a \cdot 10^3 + b \cdot 10^2 + c \cdot 10^1 + d$$

Also $(a \cdot 10^3 + b \cdot 10^2 + c \cdot 10^1 + d) \div 2 = \dfrac{a \cdot 10^3}{2}$

$$+ \frac{b \cdot 10^2}{2} + \frac{c \cdot 10^1}{2} + \frac{d}{2} = a \cdot 500 + b \cdot 50 + c \cdot 5 + \frac{d}{2}$$

Thus $abcd$ is divisible by 2 if and only if d is divisible by 2.

Hence *a number is divisible by 2 if and only if the ones digit is 0, 2, 4, 6, or 8.*

By using a similar argument, you can state a similar condition for divisibility by 5.

Now consider divisibility by 4. Since 100 is divisible by 4, each place value to the left of the tens place is divisible by 4. *Hence a number is divisible by 4 if and only if the number formed by the tens and ones digits is divisible by 4.*

Example: Which of the following are divisible by four?   **(a)** 2848, **(b)** 13,772, **(c)** 30,968, **(d)** 411,178.

Solution:

(a) 2848 is divisible by 4 since $48 = 12 \cdot 4$

(**b**) 13,772 is divisible by 4 since 72 = 18 · 4
(**c**) 30,968 is divisible by 4 since 68 = 17 · 4
(**d**) 411,178 is not divisible by 4 since 78 = 19 · 4 + 2

Extending this argument a bit more and using the fact that 1000 = 125 · 8, you should be able to give a condition for divisibility by 8.
Now examine the following statements.

$$10 = 9 + 1$$
$$100 = 9 \cdot 11 + 1$$
$$1000 = 9 \cdot 111 + 1$$
$$10,000 = 9 \cdot 1111 + 1$$
$$100,000 = 9 \cdot 11,111 + 1$$

It appears that each integral power of 10 can be expressed as a multiple of 9, plus 1. Hence

$$3825 = 3 \cdot 1000 + 8 \cdot 100 + 2 \cdot 10 + 5$$
$$= 3 \cdot (999 + 1) + 8 \cdot (99 + 1) + 2 \cdot (9 + 1) + 5$$
$$= 3 \cdot 999 + 3 + 8 \cdot 99 + 8 + 2 \cdot 9 + 2 + 5$$
$$= 3 \cdot 999 + 8 \cdot 99 + 2 \cdot 9 + 3 + 8 + 2 + 5$$
$$= 9 \, (3 \cdot 111 + 8 \cdot 11 + 2 \cdot 1) + 3 + 8 + 2 + 5$$

We see, then, that 3825 is divisible by 9 if and only if 3 + 8 + 2 + 5 is divisible by 9. Since 3 + 8 + 2 + 5 = 18 = 9 · 2, 3825 is divisible by 9. Generalizing we can say that *a number is divisible by 9 if and only if the sum of its digits is divisible by 9.*

If a number is not divisible by 9, then the sum of its digits differs from the remainder obtained, when it is divided by 9, by a multiple of 9. Why? The difference is called the *excess of nines* in the number.

Example: Find the excess of nines in (**a**) 438, (**b**) 2487.

Solution:

(**a**) 4 + 3 + 8 = 15, 1 + 5 = 6. So the excess of nines in 438 is 6.
By division, 438 = 48 · 9 + 6. The remainder, 6, is equal to the excess of nines.
(**b**) 2 + 4 + 8 + 7 = 21, 2 + 1 = 3. So 3 is the excess of nines in 2487. By division, 2487 = 276 · 9 + 3. The remainder, 3, is equal to the excess of nines.

Example: Which of the following numbers are divisible by 9? (**a**) 48,267, (**b**) 301,253, (**c**) 6480.

Solution:

(a) Since $4 + 8 + 2 + 6 + 7 = 27 = 9 \cdot 3$, 48,267 is divisible by 9.

(b) Since $3 + 0 + 1 + 2 + 5 + 3 = 14 = 9 \cdot 1 + 5$, 301,253 is not divisible by 9.

(c) Since $6 + 4 + 8 + 0 = 18 = 9 \cdot 2$, 6480 is divisible by 9.

You can argue, as we did above for 9, that *a number is divisible by 3 if and only if the sum of its digits is divisible by 3*. You should note also that since $9 = 3 \cdot 3$, any number that is divisible by 9 is also divisible by 3.   Is every number that is divisible by 3 divisible by 9?

Next consider 6.   Since $6 = 2 \cdot 3$, any multiple of 6 must be a multiple of 2 and a multiple of 3.

Example: 36 is a multiple of 6.   Show that it is a multiple of 2 and 3.

Solution:

$$36 = 6 \cdot 6 \qquad \text{also } 36 = 6 \cdot 6$$
$$= 6 \cdot (2 \cdot 3) \qquad\qquad = 6 \cdot (2 \cdot 3)$$
$$= (6 \cdot 2) \cdot 3 \qquad\qquad = 6 \cdot (3 \cdot 2)$$
$$= 12 \cdot 3 \qquad\qquad = (6 \cdot 3) \cdot 2$$
$$= 18 \cdot 2$$

Example: $k \cdot 6$, where k is an integer, is a multiple of 6.   Show that $k \cdot 6$ is also a multiple of 2 and 3.

Solution:

$$k \cdot 6 = k \cdot (2 \cdot 3) \qquad \text{also } k \cdot 6 = k \cdot (2 \cdot 3)$$
$$= (k \cdot 2) \cdot 3 \qquad\qquad = k \cdot (3 \cdot 2)$$
$$= (2k) \cdot 3 \qquad\qquad = (k \cdot 3) \cdot 2$$
$$= (3k) \cdot 2$$

Consequently, *a number is divisible by 6 if and only if it is divisible by 2 and by 3*.

In similar fashion, you may be able to devise conditions for divisibility by other numbers. Such conditions are frequently referred to as *tests for divisibility*.

The test for divisibility by 9 provides us with a simple means for checking our computations.

Let a and b be two integers. If we divide a and b by 9 division with a remainder gives us

$$\textbf{1. } a = 9q_1 + r_1. \qquad \textbf{2. } b = 9q_2 + r_2.$$

If we add a and b we get

$$\textbf{3. } a + b = 9 \cdot q_1 + 9 \cdot q_2 + r_1 + r_2 = 9 \cdot (q_1 + q_2) + (r_1 + r_2).$$

Now $9(q_1 + q_2)$ is a multiple of 9. Hence the excess of nines in $a + b$ is equal to the excess of nines in $r_1 + r_2$. We will now use this result to check an addition problem. It should be noted, however, that this check is not infallible, since it will not detect a transposition of digits which results in an error of a multiple of 9.

Example: Add 834 and 227 and check your result.

Solution:

834 + 227 = 1061

Check: Find the excess of nines in each addend and in the sum.

834: $8 + 3 + 4 = 15,\ 1 + 5 = 6$
227: $2 + 2 + 7 = 11,\ 1 + 1 = 2$
1061: $1 + 0 + 6 + 1 = 8$

Note that $6 + 2 = 8$; hence the addition checks. We can simplify the check as follows:

$$
\begin{array}{r}
834 \rightarrow 15 \rightarrow 6 \\
+ \ \ 227 \rightarrow 11 \rightarrow 2 \\
\hline
1061 \rightarrow \ \ 8 \rightarrow 8
\end{array}
$$

Example: Add and check $1037 + 284 + 6912 + 58$.

Solution:

$$
\begin{array}{r}
1037 \rightarrow 11 \longrightarrow 2 \\
284 \rightarrow 14 \longrightarrow 5 \\
6912 \rightarrow 18 \longrightarrow 0 \\
58 \rightarrow 13 \longrightarrow 4 \\
\hline
8291 \rightarrow 20 \rightarrow 2 \leftarrow 11
\end{array}
$$

Since the sum of the remainders 2, 5, 0, and 4 and the sum 8291 both leave a remainder of 2 when divided by 9, our addition is checked.

In a similar fashion, we can show that this technique may be used to check subtraction, multiplication, and division. The checking process is called *checking by casting out nines.*

Example: Compute each of the following and check by casting out nines:
   (a) $327 - 128$, (b) $437 \cdot 26$, (c) $224 \div 14$, (d) $211 \div 35$.

Solution:

  (a) $327 - 128 = 199$

      Check: $327 \rightarrow 12 \longrightarrow 3$
               $- 128 \rightarrow 11 \longrightarrow 2$
               $\overline{199 \rightarrow 19 \rightarrow 1 \leftarrow 1}$

  (b) $437 \cdot 26 = 11362$

      Check: $437 \rightarrow 14 \longrightarrow \quad 5$
             $\times \quad 26 \rightarrow 8 \longrightarrow \quad 8$
            $\overline{11362 \rightarrow 13 \rightarrow 4 \leftarrow 40}$

  (c) $224 \div 14 = 16$

      Check: $14 \longrightarrow 5$
           $\times \quad 16 \longrightarrow 7$
            $\overline{224 \rightarrow 8 \leftarrow 35}$

  (d) $211 \div 35 = 6\dfrac{1}{35}$ or $35 \cdot 6 + 1 = 211$

      Check: $35 \longrightarrow 8$
              $6 \longrightarrow 6$
                 $\overline{48 \rightarrow 12 \rightarrow 3}$
             $1 \longrightarrow 1$
           $211 \longrightarrow 4 \leftarrow 4$

Exercises 8.3

   1. State a test for divisibility by ten.
   2. State a test for divisibility by five.
   3. State a test for divisibility by twelve.
   4. State a test for divisibility by fifteen.
   5. State a test for divisibility by eighteen.
   6. State a test for divisibility by thirty-six.

Determine whether each of the following numbers is divisible by any members of the set $\{2, 3, 4, 5, 6, 8, 9, 10\}$.

7. 4128   **8.** 12,345,670
9. 14,641   **10.** 419,355
11. 10,072,432   **12.** 24,344,136

13. For what digits d will $49d37$ be divisible by 3?
14. For what digits d will $3842d8$ be divisible by 4?
15. For what digits d will $29863d$ be divisible by 6?

Compute each of the following, checking your computation by casting out nines.

16. $6348 + 2971$ **17.** $36487 - 2948$
18. $3727 \cdot 143$ **19.** $34245 \div 45$
20. $(648 \cdot 129) + (129 \cdot 352)$ **21.** $362 + 429 + 638 + 571 + 293$
$\qquad\qquad\qquad\qquad\qquad\qquad + 707$
22. $373 + 239 + 421 - 648$ **23.** $37 \cdot 21 \cdot 32$
24. $(387 + 261) \div 18$ **25.** $(1024 \div 32) + (4096 \div 32)$

Supply the reasons:

Suppose $a = 9 \cdot q_1 + r_1$
and $b = 9 \cdot q_2 + r_2$ [**26.** _____]
$a \cdot b = (9 \cdot q_1 + r_1) \cdot (9 \cdot q_2 + r_2)$ [**27.** _____]
$\qquad = 9 \cdot 9 \cdot q_1 \cdot q_2 + 9 \cdot q_1 \cdot r_2 + 9 \cdot q_2 \cdot r_1$
$\qquad\qquad + r_1 \cdot r_2$ [**28.** _____]
$\qquad = 9 \cdot (9 \cdot q_1 \cdot q_2 + q_1 \cdot r_2 + q_2 \cdot r_1) + r_1 \cdot r_2$ [**29.** _____]
$\dfrac{a \cdot b}{9} = \dfrac{9 \cdot (9 \cdot q_1 \cdot q_2 + q_1 \cdot r_2 + q_2 \cdot r_1) + r_1 \cdot r_2}{9}$ [**30.** _____]

$\qquad = (9 \cdot q_1 \cdot q_2 + q_1 \cdot r_2 + q_2 \cdot r_1) + \dfrac{r_1 \cdot r_2}{9}$ [**31.** _____]

So $a \cdot b$ is divisible by 9 if and only if $r_1 \cdot r_2$ is
divisible by 9.   [**32.** _____]

8.4 Summary

The nature of the real-number system is not altered by changing the base number of the place-value numeration system. Only the basic set of digits and the number represented by each numeral are changed. If, for example, we change the base number from ten to six, our digit set changes from $\{0, 1, 2, 3, 4, 5, 6, 7, 8, 9\}$ to $\{0, 1, 2, 3, 4, 5\}$. The numeral 432 no longer represents the number four hundred thirty-two. It becomes the symbol for one hundred sixty-four.

Since a change of the base number of the numeration system does not change the properties of the fundamental arithmetic operations, one need only learn the basic addition, multiplication, subtraction, and division facts and apply the previously learned algorithms.

Perhaps the best way to summarize Section 8.3 is to state divisibility tests discussed for base-ten numerals:

1. An integer is divisible by 2 if and only if the ones digit is divisible by 2.
2. An integer is divisible by 3 if and only if the sum of the digits is divisible by 3.
3. An integer is divisible by 4 if and only if the number formed by the rightmost two digits is divisible by 4.
4. An integer is divisible by 5 if and only if the ones digit is 0 or 5.
5. An integer is divisible by 6 if and only if it is divisible by 2 and by 3
6. An integer is divisible by 8 if and only if the number formed by the rightmost 3 digits is divisible by 8.
7. An integer is divisible by 9 if and only if the sum of the digits is divisible by 9.

8.4 Exercises—Review

Complete the sentences.

1. $\{0, 1, 2, 3\}$ is the digit set for a numeration system if _____ is the base number.
2. If twenty is the base number in a numeration system the digit set consists of _____ digits.
3. The numeral 83 is a valid symbol in a numeration system if the base number is greater than _____.
4. No matter what base number is used in a numeration system, _____ is always the additive identity and _____ is always the multiplication identity.
5. An integer is divisible by 9 if _____.
6. Casting out nines is a method for _____ computations.

Convert each of the following numerals to a base-ten numeral.

7. $22_{(two)}$ 8. $64_{(eight)}$ 9. $ET_{(twelve)}$
10. $101,101_{(two)}$ 11. $210,012_{(three)}$ 12. $5364_{(seven)}$

Convert each numeral to the indicated base.

13. $43_{\text{(five)}} \rightarrow$ _____(eight)   **14.** $T94_{\text{(twelve)}} \rightarrow$ _____(ten)

15. $502_{\text{(six)}} \rightarrow$ _____(two)   **16.** $10,111_{\text{(two)}} \rightarrow$ _____(seven)

Convert each numeral to a base-ten numeral.

17. $.10101_{\text{(two)}}$ **18.** $.E9T_{\text{(twelve)}}$

Convert each base-ten numeral to the indicated base.

19. $.8 \rightarrow$ _____(five)   **20.** $.75 \rightarrow$ _____(two)

Perform the following computations.

21. $32_{\text{(four)}} + 103_{\text{(four)}}$ **22.** $101_{\text{(two)}} \cdot 1101_{\text{(two)}}$

23. $5213_{\text{(six)}} - 4521_{\text{(six)}}$ **24.** $330_{\text{(twelve)}} \div 16_{\text{(twelve)}}$

25. $201_{\text{(five)}} + 4403_{\text{(five)}} + 10,042_{\text{(five)}}$

26. $21_{\text{(three)}} - 112_{\text{(three)}} - 1002_{\text{(three)}}$

27. $5574_{\text{(eight)}} \div 14_{\text{(eight)}}$ **28.** $100,110_{\text{(two)}} - 11,001_{\text{(two)}}$

Which elements of the set $\{2, 3, 4, 5, 6, 8, 9\}$ are factors of:

29. 3651   **30.** 80,024   **31.** 673,115

32. 8,633,206   **33.** 1,000,427   **34.** 1,233,817,245

Perform the following computations and check each result by casting out nines.

35. $3826 + 751 + 88,231$ **36.** $435 \cdot 1184$

37. $64,321 - 59,410$ **38.** $81,432 \div 104$

39.   214   **40.** $1503 \cdot 974$

      6803

      5490

   11162

$+$ 871

chapter nine

THE ARITHMETIC OF MEASUREMENT

9.0 Introduction

In this chapter we look at some applications of the real numbers to measurement. We point out that measures of physical quantities are usually approximations of some real number. A measure of 8 inches might be an approximation to 8.001 inches but the limitations of our measuring device and our own limitations as observers force us to record the measure as 8 inches.

Measures are usually in error and are consequently considered to be approximate numbers. Computations with these numbers must account for and reflect the errors in them. We discuss computation with approximate numbers as well as the related notions of accuracy, precision, and rounding in the first part of the chapter.

Square rooting, a square-root algorithm, and problems in area and volume are discussed in the latter part of the chapter.

9.1 Approximate and Exact Numbers

The numerals 8.3276115 . . . and 2.4437126 . . . are partial decimal representations of irrational numbers. We cannot add these numbers and obtain a simple decimal numeral. (Why?) We can only approximate their sum by approximating each of the irrational numbers with rational numbers and adding these rational-number approximations. We might say 8.3276115 . . . + 2.4437126 . . . is "approximately" equal to 8.328 + 2.444. The sum 10.772 is rounded to 10.77 and we call this result the sum to two decimal places.

The phrase *approximate number* is a description of the way a number is used. There is nothing approximate about ten in the sentence, "Ten people stood in line." It is possible to count the number of people in line and so ten is used here as an *exact number*. The sentence "It is ten miles to town" uses ten as an approximate number. Ten miles is a measurement and is subject to human and instrumental error. A more honest statement would be "It is approximately ten miles to town."

The difference between an exact and an approximate number is that there is always an error associated with the latter. The error associated with 8.328 in the above discussion is the difference between 8.328 and 8.3276115 . . . . This error cannot be determined exactly but it certainly is not more than .0004. (Why?) When a newspaper reports that "A crowd estimated at 10,000 met the President at the airport," it is using 10,000 as an approximate number. The error associated with 10,000 could have been determined exactly by *counting* the number of people in the crowd.

The results of measuring a quantity almost always yield approximate numbers. The errors cannot be determined exactly because they arise out of the physical limitations of the measuring devices and the individuals that do the measuring. It is always possible, however, to place some limit on the magnitude of the error.

Consider, for example, two measurements taken on the same object with different measuring tapes (see Figure 9.1). We can measure to the nearest .1 of a foot with tape 1. Closer measurement involves a guess and so error is introduced into the measurement. However, our guess cannot be more than one half the distance between two consecutive calibration marks, .05 foot. If the measurement taken with tape 1 is recorded as 6.4 feet, we imply that the exact measurement lies somewhere between 6.35 and 6.45 feet. We say the maximum error is plus or minus .05 foot, written ±.05.

Since the measure between consecutive calibrations on tape 2 is .01 foot, the maximum error associated with any measurement taken by tape 2 is ±.005 foot. If we record the tape 2 measurement as 6.42, we imply that the exact measurement lies between 6.415 and 6.425 feet.

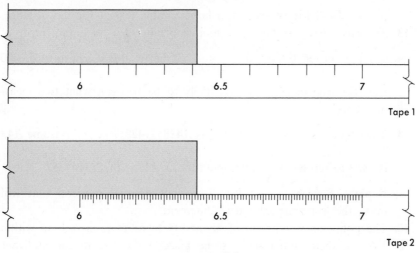

FIGURE 9.1

Exercises 9.1

State whether the underscored items in each of the following sentences name approximate or exact numbers.

1. He repeated himself 3 times.

2. They averaged 60 miles per hour on their trip to San Francisco.

3. The freeway speed limit is 65 miles per hour.

4. 80 students crowded into the room to hear the visiting professor speak.

5. The sun is 93,000,000 miles from the earth.

6. π is an irrational number.

7. Use 3.14 as the value for π in computing the area of a circle.

8. The inspection division was able to check about 2000 radios per day.

9. Is .333 the correct decimal representation for $\frac{1}{3}$?

10. The intersection of sets A and B is a set containing 43 elements.

11. Review your answers to problems 1 through 10 and then list as many ways as you can in which approximate numbers arise.

12. A forester wished to measure the distance between two points by pacing. His pace is 3 feet $\pm \frac{1}{6}$ feet. The distance measured 40

paces. Find the smallest and largest value in feet for the distance.

13. The city surveyors taping technique produced a maximum error of one part in ten thousand, $\frac{1}{10,000}$. If he records a length of 53,000 feet, the true measurement is likely to be between what two measurements?

14. The decimal representation for $\frac{1}{7}$ is .142857142857 .... Assume .143 is used to represent $\frac{1}{7}$ in computation. .143 − .142857142857 ... < E.

    Replace E with the smallest four-digit decimal numeral that will make the last sentence a true statement.

15. The politician was proud of his ability to estimate crowds to within 10% of their actual size. If he guessed the size of the audience listening to his speech as 2800, determine the minimum and maximum size of the audience.

9.2 Significant Digits and Maximum Error

The results of a computation with approximate numbers should reflect the magnitude of error associated with the numbers.

Example: Let 8.33 and 2.44 be approximations of the irrational numbers 8.3276115 ... and 2.4437126 .... Compute 8.33 × 2.44.

Solution:

$$
\begin{array}{r}
8.33 \\
2.44 \\
\hline
.3332 \\
3.332 \\
16.66 \\
\hline
20.3252
\end{array}
$$

The product 20.3252 does not reflect the magnitude of the errors associated with the factors 8.33 and 2.44. The second decimal place is in doubt in both factors and yet their product is given as a number having four decimal places. The product is more properly recorded as 20.3. We shall see why after a discussion of significant digits.

The smallest calibrations on tapes 1 and 2 of Section 9.1 are .1 and .01 foot, respectively. We call these measures the units of measure for tapes 1 and 2. The measurement taken by tape 1 is recorded as 6.4 feet, to reflect the fact that the unit of measure for the tape is .1 foot and that the maximum error in the measurement is ±.05 foot. We say 6.4 has two *significant digits* because it contains 64 units of measure, and 64 is a two-digit numeral. The measurement 6.42 taken with tape 2 has 642 units of measure and so 6.42 has three significant digits. Its maximum error is ±.005 foot.

If we know the number of significant digits in a measured quantity, we know the unit of measure. The maximum error is $\pm\frac{1}{2}$ the unit of measure. It has a face value of ±5 in the digit position following the last significant digit.

Example: The unit of measure for the distance between the earth and moon, 240,000 miles, is 1000 miles. Since 240,000 is 240 units of measure, the numeral has three significant digits. The maximum error in the measurement is $\pm\frac{1}{2} \times 1000$ miles = ±500 miles. (Note that the last three zeros of 240,000 are merely placeholders and are not significant in representing the measurement.)

Example: The platinum bar weighed 23.040 pounds. The unit of measure is .001 pound. 23.040 is 23,040 units of measure and so the numeral has five significant digits. The maximum error is ±.0005 pound. (Note that all zeros in 23.040 are significant in representing the measurement.)

Example: The quarter mile was run in 46.7 seconds. The unit of measure is .1 second. Since 46.7 is 467 units of measure, the numeral has three significant digits. The maximum error is ±.05 second.

Example: It is estimated that 0.2% of men over 40 years of age in the United States earn more than $500,000 a year. The unit of measure is 0.1%, or .001. Therefore 0.2% = .002 is 2 units of measure and so 0.2% has one significant digit. Its maximum error is ±.0005. (Note that the zeros in the tenths and hundredths places of .002 are not significant. They are only placeholders.)

We conclude from the above examples that only the significant digits of an approximate number are recorded except when zeros are necessary as placeholders. Consequently the maximum error associated with the number is known and the results of any computation involving the number must take account of this error.

Exercises 9.2

Complete the table, in which an underlined digit indicates the last significant digit of the numeral in which it appears.

	Number	Unit of Measurement	Significant Digits	Maximum Error
1.	180.3		4	
2.	220	10		
3.	16,500			±50
4.	0.003	.001		
5.	0.00050		2	
6.	56.02			±.005
*7.	240,000,000			
8.	0.000078			
9.	6001	1		
10.	856,300			±5

A measure L is more *precise* than a measure M if the maximum error associated with L is smaller than the maximum error associated with M. Use this definition to determine the more precise of each of the following pairs of measures.

11. 23 inches, 2.3 inches. $\begin{cases} \text{Since 23 inches and 2.3 inches have maximum} \\ \text{errors of } \pm.5 \text{ and } \pm.05 \text{ inch, respectively,} \\ \text{2.3 inches is the more precise measure.} \end{cases}$

12. 1000 feet, 150 feet
13. 600 miles per hour, 17,000 miles per hour
14. 180 pounds, .05 pound   **15.** .002 inch, .02 inch

Consider the two measures in problem 14. 180 pounds has a maximum error of ±.5 pound. .05 pound has a maximum error of ±.005 pound. The ratio of the maximum error of a measure to the measure is called the *relative error of the measure*.

$$\frac{.5}{180} = .002777 \ldots$$ is the relative error of the measure 180 pounds.

$$\frac{.005}{.05} = .1$$ is the relative error of the measure .05 pound.

180 pounds is a more *accurate* measure than .05 pound because it has the smaller relative error.

Determine the more accurate measure for each of the following pairs of measures. (Assume all measures are in feet.)

16. 50, .5   **17.** 50, .50
18. 240,000, 1.3   **19.** 240,000, 2.40
20. 4.58, 120   **21.** 93,000,000, 2000

22. When do two measures have the same accuracy? (*Hint:* See problems 16, 17, and 19.)

23. When do two measures have the same precision? (*Hint:* See problem 13.)

24–27. Find the percent error, to the nearest one hundredth of a percent, for each of the measures in problems 16, 18, 20, and 21.

Example: The maximum error of the measure 240,000 is 500.

$$\frac{500}{240,000} = \frac{5}{2400} = \frac{1}{480} \doteq {}^* .00208 = .208 \times 10^{-2} \doteq 0.21\%$$

$$\begin{array}{r} .00208 \\ 480\overline{)1.00000} \\ 960 \\ \hline 4000 \\ 3840 \\ \hline 160 \end{array}$$

Hence the percent error is approximately equal to 0.21%.

9.3 Computations with Approximate Numbers

Suppose you wish to determine the measure of the perimeter of the triangular piece of land shown in Figure 9.2. It certainly cannot be more

*The symbol "$\doteq$" means "is approximately equal to."

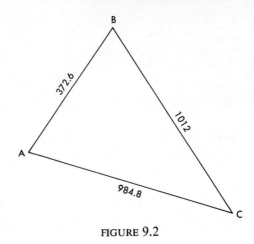

FIGURE 9.2

precise than the least precise side measure. The perimeter measure, then, is the sum $372.6 + 1012 + 984.8$ rounded to reflect the least precise measure.

$$
\begin{array}{r}
372.6 \\
1012. \\
\underline{984.8} \\
2369.4
\end{array}
$$

The perimeter is recorded as 2369 feet. Its maximum error and the maximum error of 1012, $\pm.5$ foot, are the same.

The above discussion suggests that computations involving approximate numbers follow some generally accepted rules. Before the computation is performed, all numbers should be rounded in a consistent way to one more decimal place than the least precise number in the computation. After the computation is completed, one should be certain that the magnitude of the maximum error of the computed result be consistent with the magnitudes of the maximum errors of the quantities that make up the computation. And finally the computed result should be rounded.

The rounding process commonly used in engineering practice is the following:

1. If the last *significant* digit of a computed result is *odd* and the digit following it is

(a) 5 or greater, increase the last significant digit by 1 and drop the remaining digits.
(b) less than 5, simply drop the remaining digits.

Example:

Change 532.5̲5̲ to 532.6.
Change 532.3̲7̲ to 532.4.
Change 532.7̲4̲ to 532.7.
Change 532.1̲1̲ to 532.1.

2. If the last *significant* digit of a computed result is *even* and the digit following it is

(**a**) greater than 5, increase the last significant digit by 1 and drop the remaining digits.

(**b**) 5 or less, simply drop the remaining digits.

Example:

Change 784̲6 to 785̲0.
Change 788̲9 to 789̲0.
Change 784̲5 to 784̲0.
Change 786̲2 to 786̲0.

Now consider two examples that incorporate the above ideas.

Example: Find the sum of 1003.274, 86.3512, 546.22, 791.48, and 8.6678.

Solution:

$$
\begin{array}{r}
1003.274 \\
86.351 \\
546.22 \\
791.48 \\
8.668 \\
\hline
2435.993
\end{array}
$$

The sum is 2435.99.

Example: Find the positive difference between 6483.753 and 7346.0.

Solution:

$$
\begin{array}{r}
7346.0 \\
6483.75 \\
\hline
862.25
\end{array}
$$

The positive difference is 862.2.

The straightforward manner for obtaining the number of significant digits for a sum of approximate numbers does not follow when finding a product of approximate numbers.

Example: The sides of a rectangular city lot are measured as 50.3 feet and 136.2 feet. Find the area of the lot.

Solution: The lengths 50.3 and 136.2 each have a maximum error of ±.05 foot. Therefore, the maximum dimensions of the lot are 50.35 feet by 136.25 feet and the minimum dimensions are 50.25 feet by 136.15 feet. The area of the lot, in square feet, must lie between the products 50.35 × 136.25 = 6859.1875 and 50.25 × 136.15 = 6841.5375. The area can, at best, be determined to the nearest 10 feet. It is recorded as the product 50.3 × 136.2 rounded to three significant digits.

$$
\begin{array}{r}
136.2 \\
50.3 \\
\hline
4086 \\
000 \\
6810 \\
\hline
6850.86
\end{array}
$$

The area is 6850 square feet.

The product of two approximate numbers can be found by the following procedure.

1. Round the factor having the greater number of significant digits so that it has one more significant digit than the other factor.
2. Multiply.
3. Round the product obtained so that it contains as many significant digits as the factor having the smaller number of significant digits.

Example: Find the product 183.278 × 12.4.

Solution:

$$
\begin{array}{r}
183.3 \\
12.4 \\
\hline
7332 \\
3666 \\
1833 \\
\hline
2272.92
\end{array}
$$

The product is 2270.

The procedure for the division of two approximate numbers is the following:

1. Round the approximate number having the greater number of significant digits to one more digit than the other approximate number.
2. Divide until the quotient has one more significant digit than the approximate number having the smaller number of significant digits.
3. Round the quotient so that it has the same number of significant digits as the approximate number having the smaller number of significant digits.

Example: Compute 784.263 ÷ 16.5.

Solution:

$$
\begin{array}{r}
47.52 \\
16.5\overline{)784.3.00} \\
660 \\
\overline{1243} \\
1155 \\
\overline{880} \\
825 \\
\overline{450} \\
330 \\
\overline{}
\end{array}
$$

The quotient is 47.5.

Exercises 9.3

Round each of the following approximate numbers to four significant digits.

1. 3.2347	**2.** 437.38	**3.** 12.84
4. 8760.2	**5.** 2001.9	

Round each of the following to hundredths.

6. 236.885	**7.** 3.1545	**8.** 64.355
9. 7002.118	**10.** 0.365	

Round each of the following to thousandths or five significant digits, whichever gives the smaller number of significant digits.

11. 8.3604	**12.** 3581.263	**13.** 78.457
14. 0.0007	**15.** 22.3559	

Consider the numbers in the following computations as measures of the same kind.   Find the correct rounded result for each computation.

16. 83.26 + .085 + 127.31
17. 1286.3 + 2297.88 + 485.355 + 700.034
18. 508.112 − 746.03 + 2059.552 − 63 027

19.   26.104   **20.**   832.583
        115.2   7567.106
         79.59   12092.02
        380.002   6405.998
        ‾‾‾‾‾‾‾   21.045
                                                  ‾‾‾‾‾‾‾

21. 86.339 − 28.41   **22.** 440.2 − 173.805
23.   2760.02   **24.**   10,000.1
        − 821.347   − 2108.054

25. 8.22 × 12.1   **26.** 53.5 × 17.023
27. (806.41 − 97.008) × 20.62   **28.** 15.1462 × 108.005 × 765.64
29.   156.395 $\dfrac{528.11 \times 63.068}{100.4}$
        × 14.0072   **30.**

31. (28.655 + 803 899) ÷ 415.35   **32.** 15.6 ÷ 12.11
33. 75.00 ÷ 263.2   **34.** 108)57.366
35. $\dfrac{11.08 \times 46.375 \times 8.007 + 756.03}{22.4}$ **36.** $\dfrac{24.178 - 60.22}{-15.358}$

Some of the following examples involve approximate numbers as well as exact numbers.   Consequently, some new rules must be stated.

a. The product of an approximate number and an exact number shall have as many significant digits as the approximate number.

b. The quotient of an approximate number and an exact number shall have as many significant digits as the approximate number.

37. Compute $5\sqrt{3} + 4\sqrt{2}$ to two decimal places.   Use the square-root tables on page 278 to evaluate $\sqrt{3}$ and $\sqrt{2}$.

38. The area of a circle is given as πr^2, where r is the radius of the circle. If the radius of a circle is given as 6.20 inches and π is approximated as 3.142, find the area of the circle.

39. A city lot is measured with a steel tape that is calibrated to tenths of a foot.   Find the minimum and maximum values for the area of the lot if its dimensions are given as 58.5 feet wide and 162.3 feet deep.

40. The 10- by 10-foot frame shown requires two steel tie bars for stiffness.   If each tie bar must be $10\sqrt{2} \pm .01$ feet long, how many such bars can be cut from 100 feet of bar stock ? How many frames can be supplied with stiffening elements from each 100-foot bar and what is the waste ?

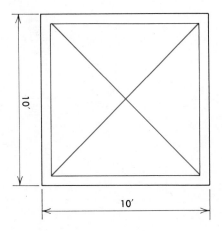

The *average* of a set of numbers is the number obtained as the sum of the elements divided by the number of elements in the set.

Example: {88, 46, 53, 92, 74} is a set of test scores. Find the average test score.

Solution:

$$\text{Average} = \frac{88 + 46 + 53 + 92 + 74}{5}$$
$$= \frac{353}{5}$$
$$= 70.6$$

The average rounded test score is 71.

41. Find the average test score for the following set of test scores: {50, 78, 99, 83, 26, 65, 75, 73}.

42. The yearly rainfall in Green County for the past 15 years is given in the following set of numbers: {30.3, 26.2, 25.1, 18.7, 36.3, 31.5, 17.0, 19.8, 25.5, 28.3, 31.2, 27.6, 16.1, 25.0, 32.9}. What was the average annual rainfall in Green County over the last 15 years ?

A *grade point average* is called a *weighted average* and is determined this way. The grades A, B, C, D, and F are given the respective weights 4, 3, 2, 1, and 0. If a student receives an A in a class, he multiplies the class units by 4. If he receives a C in another class, he multiplies the class units by 2. Adding these weighted products and dividing the sum by the total number of units, he obtains his grade point average. This number is usually rounded to the hundredths place.

Example: Find the grade point average of the student whose last semester record is shown.

Class	Units	Grade
English	3	B
French	4	C
Mathematics	3	B
History	3	A
Physics	$\frac{3}{16}$	C

Solution:

$$\text{G.P.A.} = \frac{3 \cdot 3 + 4 \cdot 2 + 3 \cdot 3 + 3 \cdot 4 + 3 \cdot 2}{16}$$

$$= \frac{44}{16} = 2.75$$

43. Find the grade point average to two decimal places for each of the three students whose records are shown.

Class	Units	Student Grade		
		1	2	3
English	3	A	B	C
Mathematics	3	C	A	B
History	3	B	B	B
Art	2	C	C	A
Physics	4	C	B	B
Speech	2	B	B	B

44. Mr. Rich's net taxable income is $86,000. His tax is computed as $31,020 plus 58% of the excess over $76,000. Find Mr. Rich's tax bill to the nearest dollar.

45. Assume that 20% of Mr. Rich's income was spent on items that carried a 4% sales tax. Compute to the nearest dollar the amount of Mr. Rich's income that was spent in sales tax.

46. If 3.5 billion dollars of a 102 billion dollar budget is spent in foreign aid, what percent of the total budget is spent on foreign aid ? Compute the result to the nearest tenth of a percent.

9.4 Denominate Numbers

Numbers that represent physical quantities are called *denominate numbers*. "10 seconds" and "3 feet" are phrases in which the numbers 3 and 10 are denominate numbers and seconds and feet are *units of measure*. If denominate numbers result as measures of physical quantities they are approximate numbers and the rules for computation with approximate numbers apply to them. There are, however, instances where denominate numbers can be considered exact numbers. Consider the following:

Example: 186,000 miles per second is an approximate measure of the speed of light. It is a denominate number. There are 60 seconds in 1 minute. Both 60 and 1 are denominate numbers and are exact. We are taking no measurement but simply state the fact that allows us to convert from one unit of time to another time unit.

Before discussing techniques for performing the arithmetic operations on denominate numbers, let us consider how a standard unit of measure, such as 1 foot and 1 gallon, is determined.

How do you decide that your living room is 20 feet long? You can measure the room's length with a tape, but how do you know that the measure between the large marks on the face of the tape is a foot? In fact, what is the measure "1 foot"? Our chain of questions leads us to the startling fact that 1 foot is really an arbitrary measure. It is the distance between two marks on a metal tape which might contract in the winter and expand in the summer.

The problem we face in trying to fix the measure 1 foot is the same problem civilizations throughout history faced. How does one find a standard unit of measure that all people can use? The United States government uses the meter as a standard unit of length. It defines the meter as the distance, determined at the temperature at which ice melts, between two marks on a platinum-iridium bar deposited at the International Bureau of Weights and Measures.

Once the standard unit of length is defined, other standard units of measure can be determined. Thus 1 foot is .3048 meter, and one inch is $\frac{1}{12}$ of a foot. A gallon of liquid is that quantity of liquid that fills a container whose volume is 231 cubic inches. So starting with a standard length measure, meters, we arrive at a standard liquid measure, gallons, which is defined in terms of another standard length measure, inches.

The English and metric systems of measure are in almost universal use today. Tables displaying these systems are on pages 276 and 277. A metric-to-English and English-to-metric conversion table is on page 277. We shall use these tables in the following examples to illustrate arithmetic operations with denominate numbers.

Example: Add the following lengths: 16 feet 3 inches, 25 feet 8 inches, and 7 feet 7 inches.

Solution:

$$
\begin{array}{ll}
16 \text{ feet} & 3 \text{ inches} \\
25 \text{ feet} & 8 \text{ inches} \\
\underline{7 \text{ feet}} & \underline{7 \text{ inches}} \\
48 \text{ feet} & 18 \text{ inches}
\end{array}
$$

Using the table on page 276 we note that 12 inches = 1 foot. Thus the sum is 49 feet 6 inches.

Example: Multiply the measured quantity, 8 hours 23 minutes, by 4.

Solution:

$$
\begin{array}{l}
8 \text{ hours } 23 \text{ minutes} \\
\underline{\qquad\qquad\qquad \times\ 4} \\
32 \text{ hours } 92 \text{ minutes}
\end{array}
$$

Since there are 60 minutes in 1 hour, the product is 33 hours 32 minutes.

Because 8 hours 23 minutes is approximate, the product 32 hours 92 minutes should be modified to satisfy our rule that the product of an exact number and an approximate number shall have as many significant digits as the approximate number (page 242). 8 hours 23 minutes (503 minutes) has only three significant digits and so the product 32 hours 92 minutes (2012 minutes) should have only three significant digits. It should be recorded as 2010 minutes or 33 hours 30 minutes.

Example: Divide the measured quantity, 1 kilometer 20 meters, by 35.

Solution: 1 kilometer = 1000 meters

$$
\begin{array}{r}
29.143 \\
35\overline{)1020.000} \\
\underline{70} \\
320 \\
\underline{315} \\
\end{array}
$$

Complete the division.

1020 meters is an approximate number and 35 is an exact number. The quotient should, therefore, have only four significant digits (see page 243) and be recorded as 29.14 meters.

Example: Convert $\frac{1}{4}$ pound to grams.

Solution: 1 pound = 0.4536 kilogram and 1 kilogram = 1000 grams. Hence

$$\frac{1}{4} \text{ pound} = \frac{1}{4} \cancel{\text{pound}} \times \frac{0.4356 \ \cancel{\text{kilogram}}}{1 \ \cancel{\text{pound}}} \times \frac{1000 \text{ grams}}{1 \ \cancel{\text{kilogram}}}$$

$$= 113.4 \text{ grams}$$

Example: Convert the velocity 30 miles per hour, $30 \ \dfrac{\text{miles}}{\text{hour}}$, to a velocity expressed in the units feet per second, $\dfrac{\text{feet}}{\text{second}}$.

Solution:

$$1 \text{ mi} = 5280 \text{ ft}$$
$$1 \text{ hr} = 60 \text{ min}$$
$$1 \text{ min} = 60 \text{ sec}$$

Therefore $30 \ \dfrac{\cancel{\text{mi}}}{\text{hr}} \times 5280 \ \dfrac{\text{ft}}{\cancel{\text{mi}}} = 30 \times 5280 \ \dfrac{\text{ft}}{\text{hr}} = 158{,}400 \ \dfrac{\text{ft}}{\text{hr}}$

$158{,}400 \ \dfrac{\text{ft}}{\cancel{\text{hr}}} \times \dfrac{1 \ \cancel{\text{hr}}}{60 \text{ min}} = \dfrac{158{,}400}{60} \ \dfrac{\text{ft}}{\text{min}} = 2640 \ \dfrac{\text{ft}}{\text{min}}$

$2640 \ \dfrac{\text{ft}}{\cancel{\text{min}}} \times \dfrac{1 \ \cancel{\text{min}}}{60 \text{ sec}} = \dfrac{2640}{60} \ \dfrac{\text{ft}}{\text{sec}} = 44 \ \dfrac{\text{ft}}{\text{sec}}$

Hence $30 \ \dfrac{\text{mi}}{\text{hr}} = 44 \ \dfrac{\text{ft}}{\text{sec}}$

The entire calculation can be written

$$30 \ \dfrac{\cancel{\text{mi}}}{\cancel{\text{hr}}} \times 5280 \ \dfrac{\text{ft}}{\cancel{\text{mi}}} \times \dfrac{1 \ \cancel{\text{hr}}}{60 \ \cancel{\text{min}}} \times \dfrac{1 \ \cancel{\text{min}}}{60 \text{ sec}} = \dfrac{30 \times 5280}{60 \times 60} \ \dfrac{\text{ft}}{\text{sec}}$$

$$= 44 \ \dfrac{\text{ft}}{\text{sec}}$$

Exercises 9.4

Use the tables on pages 276 and 277 to complete the table below. Each position in the table should have a numeral followed by the appropriate units. You are either to supply the correct numeral or the appropriate units.

1	6 ft	_____ in	_____ cm	_____ m
2	_____ mi	1000 m	1 _____	_____ ft
3	2 mi	3520 _____	10,560 _____	_____ km
4	100 min	$\frac{5}{3}$ _____	_____ days	_____ sec
5	283.5 _____	10 oz	_____ kg	$\frac{5}{8}$ _____
6	180 lb	_____ g	2880 _____	82.134 _____
7	3 gal	12 _____	24 _____	_____ liters
8	10.57 _____	10 liters	_____ gal	21.14 _____

Complete the following sentences.

9. 5 feet 10 inches is equal to _____ centimeters.
10. The 880-yard dash is equivalent to a run of _____ meters.
11. The 5000-meter run is equivalent to a run of _____ miles.
12. A car traveling at 40 miles per hour travels _____ feet per second.
13. A gas tank that holds 18 gallons can hold _____ liters.
14. A car that travels 5 kilometers on 1 liter of gas can travel _____ miles on 1 gallon of gas.
15. A hose that delivers 30 quarts of water per minute delivers _____ gallons per hour.
16. A road map uses a scale of 1 inch per mile. This is equivalent to _____ centimeters per kilometer.
17. Problems 9 through 16 use denominate numbers. In which sentences are the denominate numbers approximate and in which sentences are they exact?

Compute each of the following:

18. 26 ft + 18 ft 3 in. + 42 ft 11 in. + 6 in.
19. 3 mi + 6070 ft + 2084 ft + 8 mi + 356 ft

20. 2.8 km + 1500 m + 826 m + 7.32 km
21. 12 gal − 3 qt + 26.4 qt − 43 pt
22. 200 lb + 863 lb + 2 tons − 784 lb − $\frac{1}{4}$ ton
23. 6 qt − 14.8 qt + 4.1 gal − 2.3 qt + 20 pt
24. 10 ft 3 in. − 2 ft 7 in. + 16 ft 4 in. + 25 ft 3 in. − 6 ft 11 in.
25. An average city block in Metro City is 240 feet. Compute the distance in miles of 40 city blocks.
26. A stamping machine can stamp a 3.2-pound block of aluminum into a finished part. If the machine stamps on the average of 2830 parts a day, how many tons of aluminum does it process in 1 week?
27. The Metro City government is charged with spending $300 per minute to provide services to the people of Metro City. How much money does the government spend in a day? In a year?
28. Separate the dimension 23 feet 8 inches into six equal parts.
29. A certain scrap metal is worth $20.86 per ton. How much is 126,300 pounds of the metal worth?
30. A certain machine process is performed in five stages and takes 1 hour 36 minutes to complete. How much time is spent in each stage if each of the five stages requires the same amount of time?

9.5 Area and Square Root

Suppose the dimensions of your dining room are 10.0 feet by 12.0 feet. You wish to tile the dining room floor with square tiles that measure 1 foot on a side. How many tiles do you need to cover the floor? Your problem is solved if you imagine lining the floor as shown in Figure 9.3.

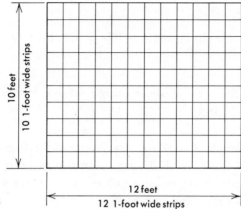

FIGURE 9.3

The floor is first divided into 10 strips each 1.0 foot by 12.0 feet and then into 12 strips each 1.0 foot by 10.0 feet. The resulting pattern on the floor is 120 squares each measuring 1.0 foot on a side. Although you have solved the problem, you might well have asked if there is an easier way.

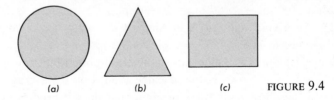

(a)   (b)   (c)   FIGURE 9.4

There is an easier way. Let us call the measure of the plane region enclosed within a figure the *area* of the figure. The measures of the shaded regions in Figure 9.4 would be called the area of a circle, the area of a triangle, and the area of a rectangle, respectively. A unit of measure for area is square feet. We say a square that measures 1 foot on a side has an area of 1 square foot. Therefore the area of any region is simply the number of 1-foot squares required to cover the region without overlapping.

You might have predicted the floor area of the room of Figure 9.3 to be 120 square feet without lining the floor. If you had observed that each of the ten 12-foot strips contained twelve 1-foot squares, you would have immediately known that you need $10 \cdot 12$, or one hundred twenty, 1-foot squares. Likewise, if your room was W feet by L feet you would have W strips each containing L 1-foot squares. You conclude then that any rectangle of width W feet and length L feet has an area of $W \cdot L$ square feet. The last sentence may be stated symbolically as $A = W \cdot L$.

Example: Find the area of a rectangle whose dimensions are 32.0 feet by 16.0 feet.

Solution: Using the formula $A = W \cdot L$ we have $A = 32.0 \times 16.0 = 512$ square feet.

Example: Find the area of the rectangle whose dimensions are exactly 18.50 feet by 13.25 feet.

Solution: The formula $A = W \cdot L$ was developed for W and L to be whole numbers. Since 18.50 and 13.25 are not whole numbers, we must either discard our formula or introduce a unit of measure that makes the dimensions of the rectangle whole numbers.

$$18.50 \text{ feet} = 18.50 \times 12 \text{ inches}$$
$$= 222 \text{ inches}$$
$$13.25 \text{ feet} = 13.25 \times 12 \text{ inches}$$
$$= 159 \text{ inches}$$

Now $A = 222 \times 159 = 35{,}298$ square inches.

We wish to convert 35,298 square inches to square feet. Figure 9.5 dis-

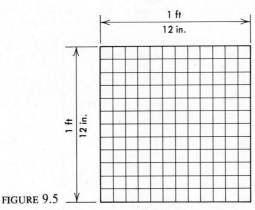

FIGURE 9.5

plays the fact that each square foot contains 144 square inches. Therefore, 35,298 square inches equals $\dfrac{35{,}298}{144}$ square feet.

```
            245.125
    144)35298.000
        288
        ───
        649
        576
        ───
        738
        720
        ───
        180
        144
        ───
        360
        288
        ───
        720
        720
        ───
        000
```

$\dfrac{35{,}298}{144}$ square feet = 245.125 square feet. But $18.50 \times 13.25 = 245.125$, and so we see that the formula, $A = W \cdot L$, also applies to this problem even though W and L are not whole numbers.

It is in general true that if the dimensions of a rectangle are *rational* numbers the area of the rectangle is the product of the dimensions.

Since a square is a rectangle whose sides all have the same measure its area is known if we know the measure of one of its sides. Now we ask if it is possible to find the measure of the sides of a square if we know its area.

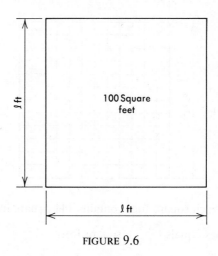

FIGURE 9.6

Assume that a plane square region (Figure 9.6) has an area of 100 square feet. What is the measure of a side of the square? Since the sides all have the same measure, l, we can use the formula for the area of a rectangle to obtain the sentence $100 = l \cdot l$ or $100 = l^2$. 100 is the square of l and l is called the square root of 100. We can write this symbolically as $l = \sqrt{100}$ where "$\sqrt{}$" is called the *radical* and "100" the *radicand*.

We have discussed the inverse operations squaring and square rooting in Chapter Five. If 100 is the square of l ($100 = l^2$), then the square root of 100 is l ($l = \sqrt{100}$). And, in general, if a is a positive real number, then the square root of a, $\sqrt{a}$, is that nonnegative number which when multiplied by itself gives the product a.

Example: Solve each of the following sentences.

(a) $x = \sqrt{25}$ (b) $y = \sqrt{81}$

(c) $r = \sqrt{144}$ (d) $s = \sqrt{225}$

Solutions:

   (a) $x = 5$ because $5 \cdot 5 = 25$

   (b) $y = 9$ because $9 \cdot 9 = 81$

   (c) $r = 12$ because $12 \cdot 12 = 144$

   (d) $s = 15$ because $15 \cdot 15 = 225$

The *whole numbers* 25, 81, 144, and 225 are called *perfect squares* because for each of these numbers there is a *whole number* that is its *square root*. All positive real numbers are not perfect squares, however, and determining their square roots can become a difficult task.

Example: Compute $\sqrt{12.25}$.

Solution: We seek a positive number which when multiplied by itself gives the product 12.25. Let us call the number we seek b. Then

$$3 < b < 4 \qquad \text{because } 3 \times 3 = 9 \text{ and } 4 \times 4 = 16$$

$$3.2 < b < 3.8 \qquad \begin{aligned} &\text{because } 3.2 \times 3.2 = 10.24 \\ &\text{and } 3.8 \times 3.8 = 14.44 \end{aligned}$$

$$3.4 < b < 3.6 \qquad \begin{aligned} &\text{because } 3.4 \times 3.4 = 11.56 \\ &\text{and } 3.6 \times 3.6 = 12.96 \end{aligned}$$

$$3.45 < b < 3.55 \qquad \begin{aligned} &\text{because } 3.45 \times 3.45 = 11.9025 \\ &\text{and } 3.55 \times 3.55 = 12.6025 \end{aligned}$$

$$b = 3.5 \qquad \text{because } 3.5 \times 3.5 = 12.25$$

The computation for the positive square root of 12.25 was performed above by a trial-and-error process. This is a lengthy process, but carefully done it can yield an exact result or as good an approximation as desired.

Example: Compute $\sqrt{2}$.

Solution: The square root of 2 is an irrational number (see problems 26 through 36 of Section 7.6), so its decimal representation is infinitely long. Therefore the trial-and-error process of the previous example cannot give us the exact decimal representation for the square root of 2. The process can, however, give a decimal representation to whatever accuracy is desired. We could use our trial-and-error process to show

$$1.4 < \sqrt{2} < 1.5$$

or to show

$$1.41 < \sqrt{2} < 1.42$$

or to show

$$1.414 < \sqrt{2} < 1.415$$

etc.

Square rooting is a common arithmetic operation. A square-root table is given on page 278. We also discuss a square-root algorithm in Section 9.6.

Exercises 9.5

Each of the following pairs of numbers represents the width and depth of a city lot. Find the area in each case.

1. (50.5 ft, 100.0 ft)   **2.** (75.4 ft, 135.8 ft)

3. (60.7 ft, 121.0 ft)   **4.** (88.3 ft, 204.6 ft)

5. (80.2 ft, 212.9 ft)

6. What is the total acreage of the five city lots of problems 1 through 5?

A parallelogram is a four-sided plane figure whose opposite sides are parallel. If we could remove the triangle *AED* from the left side of the

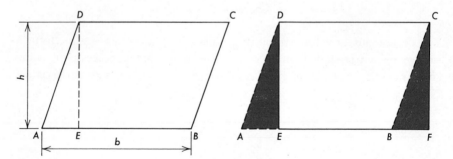

parallelogram and attach it to the right side, so that points *A, E,* and *D* are made to coincide with points *B, F,* and *C,* respectively, we would form a rectangle. The dimensions of the rectangle are *h* feet by *b* feet, so its area is *h · b* square feet. But this is the area of the parallelogram. We conclude that the area of a parallelogram is the product of its height, *h,* and its base, *b.* Find the area of each of the parallelograms shown.

7.

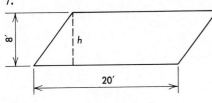

8.

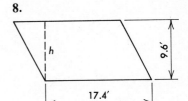

9.

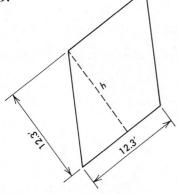

The accompanying illustration suggests that a parallelogram can always be formed from a triangle. One need only adjoin to the given triangle, *ABC*, an identical triangle *DBC*. Thus the area of a triangle is half the area of the parallelogram that can be formed from it. $A = \frac{1}{2} \cdot b \cdot h$.

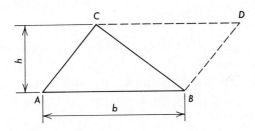

Find the areas of each of the triangles shown.

10.   **11.**

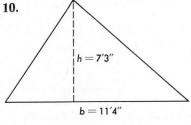
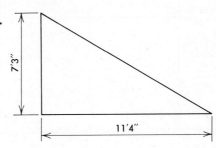

12.

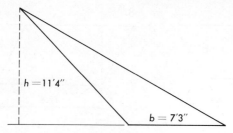

$h = 11'4''$

$b = 7'3''$

Knowing the formulas for the area of a circle ($\pi \cdot r^2$), a triangle $\left(\frac{1}{2} \cdot b \cdot h\right)$, and a rectangle ($b \cdot h$), one can easily find the areas of a great variety of plane regions.

Example: Find the area of the region *ABCDE*.

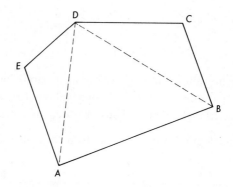

Solution: The region *ABCDE* is separated into three triangles by the dashed-line segments $\overline{AD}$ and $\overline{DB}$. The base and height of each triangle is measured and its area determined. The area of the region *ABCDE* is the sum of the areas of the three triangles. The area of *ABCDE* is approximately 2 sq in.

Triangle	Base	Height	Area
ADE	$AD = 1\frac{1}{2}$ in	$\frac{1}{2}$ in	$= \frac{3}{8}$ sq in
BDC	$BD = 1\frac{11}{16}$ in	$\frac{9}{16}$ in	$\doteq \frac{1}{2}$ sq in
ABD	$AB = 1\frac{3}{4}$ in	$1\frac{5}{16}$ in	$\doteq 1\frac{1}{8}$ sq in
			$\doteq 2$ sq in

Determine the areas of each of the shaded regions. Measure all the necessary dimensions to the nearest sixteenth of an inch.

13.   **14.**

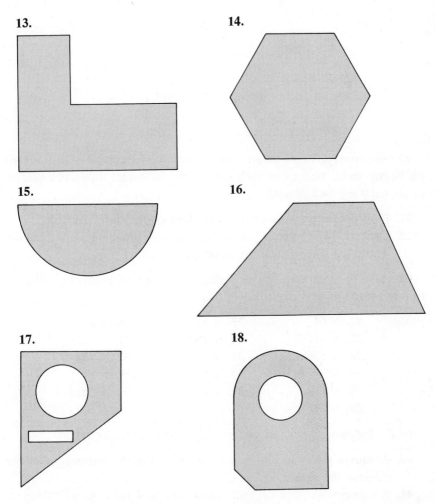

15.   **16.**

17.   **18.**

19. A foundation plan for a home is drawn to a scale of 1 in. equals 10 ft. If the foundation is rectangular and measures $4\frac{1}{4}$ in. by $7\frac{5}{8}$ in., find the first-floor area of the house.

20. The regions of problems 14, 15, and 16 are a hexagon, a semicircle, and a trapezoid, respectively. State a definition for each of these plane shapes.

21. Find the acreage of the property shown in the scale drawing, 1 in. = 100 ft, of a piece of land.

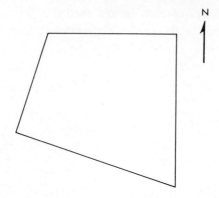

The statement "The air pressure at the surface of the earth is 14.7 pounds per square inch" means that each square inch of surface supports a column of air weighing 14.7 pounds.

22. Find the air pressure on 1 square foot of the earth's surface.
23. Convert 14.7 pounds per square inch to an equivalent quantity whose units are grams per square centimeter.

Compute the following square roots to two decimal places by using the trial-and-error process described in this section.

24. $\sqrt{64}$	**25.** $\sqrt{121}$	**26.** $\sqrt{256}$
27. $\sqrt{441}$	**28.** $\sqrt{1849}$	**29.** $\sqrt{9025}$
30. $\sqrt{10609}$	**31.** $\sqrt{3}$	**32.** $\sqrt{5}$
33. $\sqrt{7.6}$	**34.** $\sqrt{12.5}$	**35.** $\sqrt{92}$
36. $\sqrt{150}$	**37.** $\sqrt{70.3}$	**38.** $\sqrt{200.1}$
39. $\sqrt{197}$		

In the following problems you may use the square-root tables.

40. A square piece of land has 15 acres. Find the dimensions of the sides of the square in feet.
41. A rectangular piece of land whose length is twice its width has 20 acres. Find the dimensions of the rectangle in feet.

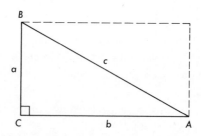

A triangle that forms half a rectangle or square (see the discussion preceding problem 10) is called a *right triangle*. The sides $\overline{AC}$ and $\overline{BC}$ are said to be perpendicular or at right angles. The diagonal of the rectangle, $\overline{AB}$, is called the *hypotenuse* of the triangle. It is the largest side of the triangle ABC. If we call the measures of the sides of the triangle a, b, and c, the relationship $a^2 + b^2 = c^2$ exists between those measures. The relationship is called the *Pythagorean theorem*. It says: "The sum of the squares of the measures of the sides of a right triangle equals the square of the hypotenuse measure."

Example: Find the length of the diagonal of a rectangle whose sides are exactly 8.0 inches and 10.0 inches.

Solution: Using the Pythagorean theorem we have

$$c^2 = 8^2 + 10^2$$
$$= 64 + 100$$
$$= 164$$

If $c^2 = 164$ then,

$$c = \sqrt{164}$$
$$\doteq 12.8$$

Find the missing dimension for each of the right triangles whose sides have measures a and b and whose hypotenuse has measure c. Assume all given measures are exact.

42. $a = 5.0$, $b = 12.0$, $c = ?$ **43.** $a = 3.0$, $b = ?$, $c = 5.0$

44. $a = ?$, $b = 15.0$, $c = 25.0$ **45.** $a = 6.0$, $b = 8.0$, $c = ?$

46. $a = 10.0$, $b = ?$, $c = 26.0$ **47.** $a = ?$, $b = 15.0$, $c = 17.0$

48. Draw the triangles in problems 43 and 45. Do you see any relationship between these triangles (compare their dimensions)? Compare the dimensions of the triangles in problems 42 and 46.

49. How long must a guy wire be if it is to support a TV antenna 70 feet 8 inches high? The antenna is based on level ground and the guy wire is to be anchored 10.0 feet from the base.

50. Cities A and B are connected by a freeway and a two-lane road. The maximum average speed that a motorist can maintain on the freeway is 60 mph. His maximum average speed on the two-lane road would be 45 mph. Using the illustration, determine which route you would choose to go from city A to city B in the least possible time.

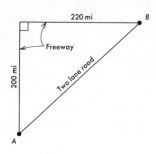

51. Car 1 travels east from High City at 50 mph. Car 2 starts 3 hours later and travels north at 60 mph. How far apart are the cars 4 hours after car 2 began its trip?

The pairs of triangles discussed in problem 48 are pairs of *similar* triangles. Similar triangles have the same shape and the ratios of their corresponding sides are equal. Comparing the corresponding sides of the triangles of problems 43 and 45 gives $\frac{3}{6} = \frac{4}{8} = \frac{5}{10}$. These ratios all equal $\frac{1}{2}$.

The above discussion might suggest a way to solve the following problems.

52. Two right triangles are similar. The sides of the larger are three times as long as the sides of the smaller. Find the area of the larger triangle if the area of the smaller triangle is 100 square inches.

53. John decided he could make a fairly good estimate of the height of the skyscraper which was about 1000 feet away. Its base was about level with his eye. He held a 4-inch-long pencil in front of him so that his line of sight through the bottom of the pencil struck the base of the building. His line of sight through the top of the pencil struck the top of the building. If he held the pencil 1 foot from his eye, how tall is the skyscraper?

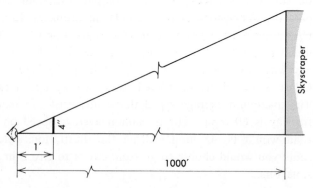

9.6 An Algorithm for Computing Square Roots

In this section we shall develop an algorithm for finding the square root of a positive number.

The pattern:

$$10^2 = 100$$
$$100^2 = 10,000$$
$$1000^2 = 1,000,000$$
$$10,000^2 = 100,000,000 \quad \text{etc.}$$

suggests that for any whole number a

1. If $0 < a < 10$, a^2 has one or two digits.
2. If $10 < a < 100$, a^2 has three or four digits.
3. If $100 < a < 1000$, a^2 has five or six digits.
4. If $1000 < a < 10,000$, a^2 has seven or eight digits.

Also, because of the inverse relationship between squaring and square-rooting, the above pattern suggests that

1. If a one- or two-digit whole number has a whole-number square root, the root must be a one-digit number.
2. If a three- or four-digit whole number has a whole-number square root, the root must be a two-digit number.

Example: Each of the following numbers is a perfect square. How many digits will there be in each of their square roots?

      (a) 225   (b) 1849   (c) 14,400
      (d) 119,716   (e) 1,221,025   (f) 17,698,849

Solution:

  (a) 2   (b) 2   (c) 3   (d) 3   (e) 4   (f) 4

Three examples below compare squaring to the inverse process of finding the square root. You should read the examples carefully, observing the clues given (in color). You may have to go over the examples many times and you may even have to construct an example of your own before you understand the square-root algorithm.

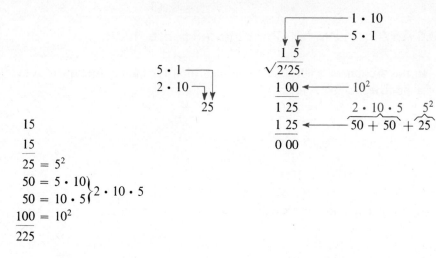

$$25 = 5^2$$
$$50 = 5 \cdot 10$$
$$50 = 10 \cdot 5 \Big\} 2 \cdot 10 \cdot 5$$
$$100 = 10^2$$
$$\overline{225}$$

The algorithm shown above follows this sequence:

(1) $$\sqrt{2'25.}$$

(2)

(3)

(4)

$$
\begin{array}{r}
\text{———}1 \cdot 10 \\
\text{———}5 \cdot 1 \\
1\ \ 5 \\
\end{array}
$$

(5)
$$
\begin{array}{r}
5 \cdot 1 \text{———} \\
2 \cdot 10 \text{———} \\
\\
25)\quad
\end{array}
\quad
\begin{array}{r}
\sqrt{2'25.} \\
1\ 00 \longleftarrow 10^2 \\
\overline{1\ 25} \qquad 2 \cdot 10 \cdot 5 \quad 5^2 \\
1\ 25 \longleftarrow \overbrace{50 + 50} + \overbrace{25} \\
\overline{0\ 00}
\end{array}
$$

Question: Why is 225 separated into a two-digit and one-digit group, 2'25 ? The answer is given in the discussion at the beginning of the section.

$$
\begin{array}{l}
43 \\
\underline{43} \\
\ \ 9 = 3^2 \\
120 = 3 \cdot 40 \\
120 = 40 \cdot 3 \\
1600 = 40^2 \\
\overline{1849}
\end{array}
\qquad
\begin{array}{r}
\text{———}4 \cdot 10 \\
\text{———}3 \cdot 1 \\
4\ \ 3 \\
\end{array}
$$

$$
\begin{array}{r}
3 \cdot 1 \text{———} \\
2 \cdot 40 \text{———} \\
\\
83)\quad
\end{array}
\quad
\begin{array}{r}
\sqrt{18'49} \\
16\ 00 \longleftarrow 40^2 \\
\overline{2\ 49} \qquad 2 \cdot 40 \cdot 3 \quad 3^2 \\
2\ 49 \longleftarrow \overbrace{120 + 120} + \overbrace{9} \\
\overline{0\ 00}
\end{array}
$$

The square-root algorithm shown above is displayed in a sequence of steps below.

(1)
$$\sqrt{18'49}$$

(2)
$$
\begin{array}{r}
\text{———}4 \cdot 10 \\
4 \\
\sqrt{18'49} \\
16\ 00 \longleftarrow 40^2
\end{array}
$$

(3)
$$
\begin{array}{r}
\text{———}4 \cdot 10 \\
4 \\
\sqrt{18'49} \\
\end{array}
$$
$$
\begin{array}{r}
2 \cdot 40 \text{———} \\
\\
8)\quad
\end{array}
\quad
\begin{array}{r}
16\ 00 \longleftarrow 40^2 \\
\overline{2\ 49}
\end{array}
$$

(4)
$$
\begin{array}{r}
\text{———}4 \cdot 10 \\
\text{———}3 \cdot 1 \\
4\ \ 3 \\
\end{array}
$$
$$
\begin{array}{r}
3 \cdot 1 \text{———} \\
2 \cdot 40 \text{———} \\
\\
83)\quad
\end{array}
\quad
\begin{array}{r}
\sqrt{18'49} \\
16\ 00 \longleftarrow 40^2 \\
\overline{2\ 49}
\end{array}
$$

$$\begin{array}{r} \text{4 · 10} \\ \text{3 · 1} \end{array}$$

(5)

$$\begin{array}{r} 4 \quad 3 \\ 3 \cdot 1 \longrightarrow \quad \sqrt{18'49} \\ 2 \cdot 40 \longrightarrow \quad 16\ 00 \longleftarrow 40^2 \\ 83)\quad\underline{}\ 2\ 49 \qquad 2\cdot 40\cdot 3 \quad 3^2 \\ 2\ 49 \longleftarrow 120 + 120 + 9 \\ \overline{0\ 00} \end{array}$$

Question: Why is 1849 separated into two two-digit groups, 18′49 ?

$$
\begin{array}{r}
346 \\
346 \\
\hline
36 = 6^2 \\
240 = 6 \cdot 40 \\
240 = 40 \cdot 6 \\
1800 = 6 \cdot 300 \\
1800 = 300 \cdot 6 \\
1600 = 40^2 \\
12000 = 40 \cdot 300 \\
12000 = 300 \cdot 40 \\
90000 = 300^2 \\
\hline
119716
\end{array}
$$

with bracket annotations: $2 \cdot 40 \cdot 6$; $2 \cdot 300 \cdot 6$; $2 \cdot 300 \cdot 40$

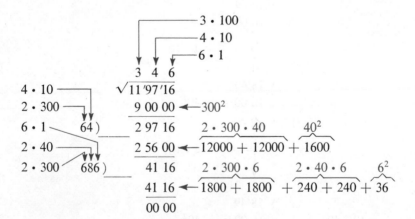

Question: Why is 119,716 separated into 3 two-digit groups, 11′97′16 ?

The examples have dealt only with perfect squares and their square roots. It is also useful to be able to compute the square root of numbers which are not perfect squares. The square roots of such numbers may be irrational. Therefore, finding the square root of numbers which are not perfect squares means finding a rational number, or a rational-number approximation to an irrational number. We can find as good a rational-number approximation as desired using the square-root algorithm.

Example: Find the square root of 56 to two decimal places.

Solution:

$$
\begin{array}{r}
7.\ 4\ 8\ 3 \\
\sqrt{56.00'00'00'} \\
\end{array}
$$

$$
\begin{array}{r}
49 \\
\hline
144)\quad 700 \\
576 \\
\hline
1488)\quad 12400 \\
11904 \\
\hline
14963)\quad 49600 \\
44889 \\
\hline
\end{array}
$$

Rounding we have 7.48 as an approximation to $\sqrt{56}$.

Exercises 9.6

Use the square-root algorithm to find:

1. $\sqrt{256}$	**2.** $\sqrt{961}$	**3.** $\sqrt{3025}$
4. $\sqrt{7569}$	**5.** $\sqrt{10816}$	**6.** $\sqrt{181476}$
7. $\sqrt{6.25}$	**8.** $\sqrt{27.5625}$	**9.** $\sqrt{.015625}$
10. $\sqrt{339.2964}$		

Use the square-root algorithm to find the following square roots rounding to thousandths.

11. $\sqrt{2}$	**12.** $\sqrt{3}$	**13.** $\sqrt{5}$
14. $\sqrt{96}$	**15.** $\sqrt{832}$	**16.** $\sqrt{2348}$
17. $\sqrt{8002}$	**18.** $\sqrt{25,411}$	**19.** $\sqrt{602,186}$

20. Use the results of problems 11 and 12 to find $\sqrt{2} \cdot \sqrt{3}$. Compare this result to $\sqrt{6}$ obtained from the square-root table on page 278.

21. Use the results of problems 11 and 13 to find $\sqrt{2} \cdot \sqrt{5}$. Compare this result to $\sqrt{10}$ obtained from the table on page 278. Use the results of problems 12 and 13 to find $\sqrt{3} \cdot \sqrt{5}$. Compare this result to $\sqrt{15}$ obtained from the table on page 278.

22. Complete the following generalization suggested by problems 20 and 21. *If a and b are positive real numbers, then* $\sqrt{a} \cdot \sqrt{b} = $ _____.

Test the generalization of problem 22 against:

23. $\sqrt{4} \cdot \sqrt{4} = \sqrt{16}$ **24.** $\sqrt{4} \cdot \sqrt{9} = \sqrt{36}$

25. $\sqrt{4} \cdot \sqrt{25} = \sqrt{100}$ **26.** $\sqrt{900} = \sqrt{25} \cdot \sqrt{36}$

27. $\sqrt{1089} = \sqrt{121} \cdot \sqrt{9}$

28. Test the truth of the following generalization:

If a and b are positive real numbers, then $\dfrac{\sqrt{a}}{\sqrt{b}} = \sqrt{\dfrac{a}{b}}$.

29. What property of addition and multiplication allows us to state the following?

$$3\sqrt{4} + 5\sqrt{4} = (3 + 5)\sqrt{4} = 8\sqrt{4}$$

30. The real number b has a real-number square root only if b is greater than or equal to zero. Why?

9.7 Volumes

How much water does the tank hold? How many oranges can be packed in the crate? How much earth fill is necessary at the freeway sight? These are questions about volume. The interior of a tank is to be filled. How does one measure the space inside the tank? An orange crate is to be filled. What space is available inside the orange crate?

As area is the number assigned to a region enclosed by some boundary, volume is the number assigned to the space occupied by some solid. A volume of 1 cubic foot is assigned to the space occupied by the cube of

Figure 9.7.   If the unit of length in Figure 9.7 was 1 inch, the cube would have a volume of 1 cubic inch.   If the unit of length was 1 yard, the volume would be 1 cubic yard; etc.

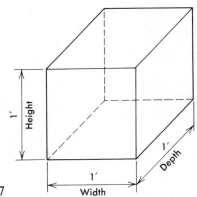

FIGURE 9.7

Example: Find the volume of the rectangular solid of Figure 9.8.

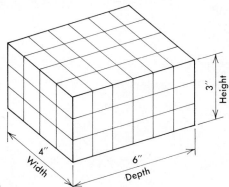

FIGURE 9.8

Solution: We attempt to find how many unit volumes, 1 cubic inch each, will form the solid.   By dividing the figure as shown (into 1-inch cubes), we see it is possible to form the solid as three layers of 24, (4 • 6), 1-inch cubes.   The volume is 3 • 4 • 6 = 72 cubic inches.

In general the volume of a rectangular solid is

$$V = height \cdot weight \cdot depth$$

Other common solid shapes and the formulas for their volumes are:

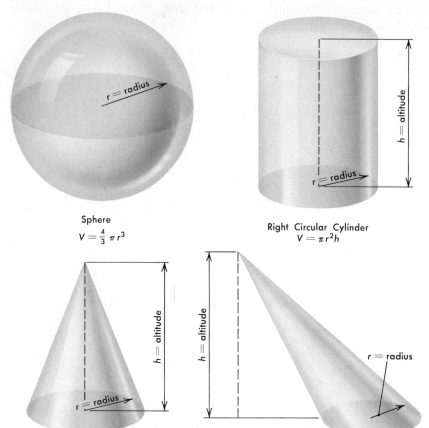

Sphere

$$V = \frac{4}{3} \pi r^3$$

Right Circular Cylinder

$$V = \pi r^2 h$$

Right Circular Cone

$$V = \frac{1}{3} \pi r^2 h$$

Oblique Circular Cone

$$V = \frac{1}{3} \pi \bar{r}^2 h$$

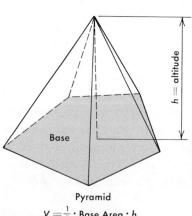

Pyramid

$$V = \frac{1}{3} \cdot \text{Base Area} \cdot h$$

Exercises 9.7

1. Find the volume of a rectangular solid whose dimensions are 6 ft 4 in. high, 2 ft 6 in. wide, and 8 ft 9 in. deep.

2. Find the volume of a sphere of radius 2 ft 2 in.

3. Find the volume of a right circular cone of base radius 7 in. and altitude 1 ft 3 in.

4. Find the volume of a pyramid whose base is a 3 ft 5 in. square and whose altitude is 10 ft 11 in.

5. Convert 1 cubic foot to cubic inches.

6. Convert 1 cubic yard to cubic feet.

7. A gallon of water occupies a volume of 231 cubic inches. What is the volume occupied by 1 quart of water? 1 pint of water?

8. If water weighs 62.5 pounds per cubic foot, how much does 1 gallon of water weigh? 1 quart of water? 1 pint of water?

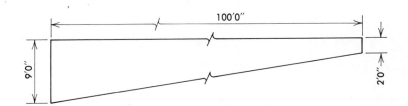

9. The figure is a side view of an excavation that is 50 ft wide. Find the volume of earth to be excavated and the cost of such an excavation if it is priced at $3.25 per cubic foot.

10. If steel weighs 490 pounds per cubic foot, what volume of steel will equal in weight 1 cubic foot of water?

11. Water pressure at any depth h is determined as the weight of a column of water having a 1-foot-square base and a height h. What is the water pressure 100 feet below the surface of the ocean? (See problem 8.)

12. Find the volume, in cubic feet, of a gas tank that holds 20 gallons of gas.

13. A concrete driveway 75 feet by 10 feet by 4 inches is to be poured. If concrete costs $8.60 a cubic yard "in place," determine the cost of the driveway.

Determine the volumes of the following shapes.

14.

15.

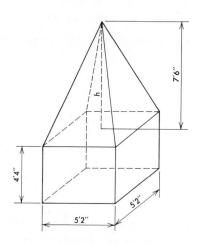

16.

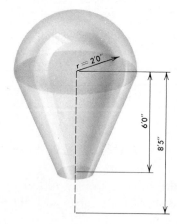

17. If water can be piped into the pool of problem 9 at the rate of 1200 gallons per minute, how long would it take to fill the pool?

18. Assume the average orange crate is 4 by $1\frac{1}{2}$ by $1\frac{1}{2}$ feet and the average orange has a $1\frac{1}{2}$ inch radius. Approximately how many oranges can be packed into an orange crate?

19. The local beach is 1000 feet long and 200 feet wide. Assume the sand depth is 1 foot and each sand particle is a cube .01 inch on a side. How many particles of sand does the local beach contain? (*Hint:* Use scientific notation.)

9.8 Summary

Measures are usually in error and so are referred to as approximate numbers. Their exact error is not known but limitations on its size can be determined. These error limitations are reflected in the recording of a measured quantity. Its maximum error is taken to be $\pm$ 5 units in the place following the last significant digit. The maximum error of measured quantities is also considered in computations involving these quantities. We round the results of a computation to reflect the least precise measure in the computation.

Denominate numbers represent physical quantities. They are approximate if they result as a measurement. Otherwise they can be considered exact. We discussed two kinds of computations with denominate numbers. One was the usual computation for approximate numbers and the other was a conversion from one set of units to another set of units. We converted feet to inches, gallons to quarts, miles per hour to feet per second, etc. In making the conversions we considered the conversion factors to be exact denominate numbers. For example, the "12" in "12 inches equals 1 foot," is exact.

Square rooting and computing areas and volumes of certain plane and solid shapes were topics discussed in the latter part of the chapter. We first looked at square rooting as a guessing process where through a sequence of guesses it is possible to come closer and closer to the square root sought. A square-root algorithm was then introduced through a set of three examples.

Exercises 9.8—Review

Complete each of the following sentences.

1. A number obtained as a result of a measurement is called a(n) _____ number.
2. A number obtained as a result of counting is called a(n) _____ number.
3. If a measurement is observed as 7.35, then ±.005 is its _____.
4. The measure 4.03 has 3 _____.
5. Computations with approximate numbers should reflect the precision of the _____ used in the computation.
6. The numbers in the phrases "eight feet," "twelve miles," and "one hundred yards" are _____ numbers.
7. One of the two equal factors of a number is called a _____ of a number.
8. The area of a rectangle is equal to the product of _____.
9. 395 is between (___)² and (___)². Replace each blank with a whole number.
10. The volume of a rectangular solid is equal to the product of _____.

True or false?

11. 3605 has three significant digits.
12. The maximum error in the measure .00620 is ±.0005.
13. A crowd estimated at 24,000, to the nearest thousand, might have contained 23,692 persons.
14. The product of the approximate numbers, 38.17 and 23.5, is best recorded as 867.
15. The sum of the approximate numbers 23.918, 4.2, 63.18, and .051 is best recorded as 91.349.
16. The product of the approximate numbers 34.82 and 63.1 is best recorded as 2197.
17. Each real number has a real-number square root.
18. 576 is a perfect square.
19. The area of a circle of radius r is $2 \cdot \pi \cdot r$.
20. The volume of a 12-inch cube is 1728 cubic inches.

Compute the following.

21. A steel tape used to measure the results of the long jump is calibrated in thirty-seconds of an inch. If a jumper's mark is reported as 21 feet $3\frac{3}{8}$ inches, between what measures must the exact value lie?

22. Compute $5\sqrt{3} - 3\sqrt{5}$ to the nearest hundredth using the tables.

23. Find the maximum and minimum areas of a circular garden plot if the radius is 6 feet, measured to the nearest sixteenth of an inch.

24. Find the average monthly gross income of Sam's Grocery, given the following receipts;

    Jan: $1287.43   Feb: $1125.01   Mar: $1146.37
    Apr: $1081.27   May: $1037.37   Jun: $1129.00
    Jul: $1048.20   Aug: $ 957.21   Sep: $1095.68
    Oct: $1111.11   Nov: $1283.14   Dec: $1301.28

25. A car that travels 60 miles per hour is traveling _____ feet per second.

26. A particular state spends a total of approximately 28 million dollars to educate its 65,000 school children. What is the approximate cost per child?

27. Find the number of acres in a rectangular plot of ground 300 yards long and 150 yards wide.

28. Compute $\sqrt{484.8}$ correct to the nearest tenth.

29. Compute $\sqrt{.0058123}$ correct to the nearest tenth.

30. Find the area measure.

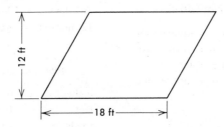

31. Find the measure of the diagonal of a rectangle 8 feet wide and 15 feet long.

32. John casts a 64-inch shadow at the same time that a flagpole casts a 12-foot shadow. If John is 6 feet tall, how tall is the flagpole? Assume all measures to the nearest inch.

33. Since $3136 = 49 \times 64$ it follows that $\sqrt{3136} =$ ____ $\times$ ____. (*Hint:* See problem 22, page 268.)

34. A spherical balloon is inflated to a diameter of 12.0 inches with water weighing 62.5 pounds per cubic foot. If the weight of the empty balloon is negligible, compute the weight of the full balloon.

35. Find the volume of a reservoir in the shape of an inverted square pyramid with base 100 feet square and depth 20 feet.

A P P E N D I X

TABLE 1. Tables of Measure, English System

Linear Measure (Length)

12 inches = 1 foot
3 feet   = 1 yard
5280 feet = 1 mile

Square Measure (Area)

144 square inches = 1 square foot
9 square feet   = 1 square yard
43,560 square feet = 1 acre
740 acres   = 1 square mile

Cubic Measure (Volume)

1728 cubic inches = 1 cubic foot
27 cubic feet   = 1 cubic yard

Liquid Measure

2 pints   = 1 quart
4 quarts   = 1 gallon
231 cubic inches = 1 gallon

Avoirdupois Weight

16 ounces = 1 pound

Time

60 seconds = 1 minute
60 minutes = 1 hour
24 hours   = 1 day
7 days   = 1 week
365 days   = 1 year
366 days   = 1 leap year
12 months = 1 year

Abbreviations

inches	in or "
feet	ft or '
yards	yd
pints	pt
quarts	qt
gallons	gal
ounces	oz
pounds	lb
seconds	sec
minutes	min
hours	hr
months	mo
square inches	sq in
square feet	sq ft
cubic inches	cu in
cubic feet	cu ft

TABLE 2. Metric Measures

Abbreviations

centimeter	cm
kilogram	kg
kilometer	km
liter	liter
meter	m
milligram	mg
millimeter	mm

Prefixes

milli-	= one thousandth	deka-	=	ten
centi-	= one hundredth	hecto-	=	one hundred
deci-	= one tenth	kilo-	=	one thousand

Metric Units Length

10 *millimeters*	= 1 *centimeter*
10 centimeters	= 1 decimeter
10 decimeters	= 1 *meter*
10 meters	= 1 dekameter
10 dekameters	= 1 hectometer
10 hectometers	= 1 *kilometer*

Capacity

10 milliliters	= 1 centiliter
10 centiliters	= 1 decoliter
10 deciliters	= 1 *liter*
10 liters	= 1 dekaliter
10 dekaliters	= 1 hectoliter
10 hectoliters	= 1 kiloliter

Weight

10 *milligrams*	= 1 centigram
10 centigrams	= 1 decigram
10 decigrams	= 1 *gram*
10 grams	= 1 dekagram
10 dekagrams	= 1 hectogram
10 hectograms	= 1 *kilogram*

Metric-English and English-Metric Conversions Length

1 meter	= 1.0936 yards
1 meter	= 39.37 inches
1 meter	= 3.2808 feet
1 kilometer	= 0.6214 mile
1 yard	= 0.9144 meter
1 foot	= 0.3048 meter
1 inch	= 2.54 centimeters
1 mile	= 1.6093 kilometers

Capacity

1 liter	= 1.0567 quarts
1 quart	= 0.9463 liter

Weight

1 kilogram	= 2.2046 pounds
1 gram	= 0.0353 ounce
1 pound	= 0.4536 kilogram
1 ounce	= 28.35 grams

TABLE 3. Table of Square Roots

N	$\sqrt{N}$	N	$\sqrt{N}$	N	$\sqrt{N}$	N	$\sqrt{N}$
1	1.000	51	7.141	101	10.05	151	12.29
2	1.414	52	7.211	102	10.10	152	12.33
3	1.732	53	7.280	103	10.15	153	12.37
4	2.000	54	7.348	104	10.20	154	12.41
5	2.236	55	7.416	105	10.25	155	12.45
6	2.449	56	7.483	106	10.30	156	12.49
7	2.646	57	7.550	107	10.34	157	12.53
8	2.828	58	7.616	108	10.39	158	12.57
9	3.000	59	7.681	109	10.44	159	12.61
10	3.162	60	7.746	110	10.49	160	12.65
11	3.317	61	7.810	111	10.54	161	12.69
12	3.464	62	7.874	112	10.58	162	12.73
13	3.606	63	7.937	113	10.63	163	12.77
14	3.742	64	8.000	114	10.68	164	12.81
15	3.873	65	8.062	115	10.72	165	12.85
16	4.000	66	8.124	116	10.77	166	12.88
17	4.123	67	8.185	117	10.82	167	12.92
18	4.243	68	8.246	118	10.86	168	12.96
19	4.359	69	8.307	119	10.91	169	13.00
20	4.472	70	8.367	120	10.95	170	13.04
21	4.583	71	8.426	121	11.00	171	13.08
22	4.690	72	8.485	122	11.05	172	13.11
23	4.796	73	8.544	123	11.09	173	13.15
24	4.899	74	8.602	124	11.14	174	13.19
25	5.000	75	8.660	125	11.18	175	13.23
26	5.099	76	8.718	126	11.22	176	13.27
27	5.196	77	8.775	127	11.27	177	13.30
28	5.292	78	8.832	128	11.31	178	13.34
29	5.385	79	8.888	129	11.36	179	13.38
30	5.477	80	8.944	130	11.40	180	13.42
31	5.568	81	9.000	131	11.45	181	13.45
32	5.657	82	9.055	132	11.49	182	13.49
33	5.745	83	9.110	133	11.53	183	13.53
34	5.831	84	9.165	134	11.58	184	13.56
35	5.916	85	9.220	135	11.62	185	13.60
36	6.000	86	9.274	136	11.66	186	13.64
37	6.083	87	9.327	137	11.70	187	13.67
38	6.164	88	9.381	138	11.75	188	13.71
39	6.245	89	9.434	139	11.79	189	13.75
40	6.325	90	9.487	140	11.83	190	13.78
41	6.403	91	9.539	141	11.87	191	13.82
42	6.481	92	9.592	142	11.92	192	13.86
43	6.557	93	9.644	143	11.96	193	13.89
44	6.633	94	9.695	144	12.00	194	13.93
45	6.708	95	9.747	145	12.04	195	13.96
46	6.782	96	9.798	146	12.08	196	14.00
47	6.856	97	9.849	147	12.12	197	14.04
48	6.928	98	9.899	148	12.17	198	14.07
49	7.000	99	9.950	149	12.21	199	14.11
50	7.071	100	10.00	150	12.25	200	14.14

ANSWERS TO

ODD-NUMBERED PROBLEMS

Exercises 1.1 (page 4)

1. {January, February, March, April, May, June, July, August, September, October, November, December}
3. {pennies, dimes, quarters, half-dollars}
5. {Idaho, Iowa, Indiana, Illinois}
7. {Atlantic, Pacific, Indian, Antarctic}
11. {presidents since 1949} **13.** {five boroughs of New York City}
15. {three major automobile manufacturers in the U.S.}
17. {primary colors} **19.** {oceans on earth} **21.** True
23. True **25.** False **27.** False **29.** False **31.** False
33. Finite **35.** Infinite **37.** Infinite **39.** Finite **41.** Infinite
43. Finite **45.** $A \nsubseteq B$ **47.** $A \subset B$ **49.** $A \nsubseteq B$ **51.** $A \nsubseteq B$
53. $A = B$ **55.** $\varnothing, \{a\}$; 2 **57.** $\varnothing, \{1\}, \{2\}, \{3\}, \{1, 2,\} \{1, 3\}, \{2, 3\},$
$\{1, 2, 3\}$; 8 **59.** False **61.** True **63.** True; each element of $\{1, 2\}$ is also an element of $\{1, 2, 3, 4\}$ **65.** False; "2" is an element of $\{1, 2, 3, 4\}$ but not a subset, by definition.
67. False; "1" is an element, by definition.

Exercises 1.2 (page 10)

1. Yes **3.** No **5.** No **7.** Yes **9.** Yes **11.** 1, 4, 7, 9, and 10
13. True **15.** True **17.** False **19.** False **21.** False **23.** True
25. True **27.** (1) 12, (2) 7, (3) 4, (5) 4, (6) 0, (7) 4, (8) 2, (11) 4, (12) 3, (13) 5, (14) 5, (15) 3, (16) 6, (17) 3, (18) 3, (19) 4, (20) 3.

Exercises 1.3   (page 13)

1. 57   **3.** 5896   **5.** 32,000,002   **7.** 90,099   **9.** 53,020,000,308
11. Three hundred thirty-three   **13.** Fifty-five thousand seven hundred four
15. Seventy million eight thousand ninety   **17.** Fifty thousand eight   **19.** Two
21. A single symbol, /, is used to write all the numerals
23. Acts as a placeholder

Exercises 1.4   (page 15)

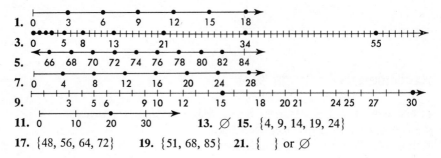

11. 0   10   20   30   **13.** ∅   **15.** {4, 9, 14, 19, 24}
17. {48, 56, 64, 72}   **19.** {51, 68, 85}   **21.** {   } or ∅

Exercises 1.5   (page 17)

1. False   **3.** True   **5.** False   **7.** True   **9.** False   **11.** True   **13.** True
15. False   **17.** {1743, 1734, 1473, 1437, 1374, 1347}
19. {1,000,000,001, 200,000,002, 30,000,003, 4,000,004, 500,005}
21. $A = \{3, 8, 13, 18, 23, 28, 33, 38, 43, 48\}$
$B = \{z, y, x, w, v, u, t, s, r, q, p, o, n, m\}$
The cardinality of B is greater than the cardinality of A

23. $A = \{7, 16, 25, 34, 43, 52, 61, 70\}$
$B = \{2, 4, 6, 8, 10, 12, 14, 16, 18, 20\}$
The cardinality of B is greater than the cardinality of A

25. $A = \{1, 4, 9, 16, 25, 36, 49, 64, 81, 100, 121, 144, 169, 196, 22\}$
$B = \{43, 44, 45, 46, 47, 48, 49, 50, 51, 52, 53, 54, 55, 56, 57\}$
The cardinality of B equals the cardinality of A

27. $8 > 7$ **29.** $3 = 3$
31. The cardinality of {natural numbers less than 6} = the cardinality of
{vowels in the alphabet}

Exercises 1.6 (page 21)

1. Not an open sentence **3.** Open sentence **5.** Not an open sentence
7. Not an open sentence **9.** Not an open sentence **11.** Not an open sentence
13. Not an open sentence **15.** Open sentence **17.** Not an open sentence
19. Open sentence **21.** True **23.** All the objects **25.** True **27.** False
29. True **31.** False **33.** False **35.** $\{n\colon 86 \leq n\} = \{86, 87, 88, \ldots\}$
37. True **39.** $\{m\colon m \leq 0\} = \{0\}$
41. $\{m\colon 7 < m\} = \{8, 9, 10, \ldots\}$

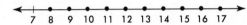

43. $\{t\colon t \not< 8\} = \{8, 9, 10, \ldots\}$

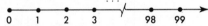

45. $\{z\colon z \not\geq 100\} = \{0, 1, 2, 3, \ldots, 99\}$

47. $\{m\colon m > 4 \text{ and } m < 13\} = \{5, 6, 7, 8, 9, 10, 11, 12\}$

49. $\{k\colon k < 6 \text{ and } 3 \leq k\} = \{3, 4, 5\}$

51. $\{z\colon 56 \leq z \text{ and } z \leq 64\} = \{56, 57, 58, \ldots, 64\}$

53. $\{d\colon 57 \leq d \text{ and } d \leq 48\} = \{\ \ \}$ **55.** $\{n\colon 0 < n \text{ and } n < 2\} = \{\ \ \}$

Exercises 1.7—Review (page 23)

1. Equivalent sets **3.** Empty set **5.** Name **7.** Is less than
9. All male math students in my class **11.** True **13.** True
15. False **17.** No **19.** Yes **21.** 0, 1, 2, 3, 4, 5, 6, 7, 8, 9
23. 8,258,003 **25.**
27. 1008 1009 1010 1011
29.
31. $3 \not< 2$ **33.** $41 \not\geq 45$ **35.** $\{n \in W\colon n < 20\}$
$\{$**37.** women students at UCLA$\}$ **39.** $\{$the doors of my house$\}$

Exercises 2.1   (page 27)

1. False   3. True   5. False   7. True   9. True
11. $\{1, 2, 4, 5, 6, 8, 9, 10\}$ 13. $\{$persons born since 1900$\}$
15. $\{$North and South American countries$\}$ 17. $\{a, e, i, o, u, m, n, p, q\}$
19. $\{$Norway, Denmark, Germany, Sweden, Finland$\}$
21. $U = N$

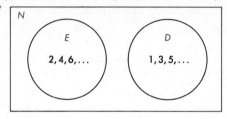

23. $U = \{1, 2, 3, 4, 5, \ldots, 10\}$

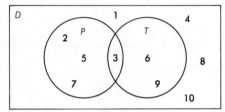

25. $U = \{n \in N : n \leq 60\}$

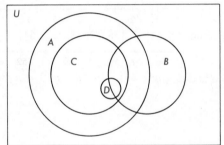

Exercises 2.2   (page 30)

1. $A \cup B = \{a, b, c, d, e, i, o, u\}$; $A \cap B = \{a, e\}$
3. $E \cup F = \{2, 4, 6, 8, 10, 12\}$; $E \cup F = \{4, 8, 12\}$
5. $K \cup L = \{3, 4, 6, 8, 9, 12, 15, 16, 18, 20, 21, 24, 27, 28, 30, 32, 33, 36, 39, 40\}$;
   $K \cap L = \{12, 24, 36\}$
7. $Q \cup R = \{3, 5, 6, 9, 10, 12, 15, 18, 21, 24, 25, 27, 30, 33, 35, 36, 39, 40,$
   $42, 45, 48, 50, 51, 54, 55, 57, 60\}$; $Q \cap R = \{15, 33, 45, 60\}$
9. (a) $A \cup B = \{$natural numbers 3 through 11$\}$; $A \cap B = \{$natural numbers
       5 through 8$\}$
   (b) $A \cup B = \{3, 4, 5, 6, 7, 8, 9, 10, 11\}$; $A \cap B = \{5, 6, 7, 8\}$

11. (a) $A \cup B = \{$whole numbers 0 through 24$\}$; $A \cap B = \varnothing$

(b) $A \cup B = \{0, 1, 2, 3, 4, \ldots, 24\}$; $A \cap B = \{\;\;\}$

13. (a) $U = \{$people in the assembly hall$\}$, $A = \{$democrats in the assembly hall$\}$, $B = \{$republicans in the assembly hall$\}$

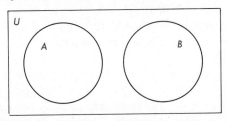

(b) $U = \{$students$\}$, $A = \{$students taking Spanish$\}$, $B = \{$students taking French$\}$, $C = \{$students taking German$\}$

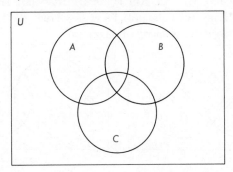

(c) $U = \{$students at the meeting$\}$, $A = \{$honor students at the meeting$\}$, $B = \{$student government members at the meeting$\}$, $C = \{$athletes at the meeting$\}$

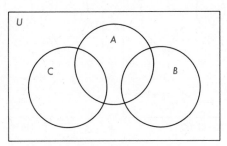

Exercises 2.3 (page 33)

1. $A \cup B = \{a, e, i, o, u\}$ and $B \cup A = \{a, e, i, o, u\}$
$A \cap B = \{a, e, i\}$ and $B \cap A = \{a, e, i\}$

3. $A \cup B = \{$natural numbers$\}$ and $B \cup A = \{$natural numbers$\}$
$A \cap B = \varnothing$ and $B \cap A = \varnothing$

5. $A \cup B = A$ and $B \cup A = A$; $A \cap B = \varnothing$ and $B \cap A = \varnothing$

7. $(A \cup B) \cup C = \{1, 2, 3, 4, 5, 6, 7\} \cup \{1, 3, 5, 7\} = \{1, 2, 3, 4, 5, 6, 7\}$
$A \cup (B \cup C) = \{1, 2, 3, 4, 5\} \cup \{1, 3, 4, 5, 6, 7\} = \{1, 2, 3, 4, 5, 6, 7\}$
$(A \cap B) \cap C = \{3, 4, 5\} \cap \{1, 3, 5, 7\} = \{3, 5\}$
$A \cap (B \cap C) = \{1, 2, 3, 4, 5\} \cap \{3, 5, 7\} = \{3, 5\}$

9. $(A \cup B) \cup C = W \cup C = W$; $A \cup (B \cup C) = N \cup W = W$
$(A \cap B) \cap C = N \cap \{n \in N: n$ is an odd number$\} = \{n \in N: n$ is an odd number$\}$
$A \cap (B \cap C) = N \cap \{n \in W: n$ is an odd number$\} = \{n \in N: n$ is an odd number$\}$

11. **(7)** $U = \{n \in N: n < 8\}$ **(8)** $\{$registered voters in Los Angeles$\}$
(9) $U = \{$whole numbers$\}$ **(10)** $U = \{$students at O.K. College$\}$

13. **(a)** True **(b)** False **(c)** False **(d)** True **(e)** True **(f)** False **(g)** True
(h) True **(i)** False **(j)** True **(k)** False **(l)** True **(m)** True

15. **(a)** True **(b)** True **(c)** False **(d)** False **(e)** True **(f)** True

17. True by the associative property of union

19.

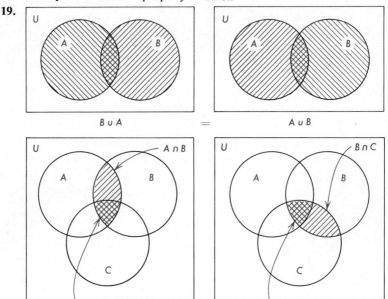

Exercises 2.4   (page 38)

1.

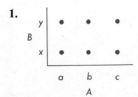

3. 6 **5.** 100 **7.** 90 **9.** False **11.** True **13.** False
15. True   **17.** True **19.** $A = B$ **21.** Infinite

Exercises 2.5—Review (page 40)

1. Universal set **3.** Disjoint **5.** Union **7.** B with A
9. Subset **11.** 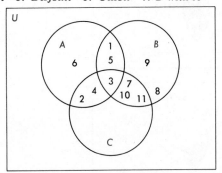 **13.** 1, 3, 5 **15.** 3

17. $U = \{0, 2, 3, 100, 101, 108, 250\}$
19. {Mississippi River, Missouri River, Lake Michigan, Lake Tahoe}
21. {9, 10, 11, 12, 13, 14, 15, 16} **23.** {9, 10, 14, 15}
25. (a)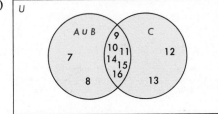

(b)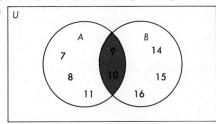

(c)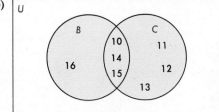

(d)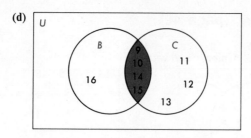

(e)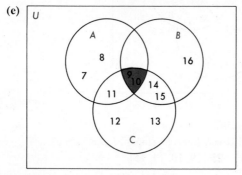

27. False: Let $A = \{1, 2, 3\}$ and $B = \{4, 5, 6\}$; $A \cup B = \{1, 2, 3, 4, 5\}$, which is not a subset of A **29.** True   **31.** True

33. $A \cap B = \{9, 10\}$ and $B \cap A = \{9, 10\}$

35. $(A \cap B) \cap C = \{9, 10\} \cap \{9, 10, 11, 12, 13, 14, 15\} = \{9, 10\}$; $A \cap (B \cup C) = \{7, 8, 9, 10, 11\} \cup \{9, 10, 14, 15\} = \{9, 10\}$

37. $A \cup (B \cup C) = \{7, 8, 9, 10, 11\} \cup \{9, 10, 11, 12, 13, 14, 15, 16\} = \{7, 8, 9, 10, 11, 12, 13, 14, 15, 16\}$; this set contains C

39. $A \cup (B \cap C) = \{7, 8, 9, 10, 11\} \cup \{9, 10, 14, 15\} = \{7, 8, 9, 10, 11, 14, 15\}$; $(A \cup B) \cap (A \cup C) = \{7, 8, 9, 10, 11, 14, 15, 16\} \cap \{7, 8, 9, 10, 11, 12, 13, 14, 15\} = \{7, 8, 9, 10, 11, 14, 15\}$

41. $\{(r, a), (r, b)\}$ **43.** $\{(r, w), (r, x), (r, y)\}$

45. $\{(a, r, w), (a, r, x), (a, r, y), (b, r, w), (b, r, x), (b, r, y)\}$

47. Yes   **49.** Yes   **51.** No

Exercises 3.1   (page 46)

1. Let $A = \{a, b, c\}$, $B = \{1, 2, 3, 4, 5, 6, 7\}$; $a + b = n(A \cup B)$; $3 + 7 = 10$

3. Let $A = \{\ \ \}$, $B = \{1, 2, 3, \ldots, 23\}$; $n(A) = 0$, $n(B) = 23$; $0 + 23 = 23$

5. Let $A = \{1, 2, 3, 4, 5, 6\}$, $B = \{a, b, c, d, e, f\}$; $n(A) = 6$, $n(B) = 6$; $n(A \cup B) = 12$; $6 + 6 = 12$

7. 6   **9.** 20   **11.** 9   **13.** 30   **15.** 34   **17.** 13   **19.** 39   **21.** 43   **23.** 34

25. 36   **27.** 43   **29.** 13;

```
            4                    9
     +--+--+--+--+--+--+--+--+--+--+--+--+--+--+>
     0     2     4     6     8    10    12    14
```

31. 11;

```
                8           3
     +--+--+--+--+--+--+--+--+--+--+--+>
     0     2     4     6     8    10    12
```

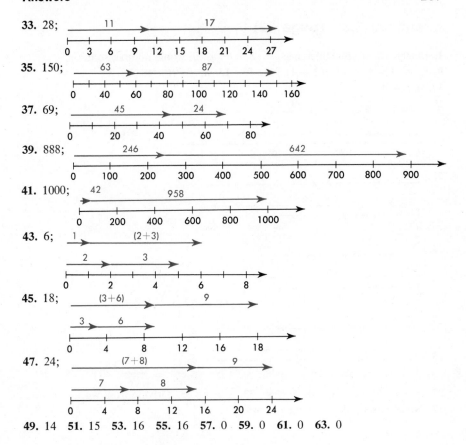

33. 28;

35. 150;

37. 69;

39. 888;

41. 1000;

43. 6;

45. 18;

47. 24;

49. 14   **51.** 15   **53.** 16   **55.** 16   **57.** 0   **59.** 0   **61.** 0   **63.** 0

Exercises 3.2   (page 48)

1. Commutative property   **3.** Associative property
5. Identity property; $0 + 0 = n(\varnothing) + n(\varnothing) = n(\varnothing \cup \varnothing) = n(\varnothing) = 0$
7. Commutative property   **9.** Identity property; $687 + 0 = n(A) + n(\varnothing) =$
$n(A \cup \varnothing) = n(A) = 687$ **11.** Identity property   **13.** Associative property
15. Commutative property   **17.** True   **19.** True

21.

+	0	1	2	3	4	5	6	7	8	9
0	0	1	2	3	4	5	6	7	8	9
1	1	2	3	4	5	6	7	8	9	10
2	2	3	4	5	6	7	8	9	10	11
3	3	4	5	6	7	8	9	10	11	12
4	4	5	6	7	8	9	10	11	12	13
5	5	6	7	8	9	10	11	12	13	14
6	6	7	8	9	10	11	12	13	14	15
7	7	8	9	10	11	12	13	14	15	16
8	8	9	10	11	12	13	14	15	16	17
9	9	10	11	12	13	14	15	16	17	18

23. Identity property   **25.** 0   **27.** $k, k \in W$ **29.** Associative, commutative,
and identity properties   **31.** Commutative property   **33.** Commutative and identity
properties   **35.** Associative and commutative properties   **37.** Closed   **39.** Closed
41. Closed   **43.** Not closed   **45.** $((3 + 4) + (7 + 8)) + ((14 + 6) + 5)$

Exercises 3.3 (page 52)

1. Binary **3.** 0 **5.** Difference **7.** $2 - 6$ has no whole number solution
9. $(7 - 2) - 1 \neq 7 - (2 - 1)$ **11.** 13 **13.** $a, a \in W$ **15.** 23
17. $a, a \in W$
19.

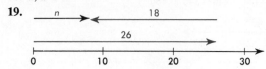

21.

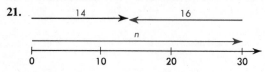

23.

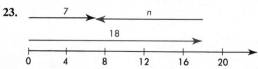

25.

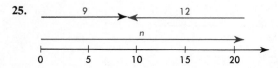

27. $x > y$ **29.** $x = y$ **31.** $x < y$ **33.** $x > y$ **35.** Driving from work
37. None exists **39.** Untying a knot

Exercises 3.4 (page 54)

1. $26 + 12 = (20 + 6) + (10 + 2)$ [renaming]
          $= (20 + 10) + (6 + 2)$ [regrouping]
          $= 30 + 8$ [addition facts]
          $= 38$ [renaming]
3. $268 + 31 = (200 + 60 + 8) + (30 + 1)$ [renaming]
          $= 200 + (60 + 30) + (8 + 1)$ [regrouping]
          $= 200 + 90 + 9$ [addition facts]
          $= 299$ [renaming]
5. 42 **7.** 240 **9.** 10096 **11.** The sum of two even numbers is an even number

16	376	7758
58	616	17854

13. {62} **15.** {12,904} **17.** {66,666} **19.** {25} **21.** {235} **23.** {3441}
25. The sum of an odd number and an even number is an odd number
27. {220} **29.** {58,440}

31. The sums are all in the set; addition in this set is closed
33. 196   **35.** 2203   **37.** 157,490   **39.** 1,489,960

Exercises 3.5   (page 57)

1. $78 - 26 = (70 + 8) - (20 + 6)$
$= (70 - 20) + (8 - 6)$
$= 50 + 2$
$= 52$

3. $671 - 468 = (600 + 70 + 1) - (400 + 60 + 8)$
$= (600 - 400) + (70 - 60) + (1 - 8)$
$= (600 - 400) + (60 - 60) + (11 - 8)$
$= 200 + 0 + 3$
$= 203$

5. $2004 - 625 = (2000 + 4) - (600 + 20 + 5)$
$= 1000 + (1000 - 600) + (0 - 20) + (4 - 5)$
$= 1000 + (900 - 600) + (100 - 20) + (4 - 5)$
$= 1000 + (900 - 600) + (90 - 20) + (14 - 5)$
$= 1000 + 300 + 70 + 9$
$= 1379$

7. $\{41\}$ **9.** $\{187\}$ **11.** $\{6747\}$ **13.** $\{110,477\}$

15.

—	0	1	2	3	4	5	6	7	8	9
0	0	*	*	*	*	*	*	*	*	*
1	1	0	*	*	*	*	*	*	*	*
2	2	1	0	*	*	*	*	*	*	*
3	3	2	1	0	*	*	*	*	*	*
4	4	3	2	1	0	*	*	*	*	*
5	5	4	3	2	1	0	*	*	*	*
6	6	5	4	3	2	1	0	*	*	*
7	7	6	5	4	3	2	1	0	*	*
8	8	7	6	5	4	3	2	1	0	*
9	9	8	7	6	5	4	3	2	1	0

17. **(a)** The difference between two even numbers is an even number. Let a = even number greater than b. Let b = even number. $a - b = c$; c must be an even number because $c + b$ must equal a, which is even.

(b) The difference between two odd numbers is an even number. Let a = odd number greater than b. Let b = odd number. $a - b = c$; c must be an even number because $b + c$ must equal a, an odd number.

(c) The difference between an odd number and an even number is an odd number. Let a = even number greater than b. Let b = odd number. If $a - b = c$, c must be an odd number because the sum of $b + c$ must be an even number. Let d = odd number greater than e. Let e = even number. If $d - e = g$, then f must be an odd number because $e + f$ must equal d, an odd number.

19. $\{38\}$ **21.** $\{4562\}$ **23.** Yes; $\{1168\}$

Exercises 3.6   (page 63)

1. Let $A = \{1, 2\}$ and $B = \{a, b, c, d, e, f, g, h\}$, $n(A \times B) = 16$; hence $2 \cdot 8 = 16$

3. Let $A = \{1, 2, 3, \ldots, 9\}$ and $B = \{a, b, c, \ldots, f\}$, $n(A \times B) = 54$; hence $9 \cdot 6 = 54$

5. Commutative property: Let $n(A) = 4$ and $n(B) = 3$;
$4 \cdot 3 = n(A) \cdot n(B) = n(A \times B) = n(B \times A) = n(B) \cdot n(A) = 3 \cdot 4$

7. Associative property: Let $n(A) = 3$, $n(B) = 7$, $n(C) = 2$; $(3 \cdot 7) \cdot 2 = n(A \times B) \cdot n(C) = n[(A \times B) \times C] = n[A \times (B \times C)] = n(A) \cdot n(B \times C) = 3 \cdot (7 \cdot 2)$

9. Identity property; see 13 for verification

11. Commutative property; see 5 for verification

13. Identity property: Let $n(A) = 63$, $n(B) = 1$; $63 \cdot 1 = n(A) \cdot n(B) = n(A \times B) = n(A) = 63$

15. Identity property; see 13 for verification

17. Distributive property; Let $n(A) = 1$, $n(B) = 12$, and $n(C) = 6$;
$1 \cdot (12 + 6) = n(A) \cdot [n(B) + n(C)] = n(A) \cdot n(B \cup C) = n[A \times (B \cup C)] = n[(A \times B) \cup (A \times C)] = n(A \times B) + n(A \times C) = n(A) \cdot n(B) + n(A) \cdot n(C) = 1 \cdot 12 + 1 \cdot 6$

19. Distributive property; see 17 for verification   **21.** True   **23.** True

27. They are the same; commutative property   **29.** Yes, the identity property

31. Zero-factor property   **33.** Commutative property   **35.** Distributive property

37. Distributive property

Exercises 3.7   (page 67)

1. 1   **3.** Binary   **5.** Quotient   **7.** False   **9.** False   **11.** 56   **13.** 28

15. 42   **17.** $a, a \in N$ **19.** Division by 0 is undefined, $\varnothing$

21. $n \cdot 209 = 836$; $\{4\}$ **23.** $n \cdot 500 = 5000$; $\{10\}$ **25.** $n \cdot 115 = 345$; $\{3\}$

27. $n \cdot 10 = 0$; $\{0\}$ **29.** Division by 0 is undefined, $\varnothing$

Exercises 3.8   (page 69)

1. $22 \cdot 5 = (20 + 2) \cdot (5)$ [renaming]
$\qquad = (20) \cdot 5 + (2) \cdot 5$ [distributive property]
$\qquad = 100 + 10$ [multiplication facts]
$\qquad = 110$ [renaming]

3. $145 \cdot 68 = (100 + 40 + 5) \cdot (60 + 8)$ [renaming]

$= (100 + 40 + 5) \cdot 60 + (100 + 40 + 5) \cdot 8$ [distributive property]

$= 6000 + 2400 + 300 + 800 + 320 + 40$ [multiplication facts]

$= (6000+2000)+(400+300+300+800)+(20+40)$ [renaming, regrouping]

$= 8000 + 1800 + 60$ [addition facts]

$= (8000 + 1000) + 800 + 60$ [renaming, regrouping]

$= 9860$ [renaming]

5. 2226   **7.** 28,392   **9.** 1,400,976   **11.** $\{60\}$

13. $\{6000\}$ **15.** $\{2300\}$ **17.** $\{580\}$ **19.** $\{764,000\}$

21. The place value of a natural number multiplied by 10, 100, 1000, etc., is changed by adding one, two, three, etc., zeros to it.

23. $\{52\}$ **25.** $\{332\}$ **27.** $\{12,298\}$ **29.** $\{16,990,104\}$ **31.** $\{6666\}$

33. $\{20\}$ **35.** $\{105\}$ **37.** $\{410\}$ **39.** $\{107,750\}$

41. Multiplication of a natural number by 5 results in a natural number product whose ones digit is 5 or 0

43. $\{55\}$ **45.** $\{5871\}$ **47.** $\{4,380,923\}$

49. (a)

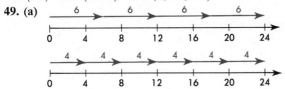

(b)

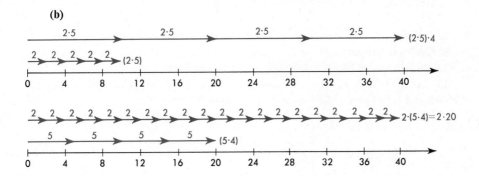

51. $8 \cdot (146) = 8 \cdot (100 + 40 + 6) = 8(100) + 8(40) + 8(6)$

53. Closed   **55.** Closed   **57.** Not closed

Exercises 3.9   (page 73)

1. $288 = 12 \cdot n$
$\quad 20 < n < 30$
$\quad$ Let $n = a \cdot 10 + b$
$\quad (20 + b) \cdot 12 = 288$
$\quad\quad 240 + 12b = 288$
$\quad\quad\quad 12b = 48$
$\quad\quad\quad\quad b = 4$
$\quad\quad\quad\quad n = 24$

3. $196 = 14 \cdot n$
$\quad 10 > n > 20$
$\quad$ Let $n = a \cdot 10 + b$
$\quad (10 + b) \cdot 14 = 196$
$\quad\quad 140 + 14b = 196$
$\quad\quad\quad 14b = 56$
$\quad\quad\quad\quad b = 4$
$\quad\quad\quad\quad n = 14$

5. $\{6\}$ **7.** Division cannot be performed, $\varnothing$ **9.** $\{216\}$
11. Division cannot be performed, $\varnothing$ **13.** Division cannot be performed, $\varnothing$
15. Only natural numbers whose ones place is 0 can be divided by 10; only natural numbers whose ones place is 0 or 5 can be divided by 5
17. $\{5\}$ **19.** $\{13\}$ **21.** $\{11\}$ **23.** $\{113\}$
25. Division of two odd numbers gives an odd quotient
27. Division cannot be performed, $\varnothing$ **29.** Division cannot be performed, $\varnothing$
31. $28 \div 4 = 7$ **33.** $\{12\}$ **35.** $\{14\}$ **37.** $\{103\}$ **39.** $\{9\}$ **41.** $\{38\}$

Exercises 3.10   (page 78)

1. \$219   **3.** \$208   **5.** 27   **7.** $P = 120$; $A = 864$ **9.** 114 mph
11. Station wagon—14 miles; coupe—21 miles.   **13.** \$335 gain   **15.** \$248

Exercises 3.11—Review   (page 81)

1. Disjoint   **3.** Associative property   **5.** Inverse   **7.** Not closed
9. Cartesian product   **11.** $n(A)$
13. A plan, or set of rules, for performing an operation
15. Let $A = \{a, b, c\}$, $n(A) = 3$, and $B = \{1, 2, 3, 4, 5, 6\}$, $n(B) = 6$;
then $n(A \cup B) = 3 + 6$, $n(A \cup B) = 9$, hence $9 = 3 + 6$

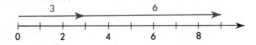

17. Let $A = \{a, e, i, o, u\}$, $B = \{1, 2, 3, \ldots, 7\}$; then
$n(A) = 5$, $n(B) = 7$, $n(A \cup B) = 12$, hence $5 + 7 = 12$

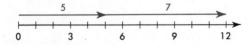

19. Let $A = \{a, b, c, d, e, f, g\}$, $B = \{1\}$; then
$n(A) = 7$, $n(B) = 1$, $n(A \times B) = 7$, hence $7 \cdot 1 = 7$

$$B \quad 1 \quad \bullet \ \bullet \ \bullet \ \bullet \ \bullet \ \bullet \ \bullet$$
$$a \ b \ c \ d \ e \ f \ g$$
$$A$$

21. Let $A = \{1, 2, 3, 4\}$, $n(A) = 4$, $B = \{a, b, c, d, e, f, g\}$, $n(B) = 6$;
then $n(A \times B) = 24$, hence $4 \cdot 6 = 24$

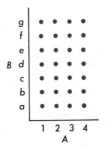

23. $n \cdot 4 = 8$; $\{2\}$ **25.** $n \cdot 9 = 9$; $\{1\}$ **27.** $n + 56 = 108$; $\{52\}$
29. Division by 0 is undefined
31. $68 + 46 = (60 + 8) + (40 + 6)$ [renaming]
          $= (60 + 40) + (8 + 6)$ [regrouping]
          $= 100 + 14$ [addition facts]
          $= 114$ [renaming]
33. $108 \cdot 25 = (100 + 8) \cdot (20 + 5)$ [renaming]
          $= (100 + 8) \cdot 20 + (100 + 8) \cdot 5$ [distributive property]
          $= 2000 + 160 + 500 + 40$ [multiplication facts]
          $= 2000 + (100 + 500) + (60 + 40)$ [renaming and regrouping]
          $= 2000 + 600 + 100$ [addition facts]
          $= 2000 + (600 + 100)$ [associative property]
          $= 2700$ [addition fact and renaming]
35. Commutative property of addition   **37.** Distributive property
39. Identity property of multiplication

Exercises 4.1   (page 85)

1. Whole numbers, opposites   **3.** Less than   **5.** Less than   **7.** $^-6$ **9.** $1 > ^-1$
11. $^-15 < ^-11$ **13.** $3 > ^-3$ **15.** $^-926 > ^-1005$ **17.** $^-(5 + 4) < 0$
19.

$$\leftarrow\!\!+\!\!-\!\!\bullet\!\!-\!\!+\!\!-\!\!\bullet\!\!-\!\!+\!\!-\!\!+\!\!\rightarrow$$
$$^-5 \quad ^-4 \quad ^-3 \quad ^-2 \quad ^-1 \quad 0$$

21.

$$\leftarrow\!\!\bullet\!\!-\!\!+\!\!-\!\!\bullet\!\!-\!\!+\!\!-\!\!\bullet\!\!-\!\!+\!\!-\!\!\bullet\!\!-\!\!+\!\!\rightarrow$$
$$^-6 \quad ^-4 \quad ^-2 \quad 0 \quad 2 \quad 4 \quad 6 \quad 8$$

23.

$$\leftarrow\!\!\bullet\!\!+\!\!\bullet\!\!+\!\!+\!\!\bullet\!\!+\!\!+\!\!+\!\!\bullet\!\!+\!\!+\!\!+\!\!\bullet\!\!+\!\!+\!\!\bullet\!\!\rightarrow$$
$$^-12 \ ^-10 \ ^-8 \ ^-6 \ ^-4 \ ^-2 \ 0 \ 2 \ 4 \ 6 \ 8$$

25.

$$^-1057 \qquad\qquad\qquad 896 \quad 904$$
$$\leftarrow\!\!\bullet\!\!+\!\!-\!\!+\!\!-\!\!+\!\!-\!\!+\!\!-\!\!\bullet\!\!\bullet\!\!\rightarrow$$
$$^-1000 \quad ^-500 \quad 0 \quad 500 \quad 1000$$

27. $\{n \in J: n < ^-6\}$ **29.** $\{n \in J: n \leq 0\}$

31. {⁻11, ⁻10, ⁻9}   **33.** |⁻3| > 2   **35.** 5 < |10| **37.** |⁻4| = |4|
39. |⁻12| = |12| **41.** 7 = |7| **43.** U = {set of integers}

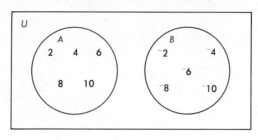

Exercises 4.2   (page 90)

1.

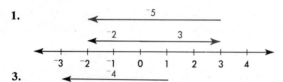

3.

5.

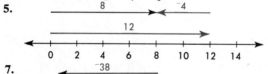

7.

9.

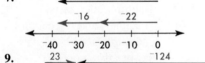

11. ⁻38 + 15 = ⁻(|⁻38| − |15|)   **13.** 286 + (⁻16) = (|286| − |⁻16|)
          = ⁻(38 − 15)   = (286 − 16)
          = ⁻(23)   = 270
          = ⁻23

15. ⁻36 + ⁻28   **17.** ⁻965 + 2804   **19.** ⁻4821 + 3765
     = ⁻(|36| + |28|)   = |2804| − |⁻965| = ⁻(|⁻4821| − |3765|)
     = ⁻(64)   = (2804 − 965)   = ⁻(1056)
     = ⁻64   = 1839   = 1056

23.

25.

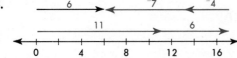

27.

29. $5 + {}^-7 + 2$
$= (5 + {}^-7) + 2$
$= {}^-(|{}^-7| - |5|) + 2$
$= {}^-(2) + 2$
$= 0$

31. ${}^-8 + {}^-5 + 3 + {}^-3$
$= ({}^-8 + {}^-5) + (3 + {}^-3)$
$= {}^-(|{}^-8| + |{}^-5|) + 0$
$= {}^-(13) + 0$
$= {}^-13$

33. $\{{}^-368\}$ **35.** $\{{}^-375\}$ **37.** $\{{}^-2281\}$ **39.** $\{{}^-6\}$ **41.** $\{{}^-526\}$ **43.** \$512
45. Yes; if $a \in W$, ${}^-a$ may be interpreted as "subtract a"; ${}^-a$ is often written $-a$.

Exercises 4.3 (page 94)

1. $\{{}^-7\}$ **3.** $\{80\}$ **5.** $\{{}^-28\}$ **7.** $8 - {}^-12 =$ **9.** ${}^-46 - 29 =$
                          $8 + 12 = 20$ ${}^-46 + {}^-29 = {}^-75$
11. ${}^-456$ **13.** ${}^-15,777$ **15.** ${}^-116,730$ **17.** ${}^-106$ **19.** 106
21. 45 **23.** 3 **25.**

27.   **31.** 402 **33.** ${}^-166$ **35.** $37,651$ **37.** 126

Exercises 4.4 (page 99)

1. Rule I: The product of a positive integer and a negative integer is a negative
integer; Rule II: The product of two negative integers is a positive integer
3. $\{70\}$ **5.** $\{35,483\}$ **7.** $\{152\}$ **9.** $\{186\}$ **11.** $\{11682\}$ **13.** 1200
15. ${}^-2079$ **17.** 16 **19.** 666
21. It changes the signs inside the grouping symbols to their opposites.
23. ${}^-1096$ ft
25. (a) ${}^-3 \cdot 4 = {}^-3 + {}^-3 + {}^-3 + {}^-3 = {}^-12$
    (b) $4 \cdot {}^-3 = {}^-3 \cdot 4$; therefore, by (a), $4({}^-3) = 12$ (c) Rule I
27. ${}^-9$ **29.** ${}^-7$ **31.** ${}^-19$

Exercises 4.5 (page 102)

1. Rule I: If a division involving a positive integer and a negative integer can be performed, the quotient is always a negative integer; Rule II: If a division involving two negative integers can be performed, the quotient is always a positive integer **3.** $\{^-16\}$ **5.** $\{^-28\}$ **7.** No integral solution **9.** No integral solution **11.** No integral solution **13.** $\{30\}$ **19.** 8 o'clock, $^-38°$

Exercises 4.6—Review (page 104)

1. Absolute value **3.** Greater **5.** Whole numbers **7.** An addition problem **9.** Division **11.** False **13.** True **15.** False **17.** False **19.** False **21.** False **23.** False **25.** False **27.** True **29.** False **31.** $^-91$ **33.** 60 **35.** $^-924$ **37.** $^-11$ **39.** $^-16$ **41.** Commutative property of addition **43.** Associative property of addition **45.** Identity property of multiplication

Exercises 5.1 (page 110)

1. $3 \cdot 3 \cdot 3 \cdot 3$ **3.** $(^-17) \cdot (^-17) \cdot (^-17)$ **5.** $19 \cdot 19$ **7.** $9 \cdot 9 \cdot 9 \cdot 9 \cdot 9 \cdot 9 \cdot 9 \cdot 9 \cdot 9$ **9.** $3 \cdot 3 \cdot 4 \cdot 4 \cdot 5 \cdot 5$ **11.** $3 \cdot 3 \cdot 3 \cdot 3 \cdot 3 \cdot 3 \cdot 2 \cdot 2 \cdot 5 \cdot 5 \cdot 5$ **13.** 3^6 **15.** 23^5 **17.** $3^2 \cdot 4^3 \cdot 5^5$ **19.** $2^2 \cdot 3^3 \cdot 4^4 \cdot 5^2$ **21.** $7^3 \cdot 9^5$ **23.** $3^3 \cdot 5^5 \cdot 7^5$ **25.** $2^7 \cdot 3^3$ **27.** $5^7 \cdot 7^5$ **29.** 3^4 **31.** $5^3 \cdot 7$ **33.** 9 **35.** $2^9 \cdot 3^{12}$ **37.** $3^{72} \cdot 5^{90}$ **39.** 9 **41.** 144 **43.** 225 **45.** 361 **47.** 225 **49.** 16 **51.** $(a + b)^2$ **53.** 11 **55.** There is none **57.** $^-4$ **59.** $^-14$ **61.** $^-12$ **63.** $a + b$ **65.** $a - b$ **67.** $^-729$ **69.** 216 **71.** $21a^3$ **73.** $^-4$ **75.** 6 **77.** $7a^2b$ **79.** True **81.** False **83.** False **85.** $16, $512, $526,848, $539,492,352

Exercises 5.2 page 113)

1. 2 **3.** 4 **5.** 5 **7.** 4 **9.** 8 **11.** 6 **13.** 4 **15.** 9 **17.** 4 **19.** 5, 23, 31, 47 **21.** 2, 3, 5, 7, 11, 13, 17, 19, 23, 29, 31, 37, 41, 43, 47, 53, 59, 61, 67, 71, 73, 79, 83, 89, 97, 101, 103, 107, 109, 111, 113, 119, 127, 131, 133, 137, 139, 141, 143, 149, 151, 157, 161, 163, 167, 173, 179, 181, 183, 187, 191, 193, 197, 199, 201, 203, 207, 209, 211, 221, 223, 227, 229, 233, 239, 241, 247 **23.** 29; see answer for problem 21. **25.** Yes **27.** Yes, 1 **29.** Yes **31.** (1; 1), (4; 1, 2, 4), (9; 1, 3, 9), (16; 1, 2, 4, 16), (25; 1, 5, 25), (36; 1, 2, 3, 4, 6, 9, 12, 36), (49; 1, 7, 49), (64; 1, 2, 4, 8, 16, 32, 64), (81; 1, 3, 9, 27, 81), (100; 1, 2, 4, 5, 10, 20, 25, 50, 100)

Exercises 5.3 (page 115)

1. (a) $\{1, 2, 4\}$ (b) 2^2 **3.** (a) $\{1, 2, 4, 8\}$ (b) 2^3 **5.** (a) $\{1, 2, 5, 10\}$
(b) $2 \cdot 5$ **7.** (a) $\{1, 2, 7, 14\}$ (b) $2 \cdot 7$ **9.** (a) $\{1, 2, 4, 16\}$ (b) 2^4
11. (a) $\{1, 2, 4, 5, 10, 20\}$ (b) $2^2 \cdot 5$ **13.** (a) $\{1, 2, 11, 22\}$ (b) $2 \cdot 11$
15. (a) $\{1, 5, 25\}$ (b) 5^2 **17.** (a) $\{1, 3, 9, 27\}$ (b) 3^3
19. (a) $\{1, 2, 4, 6, 10, 15, 30\}$ (b) $2 \cdot 3 \cdot 5$
21. (a) $\{1, 2, 3, 4, 6, 12, 18, 24, 36, 72\}$ (b) $2^3 \cdot 3^2$
23. (a) $\{1, 2, 3, 4, 6, 8, 12, 16, 24, 32, 48, 96\}$ (b) $2^5 \cdot 3$
25. (a) $\{1, 2, 4, 19, 38, 76\}$ (b) $2^2 \cdot 19$ **27.** (a) $\{1, 3, 9, 27, 81\}$ (b) 3^4
29. (a) $\{1, 5, 17, 85\}$ (b) $5 \cdot 17$ **31.** $\{1, 3, 5, 9, 15, 27, 45, 135\}$
33. $\{1, 2, 3, 5, 9, 15, 25, 30, 45, 50, 75, 90, 150, 250, 450, 750, 1125, 2250\}$
35. $\{1, 2, 3, 6, 9, 18, 27, 54, 81, 162\}$ **37.** $2^4, 7^2, 2^2 \cdot 5^2, 11^2, 2^4 \cdot 3^2$
39. $2^6, 7^3, 2^3 \cdot 5^3, 11^3, 2^6 \cdot 3^3$; the factors of a whole number are cubed when
the number is cubed.

Exercises 5.4 (page 117)

1. 2^5 **3.** $2 \cdot 17$ **5.** $2^2 \cdot 3^2$ **7.** $3 \cdot 13$ **9.** $2 \cdot 3 \cdot 7$ **11.** $3^2 \cdot 5$
13. $2^4 \cdot 3$ **15.** $2 \cdot 5^2$ **17.** $2^2 \cdot 13$ **19.** $5 \cdot 11$ **21.** $3 \cdot 19$ **23.** $2^2 \cdot 3 \cdot 5$
25. $2^4 \cdot 3 \cdot 13$ **27.** 2^{10} **29.** 2^8 **31.** $19 \cdot 67$ **33.** $2^3 \cdot 5 \cdot 117$
35. $3^3 \cdot 7 \cdot 11 \cdot 13 \cdot 37$ **37.** $^-1 \cdot 2 \cdot 5$ **39.** $^-1 \cdot 2^3 \cdot 3^2$ **41.** $^-1 \cdot 11^2$
43. $^-1 \cdot 5 \cdot 13$ **45.** $\{^-10, ^-5, ^-2, ^-1, 1, 2, 5, 10\}$
47. $\{^-36, ^-18, ^-9, ^-6, ^-4, ^-3, ^-2, ^-1, 1, 2, 3, 4, 6, 9, 18, 36\}$
49. $\{^-60, ^-30, ^-20, ^-15, ^-12, ^-10, ^-6, ^-5, ^-4, ^-3, ^-2, ^-1, 1, 2, 3, 4, 5, 6, 10, 12,$
$15, 20, 30, 60\}$
51. $\{^-80, ^-40, ^-20, ^-16, ^-10, ^-8, ^-5, ^-4, ^-2, ^-1, 1, 2, 4, 5, 8, 10, 16, 20, 40, 80\}$

Exercises 5.5 (page 120)

1. Multiples **3.** Factors **5.** Factor **7.** 9: (a) $\{9, 18, 27, 36, \ldots\}$, (b) $\{1, 3, 9\}$;
12: (a) $\{12, 24, 36, \ldots\}$ (b) $\{1, 2, 3, 4, 6, 12\}$ (c) $\{36, 72, \ldots\}$ (d) $\{1, 3\}$
(e) 36 (f) 3
9. 12: (a) $\{12, 24, 36, 48, \ldots\}$, (b) $\{1, 2, 3, 4, 6, 12\}$; 16: (a) $\{16, 32, 48, \ldots\}$
(b) $\{1, 2, 4, 8, 16\}$ (c) $\{48, 96, \ldots\}$ (d) $\{1, 2, 4\}$ (e) 48 (f) 4
11. 16: (a) $\{16, 32, 48, \ldots\}$ (b) $\{1, 2, 4, 8, 16\}$; 36: (a) $\{36, 72, 108, \ldots\}$
(b) $\{1, 2, 3, 4, 6, 9, 12, 18, 36\}$ (c) $\{144, 288, \ldots\}$ (d) 1, 2, 4 (e) 144 (f) 4
13. 36: (a) $\{36, 72, 108, \ldots\}$, (b) $\{1, 2, 3, 4, 6, 9, 12, 18, 36\}$;
48: (a) $\{48, 96, 144, \ldots\}$, (b) $\{1, 2, 3, 4, 6, 12, 16, 24, 48\}$,
(c) $\{144, 288, 432, \ldots\}$, (d) $\{1, 2, 3, 4, 6, 12\}$, (e) 144, (f) 12

15. 64: **(a)** {64, 128, 192, ...}, **(b)** {1, 2, 4, 8, 16, 32, 64};
144: **(a)** {144, 288, 432, ...}, **(b)** {1, 2, 3, 4, 6, 8, 9, 12, 16, 18, 24, 36, 48, 72, 144},
(c) {576, 1152, ...}, **(d)** {1, 2, 4, 8, 16}, **(e)** 576, **(f)** 16
17. 72: **(a)** {72, 144, 216, ...}, **(b)** {1, 2, 3, 4, 6, 8, 9, 12, 18, 24, 36, 72};
156: **(a)** {156, 312, 468, ...}, **(b)** {1, 2, 3, 4, 6, 12, 13, 16, 39, 52, 78, 156},
(c) {936, 1872, ...}, **(d)** {1, 2, 3, 4, 6, 12}, **(e)** 936, **(f)** 12
19. 100: **(a)** {100, 200, 300, ...}, **(b)** {1, 2, 4, 5, 10, 20, 25, 50, 100};
250: **(a)** {250, 500, 750, ...}, **(b)** {1, 2, 5, 10, 25, 125, 250},
(c) {500, 1000, 1500, ...}, **(d)** {1, 2, 5, 10, 25}, **(e)** 500, **(f)** 25
21. 37: **(a)** {37, 74, 111, ...}, **(b)** {1, 37}; 39: **(a)** {39, 78, 117, ...},
(b) {1, 3, 13, 39}, **(c)** {4329, 8658, ...}, **(d)** {1}, **(e)** 4329, **(f)** 1
23. 576 • 16 = 64 • 144   **25.** 336 • 12 = 48 • 84
           9216 = 9216   4032 = 4032

Exercises 5.6   (page 121)

1. 5^3 **3.** Square   **5.** A composite number
7. Every whole number can be renamed in a unique way as a product of primes.
9. Least common multiple   **11.** $^-2$ • $^-2$ • $^-2$ • $^-2$ • $^-2$
13. 3 • 3 • 3 • 3 • $^-5$ • $^-5$ • $^-5$ • 7 • 7   **15.** $(^-6)^2$ • 8^4 • 3
17. **(11)** $^-32$, **(12)** 1125, **(13)** $^-506$, 125   **21.** Composite   **23.** Prime
25. Composite   **27.** $^-1$ • 17   **29.** $^-1$ • 5 • 7^2 **31.** 60, 1   **33.** 900, 15

Exercises 6.1   (page 127)

1. Commutative property of addition   **3.** Closure property of addition

5. $\dfrac{a}{b} \cdot b = a$ **7.** Distributive property for multiplication over addition

9. $\dfrac{a}{b} \cdot b = a$ **11.** Definition of subtraction

13. $p + (s + t) = (p + s) + t$ **15.** Identity property of multiplication
17. Commutative property of addition   **19.** Definition of subtraction
21. Distributive property for multiplication over addition

23. Identity property of addition   **25.** $\dfrac{a}{b} = a \cdot \dfrac{1}{b}$ **27.** $\dfrac{a}{b} = a \cdot \dfrac{1}{b}$

29. $a \cdot \dfrac{1}{b} = \dfrac{a}{b}$ **31.** Division property   **33.** True   **35.** True   **37.** False

39. True   **41.** 8   **43.** 5   **45.** 7   **47.** $1 \cdot \dfrac{1}{5}$ **49.** $28 \cdot \dfrac{1}{3}$

Exercises 6.2 (page 132)

1. True **3.** False **5.** False **7.** True **9.** False **11.** False **13.** True
15. True **17.** True **19.** False **21.** $\dfrac{5}{9}$ **23.** $\dfrac{4}{9}$ **25.** $\dfrac{-2}{3}$ **27.** $\dfrac{-2}{5}$ **29.** $\dfrac{4}{-3}$

31. $\dfrac{2}{-3}$ **33.** $\dfrac{-2}{-3}$ **35.** $\dfrac{-1}{-2}$ **37.** 9 **39.** 2 **41.** 9 **43.** $^-12$ **45.** $^-40$ **47.** 1

49. $\dfrac{-6}{7}$ **51.** Fraction **53.** Denominator **55.** $\dfrac{a}{b}$ **57. (a)** $\dfrac{r}{s} = \dfrac{rt}{st}$

(b) $\dfrac{a}{b} \cdot b = a$ **(c)** $\dfrac{a}{1} = a$

Exercises 6.3 (page 138)

1. $\dfrac{a}{c} + \dfrac{b}{c} = \dfrac{a+b}{c}$ **3.** $\dfrac{a}{b} = \dfrac{a \cdot c}{b \cdot c}$ **5.** $\dfrac{^-\left(\dfrac{a}{b}\right)} = \dfrac{a}{-b}$

7. $\dfrac{a}{b} = \dfrac{a \cdot c}{b \cdot c}$ **9.** $^-\left(\dfrac{2}{3}\right) = \dfrac{-2}{3}$ **11.** $\dfrac{8}{7}$ **13.** $\dfrac{1}{1}$ **15.** $\dfrac{3}{110}$ **17.** $\dfrac{31}{35}$ **19.** $\dfrac{4}{21}$

21. $\dfrac{15}{56}$ **23.** $\dfrac{-1}{12}$ **25.** $\dfrac{9}{20}$ **27.** $\dfrac{27}{56}$ **29.** $\dfrac{89}{36}$ **31.** $\dfrac{123}{1000}$ **33.** $\dfrac{1}{1}$ **35.** $\dfrac{177}{500}$ **37.** $\dfrac{111}{100}$

39. $\dfrac{447}{1000}$ **41.** True **43.** False **45.** True **47.** True **49.** True **51.** $\{16\}$

53. $\{6\}$ **55.** $\{4\}$ **57.** $\{^-30\}$ **59.** $\{10\}$ **61.** $40\dfrac{5}{12}$ yards **63.** $40\dfrac{5}{12}$ yards

65. $33\dfrac{5}{6}$ yards **67.** 1 inch **69.** 106 feet; $4\dfrac{1}{2}$ feet

Exercises 6.4 (page 148)

1. $\dfrac{1}{12}$ **3.** $\dfrac{3}{8}$ **5.** $\dfrac{-3}{5}$ **7.** $\dfrac{-4}{5}$ **9.** $\dfrac{1}{2}$ **11.** $\dfrac{2}{-3}$ **13.** $\dfrac{289}{144}$ **15.** $\dfrac{1}{2}$ **17.** $\dfrac{-1}{36}$ **19.** $\dfrac{-5}{24}$

21. $\dfrac{6}{49}$ **23.** $\dfrac{1}{100,000}$ **25.** $\dfrac{9}{16}$ **27.** $\dfrac{10,000}{1}$ **29.** $\dfrac{17}{72}$ **31.** 25 **33.** $\dfrac{4}{3}$ **35.** $\dfrac{8}{5}$

37. $\dfrac{1}{1}$ **39.** 100 **41.** $\{^-3\}$ **43.** $\{2, ^-2\}$ **45.** $\{3\}$ **47.** $\left\{\dfrac{1}{100}\right\}$ **49.** $\left\{\dfrac{1}{3}\right\}$

51. (a) $\dfrac{r}{s} = \dfrac{r \cdot t}{s \cdot t}$, **(b)** $1 \cdot p = p$, and $\dfrac{a}{b} \cdot \dfrac{b}{a} = 1$ **(c)** $\dfrac{r}{1} = r$ **53.** $172\dfrac{1}{2}$ cents
55. 1240 freshmen, 930 sophomores, 744 juniors, 806 seniors **57.** \$1200

Exercises 6.5 (page 155)

1. $\frac{2}{1}$ **3.** $\frac{2}{7}$ **5.** $\frac{2}{1}$ **7.** $\frac{13}{12}$ **9.** $\frac{^-15}{14}$ **11.** $\frac{3}{2}$ **13.** $\frac{155}{128}$ **15.** $\frac{2}{7}$ **17.** $\frac{5}{16}$ **19.** $\frac{1}{5}$

21. $\frac{2}{1}$ **23.** $\frac{1}{10}$ **25.** $\frac{^-1}{5}$ **27.** $\frac{10}{1}$ **29.** $\frac{^-9}{13}$ **31.** $3\frac{3}{5}$ **33.** $7\frac{7}{15}$ **35.** $16\frac{1}{2}$

37. $31\frac{11}{12}$ **39.** $145\frac{4}{5}$ **41.** True **43.** True **45.** True **47.** False **49.** True

51. $\{21\}$ **53.** $\left\{\frac{1}{2}\right\}$ **55.** $\{5\}$ **57.** $\{4\}$ **59.** $\left\{\frac{5}{4}\right\}$ **61.** Q **63.** $\{10\}$ **65.** 18

67. $\frac{6}{125}$ **69.** $\frac{8}{9}$ **71.** $\frac{24}{11}$ **73.** $\frac{^-1}{12}$ **75.** $\frac{1}{1}$

Exercises 6.6 (page 160)

1.

3.

5.

7.

9.

11.

13. $\left\{\frac{4}{7}, \frac{^-5}{10}, \frac{^-3}{8}\right\}$ **15.** $\left\{\frac{^-123}{100}, \frac{^-1205}{1000}, \frac{^-12}{10}, \frac{^-26}{50}\right\}$

17. $\frac{2}{3} > \frac{1}{2}$ **19.** $\frac{5}{6} > \frac{3}{4}$ **21.** $\frac{^-11}{7} > \frac{^-18}{7}$ **23.** $\frac{^-5}{8} > \frac{2}{^-3}$ **27.** $\frac{1}{2}$ **29.** $\frac{9}{40}$

31. $\frac{17}{48}$ **33.** $\frac{61}{200}$ **35.** No **37.** Yes

Exercises 6.7 (page 166)

3. $\dfrac{1}{3}$ **5.** $\dfrac{1}{5}$ **7.** \$32, \$96 **9.** $\dfrac{7}{10}$ **11.** 24 points **13.** $6\dfrac{7}{120}$ miles **15.** 18 feet

17. $666\dfrac{2}{3}$ miles **19.** 64 ounces **21.** $1\dfrac{4}{5}$ units **23.** $3\dfrac{3}{8}$ tons

Exercises 6.8—Review (page 169)

1. Subset **3.** Equivalent **5.** Least common multiple **7.** $\dfrac{3}{8}$ **9.** Ratio

11. 3 **13.** $^-6$ **15.** 2 **17.** $\dfrac{7}{-8}$ **19.** $^-16$ **21.** They are not equal

23. $\dfrac{^-7}{2} = \dfrac{21}{^-6}$ **25.** $\dfrac{3}{6}, \dfrac{4}{6}$ **27.** $\dfrac{^-81}{63}, \dfrac{90}{63}, \dfrac{35}{^-63}$ **29.** $\dfrac{41}{40}$ **31.** $\dfrac{27}{16}$ **33.** $\dfrac{4}{9}$ **35.** $^-6$

37. $^-1$ **39.** 10 **41.** $\dfrac{4}{3}$ **43.** 100 **45.** $\dfrac{35}{81}$ **47.** $3\dfrac{2}{3}, 11 = 3 \cdot 3 + 2$

49. $25\dfrac{1}{15}, 376 = 15 \cdot 25 + 1$ **51.** $\left\{\dfrac{^-1}{2}, \dfrac{3}{8}, \dfrac{2}{3}\right\}$ **53.** $\left\{2, \dfrac{15}{6}, \dfrac{21}{3}, \dfrac{100}{14}, 8\dfrac{1}{4}\right\}$ **55.** $\dfrac{3}{8}$

Exercises 7.1 (page 174)

1. $20\dfrac{5}{100}$, twenty and five hundredths **3.** $56\dfrac{37}{1000}$, fifty-six and

thirty-seven thousandths **5.** $1000\dfrac{1}{10,000}$; one thousand and one ten-thousandth

7. Ten and sixty-three thousandths
9. Twenty-eight and three thousand three hundred sixty-five ten-thousandths
11. Three hundred twenty-six and eighty thousand three hundred
twenty-one one-hundred-thousandths
13. Ninety-nine and nine hundred ninety-three thousand forty-six millionths
15. Twelve and eighty thousand five hundred ten-millionths
17. 8.3 **19.** .0009 **21.** 6,000,000.07002 **23.** 520.036 **25.** 79,003.89216

27. 11.30 **29.** 17.064 **31.** $\dfrac{38}{100}$ **33.** $529\dfrac{1}{1000}$ **35.** $\dfrac{107}{100,000}$ **37.** $817\dfrac{64}{1000}$

39. .008 **41.** .00042 **43.** .0253 **45.** 2.5 **47.** 3×10^{-1} **49.** 206×10^{-3}

51. 10906×10^{-5} **53.** 5007×10^{-6}

Exercises 7.2 (page 178)

1. $8.65 + 3.42 = \left(8 + \dfrac{6}{10} + \dfrac{5}{100}\right) + \left(3 + \dfrac{4}{10} + \dfrac{2}{100}\right)$ [renaming]

$\qquad\qquad = (8 + 3) + \left(\dfrac{6}{10} + \dfrac{4}{10}\right) + \left(\dfrac{5}{100} + \dfrac{2}{100}\right)$ [regrouping]

$\qquad\qquad = 11 + \dfrac{10}{10} + \dfrac{7}{100}$ [addition of rationals]

$\qquad\qquad = (11 + 1) + \dfrac{7}{100}$ [renaming and regrouping]

$\qquad\qquad = 12.07$ [renaming]

3. $851.007 + 68.346 = \left(800 + 50 + 1 + \dfrac{7}{1000}\right) +$ [renaming]

$\qquad\qquad \left(60 + 8 + \dfrac{3}{10} + \dfrac{4}{100} + \dfrac{6}{1000}\right)$

$\qquad\qquad = 800 + (50 + 60) + (1 + 8) +$ [regrouping]

$\qquad\qquad \dfrac{3}{10} + \dfrac{4}{100} + \left(\dfrac{7}{1000} + \dfrac{6}{1000}\right)$

$\qquad\qquad = 800 + 110 + 9 + \dfrac{3}{10} +$ [addition of rationals]

$\qquad\qquad \dfrac{4}{100} + \dfrac{13}{1000}$

$\qquad\qquad = (800 + 100) + (10 + 9) + \dfrac{3}{10} +$ [renaming and

$\qquad\qquad \left(\dfrac{4}{100} + \dfrac{1}{100}\right) + \dfrac{3}{1000}$ regrouping]

$\qquad\qquad = 900 + 19 + \dfrac{3}{10} + \dfrac{5}{100} + \dfrac{3}{1000}$ [addition of rationals]

$\qquad\qquad = 919.353$ [renaming]

5. $896.04 + 755.079 = \left(800 + 90 + 6 + \dfrac{4}{100}\right) +$ [renaming]

$\qquad\qquad \left(700 + 50 + 5 + \dfrac{7}{100} + \dfrac{9}{1000}\right)$

$\qquad\qquad = (800 + 700) + (90 + 50) +$ [regrouping]

$\qquad\qquad (6 + 5) + \left(\dfrac{4}{100} + \dfrac{7}{100}\right) + \dfrac{9}{1000}$

$$= 1500 + 140 + 11 + \frac{11}{100} + \frac{9}{1000} \quad \text{[addition of rationals]}$$

$$= 1000 + (500 + 100) + \quad\quad \text{[renaming and}$$

$$(40 + 10) + 1 + \frac{1}{10} + \quad\quad \text{regrouping]}$$

$$\frac{1}{100} + \frac{9}{1000}$$

$$= 1000 + 600 + 50 + 1 + \quad\quad \text{[addition of rationals]}$$

$$\frac{1}{10} + \frac{1}{100} + \frac{9}{1000}$$

$$= 1651.119 \quad\quad \text{[renaming]}$$

7. {60.01}   **9.** {1583.0146}   **11.** {12,266.5006}

13. $8.57 - 5.32 = \left(8 + \frac{5}{10} + \frac{7}{100}\right) - \left(5 + \frac{3}{10} + \frac{2}{100}\right)$ [renaming]

$$= (8 - 5) + \left(\frac{5}{10} - \frac{3}{10}\right) + \left(\frac{7}{100} - \frac{2}{100}\right) \quad \text{[regrouping]}$$

$$= 3 + \frac{2}{10} + \frac{5}{100} \quad \text{[subtraction of rationals]}$$

$$= 3.25 \quad \text{[renaming]}$$

15. $10.04 - 3.26 = \left(10 + \frac{4}{100}\right) - \left(3 + \frac{2}{10} + \frac{6}{100}\right)$ [renaming]

$$= (10 - 3) + \left(0 - \frac{2}{10}\right) + \left(\frac{4}{100} - \frac{6}{100}\right) \quad \text{[regrouping]}$$

$$= (9 - 3) + \left(\frac{9}{10} - \frac{2}{10}\right) + \left(\frac{14}{100} - \frac{6}{100}\right) \quad \text{[renaming]}$$

$$= 6 + \frac{7}{10} + \frac{8}{100} \quad \text{[subtraction of rationals]}$$

$$= 6.78 \quad \text{[renaming]}$$

17. $82.49 - 15.5 = \left(80 + 2 + \frac{4}{10} + \frac{9}{100}\right) - \left(10 + 5 + \frac{5}{10}\right)$ [renaming]

$$= (80 - 10) + (2 - 5) + \left(\frac{4}{10} - \frac{5}{10}\right) + \frac{9}{100} \quad \text{[regrouping]}$$

$$= (70 - 10) + (11 - 5) + \left(\frac{14}{10} - \frac{5}{10}\right) + \frac{9}{100} \quad \text{[renaming]}$$

$$= 60 + 6 + \frac{9}{10} + \frac{9}{100} \quad \text{[subtraction of rationals]}$$

$$= 66.99 \quad \text{[renaming]}$$

19. $\{6.77\}$ **21.** $\{108.5046\}$ **23.** $\{59.1405\}$ **27.** 436.322   **29.** ‾44.315

31. ‾595.379   **33.** ‾74.023   **35.** 981.684   **37.** 315.30 acres

39. $A = 10.572$ inches, $B = 14.803$ inches, $C = 4.283$ inches, $D = 6.152$ inches

Exercises 7.3   (page 183)

1. 800   **3.** .68   **5.** .001   **7.** .001   **9.** 5.462

11. $5.3 \times 10^3 = (5 + 3 \times 10^{-1})10^3$
$$= (5 \times 10^3) + (3 \times 10^{-1} \times 10^3)$$
$$= 5000 + 3 \times 10^2$$
$$= 5300$$

13. $.25 \times 10^4 = (2 \times 10^{-1} + 5 \times 10^{-2})10^4$
$$= (2 \times 10^{-1} \times 10^4) + (5 \times 10^{-2} \times 10^4)$$
$$= 2 \times 10^3 + 5 \times 10^2$$
$$= 2500$$

15. $8.5 \times 10^{-3} = (8 + 5 \times 10^{-1})10^{-3}$
$$= (8 \times 10^{-3}) + (5 \times 10^{-1} \times 10^{-3})$$
$$= 8 \times 10^{-3} + 5 \times 10^{-4}$$
$$= .0085$$

17. $\{2642.3\}$ **19.** $\{8.651\}$ **21.** $\{78,362.1\}$ **23.** $\{1,000,000\}$ **25.** $\{1,000,000\}$

27. 361×10^{-1} **29.** 4121×10^{-3} **31.** $58,213 \times 10^{-3}$ **33.** 219×10^{-3}

35. $60,072 \times 10^{-3}$ **37.** 3041×10^{-1} **39.** $71,171 \times 10^{-3}$

41. $5.81 \times 53.064 = (581 \times 10^{-2}) \times (53064 \times 10^{-3})$
$$= (581 \times 53064) \times (10^{-2} \times 10^{-3})$$
$$= 30830184 \times 10^{-5}$$
$$= 308.30184$$

43. $125.26 \times 87.02 = (12526 \times 10^{-2}) \times (8702 \times 10^{-2})$
$$= (12526 \times 8702) \times (10^{-2} \times 10^{-2})$$
$$= 109001256 \times 10^{-4}$$
$$= 10900.1256$$

45. $.123 \times .0987 = (123 \times 10^{-3}) \times (987 \times 10^{-4})$
$$= (123 \times 987) \times (10^{-3} \times 10^{-4})$$
$$= 121401 \times 10^{-7}$$
$$= .0121401$$

47. See page 181   **49.** 3868.2427   **51.** 482.008   **53.** 37.426

55. .37426   **57.** 83   **59.** 57.11415   **61.** 13,527.17674344   **63.** $2.85 more

65. It is written as an integer multiplied by an integral power of 10

67. 9.3×10^7 **69.** 9.3×10^{-6} **71.** 1.64×10^{12} **73.** 2.6535×10^6

75. 3.339×10^4 **77.** 2.325 feet

Exercises 7.4   (page 190)

1. {86} **3.** {104} **5.** {24} **7.** {300} **9.** {.1}

11.

$$\xleftarrow{\hspace{2cm}} \underset{0}{\;|\;} \overset{.2\;\to}{\underset{.2}{\;|\;}} \overset{.2\;\to}{\underset{.4}{\;|\;}} \overset{.2\;\to}{\underset{.6}{\;|\;}} \xrightarrow{\hspace{2cm}}$$

13.

$$\xleftarrow{\hspace{2cm}} \underset{0}{\;|\;} \overset{.04\;\to}{\underset{.04}{\;|\;}} \overset{.04\;\to}{\underset{.08}{\;|\;}} \overset{.04\;\to}{\underset{.12}{\;|\;}} \overset{.04\;\to}{\underset{.16}{\;|\;}} \overset{.04\;\to}{\underset{.20}{\;|\;}} \xrightarrow{\hspace{1cm}}$$

15.

$$\xleftarrow{\hspace{2cm}} \underset{0}{\;|\;} \overset{.3\;\to}{\underset{.3}{\;|\;}} \overset{.3\;\to}{\underset{.6}{\;|\;}} \overset{.3\;\to}{\underset{.9}{\;|\;}} \overset{.3\;\to}{\underset{1.2}{\;|\;}} \xrightarrow{\hspace{1cm}}$$

17. $\dfrac{2}{5} = \dfrac{20}{50} = \dfrac{20}{5} \times \dfrac{1}{10} = 4 \times 10^{-1} = .4$

19. $\dfrac{5}{16} = \dfrac{40,000}{160,000} = \dfrac{50,000}{16} \times \dfrac{1}{10,000} = 3125 \times 10^{-4} = .3125$

21. .625 **23.** .25 **25.** .08 **27.** 1.281205 **29.** 4.375 **31.** $\dfrac{1}{4}$ **33.** $\dfrac{7}{8}$

35. $\dfrac{1}{20}$ **37.** $\dfrac{9}{2000}$ **39.** $6\dfrac{21}{50}$ **43.** {.25} **45.** {.01} **47.** {.004} **49.** {.05}

51. 2.6×10^6 **53.** 10 **55.** 60.164609 mph **57.** 26; 58; 9.16 feet waste

59. .142857142857 . . .

Exercises 7.5   (page 195)

1. 7.2 hours per day are spent in sleep **3.** Tom has hit safely 310 times out of 1000 times at bat **5.** My house is worth $\dfrac{1}{4}$ more than when I bought it

7.

Fraction	Decimal	Percent
$\dfrac{1}{2}$	.5	50%
$\dfrac{3}{20}$	.15	15%
$\dfrac{37}{100}$	.37	37%
$\dfrac{1}{4}$	.25	25%
$\dfrac{1}{1}$	1.00	100%
$\dfrac{1}{8}$	.125	12.5%
$\dfrac{7}{5}$	1.40	140%
$\dfrac{11}{5}$	2.2	220%
$\dfrac{8}{5}$	1.60	160%

9. $62\frac{1}{2}\%$ **11.** $66\frac{2}{3}\%$ **13.** 10 **15.** 50% **17.** 90

19. 144 **21.** 300 **23.** 300% **25.** No **27.** 340.5% **29.** $11.66 **35.** $36.40
37. 548.275 pounds **39.** 150%, 29.84%

Exercises 7.6   (page 203)

1. Rational   **3.** The set of irrational numbers   **5.** Rational numbers
7. Infinitely   **9.** 5   **11.** 9   **13.** 15   **15.** 30   **17.** 125   **19.** 1   **21.** 343   **23.** 5
25. 1331   **27.** Irrational   **29.** Irrational   **31.** Rational   **33.** Irrational
35. Rational   **37.** Commutative property of addition
39. Identity property of multiplication
41. Distributive property and commutative property of multiplication
43. Commutative property of addition and identity property of addition
45. Commutative and associative properties of multiplication
47. The product of two square roots of the same number is the number itself
49. The product of three cube roots of the same number is the number itself
51. {3}   **53.** {6}   **55.** Each is a nonterminating and nonrepeating decimal
61. 1   **63.** $\dfrac{212}{666}$
65. Rational number   **67.** One-to-one correspondence

Exercises 7.7—Review   (page 207)

1. Exponent   **3.** Place-value   **5.** Rational   **7.** Rational, irrational
9. Whole numbers   **11.** False   **13.** False   **15.** True   **17.** True   **19.** False
21. 147.55   **23.** 207.599   **25.** 163.4128   **27.** 3.2   **29.** 21.2863×10^{-8}
31. 187.52   **33.** 168
35.

Date	Withdrawals		Deposits	Balance
1				283.47
5	34.10	25.61		223.76
7			38.59	262.35
14	87.50		38.59	213.44
15	10.00			203.44
21	8.76		38.59	233.27
28			38.59	271.86
29	15.00			256.86
31	2.81	11.98		242.07

37. 86.626%   **39.** $42.50

Exercises 8.1 (page 216)

1. 1, 10, 11, 100, 101, 110, 111, 100, 1001, 1010, 1000, 1100, 1101, 1110, 1111, 10,000, 10,001, 10,010, 10,011, 10,100, 10,101, 11,110, 11,111, 100,000, 100,001, 100,010, 100,011, 100,100, 100,101, 100,110, 100,111, 101,000, 101,001, 101,010, 101,011, 101,100, 101,101, 101,110, 101,111, 110,000, 110,001, 110,010

3. 1, 2, 3, 10, 11, 12, 13, 20, 21, 22, 23, 30, 31, 32, 33, 100, 101, 102, 103, 110, 111, 112, 113, 120, 121, 122, 123, 130, 131, 132, 133, 200, 201, 202, 203, 210, 211, 212, 213, 220, 221, 222, 223, 230, 231, 232, 233, 300, 301, 302

5. 1, 2, 3, 4, 5, 10, 11, 12, 13, 14, 15, 20, 21, 22, 23, 24, 25, 30, 31, 32, 33, 34, 35, 40, 41, 42, 43, 44, 45, 50, 51, 52, 53, 54, 55, 100, 101, 102, 103, 104, 105, 110, 111, 112, 113, 114, 115, 120, 121, 122

7. 1, 2, 3, 4, 5, 6, 7, 10, 11, 12, 13, 14, 15, 16, 17, 20, 21, 22, 23, 24, 25, 26, 27, 30, 31, 32, 33, 34, 35, 36, 37, 40, 41, 42, 43, 44, 45, 46, 47, 50, 51, 52, 53, 54, 55, 56, 57, 60, 61, 62

9. 1, 2, 3, 4, 5, 6, 7, 8, 9, T, E, 10, 11, 12, 13, 14, 15, 16, 17, 18, 19, $1T$, $1E$, 20, 21, 22, 23, 24, 25, 26, 27, 28, 29, $2T$, $2E$, 30, 31, 32, 33, 34, 35, 36, 37, 38, 39, $3T$, $3E$, 40, 41, 42

11. 137   **13.** 229   **15.** 59   **17.** 192   **19.** 1033   **21.** 422   **23.** 100,011

25. $12E2$ **27.** 2202   **29.** 3636   **31.** 210   **33.** 343   **35.** 66   **37.** $88E0$ **39.** $E0$

43. Each odd number has a 1 in the ones place   **49.** 545   **51.** .8125

53. .470444 . . .   **55.** .259259 . . .   **57.** .24   **59.** .31

Exercises 8.2 (page 222)

1.

+	0	1	2	3	4	5	6	7
0	0	1	2	3	4	5	6	7
1	1	2	3	4	5	6	7	10
2	2	3	4	5	6	7	10	11
3	3	4	5	6	7	10	11	12
4	4	5	6	7	10	11	12	13
5	5	6	7	10	11	12	13	14
6	6	7	10	11	12	13	14	15
7	7	10	11	12	13	14	15	16

·	0	1	2	3	4	5	6	7
0	0	0	0	0	0	0	0	0
1	0	1	2	3	4	5	6	7
2	0	2	4	6	10	12	14	16
3	0	3	6	11	14	17	22	25
4	0	4	10	14	20	24	30	34
5	0	5	12	17	24	31	36	43
6	0	6	14	22	30	36	44	52
7	0	7	16	25	34	43	52	61

3.

+	0	1
0	0	1
1	1	10

·	0	1
0	0	0
1	0	1

5.

+	0	1	2	3	4	5	6	7	8	9	T	E
0	0	1	2	3	4	5	6	7	8	9	T	E
1	1	2	3	4	5	6	7	8	9	T	E	10
2	2	3	4	5	6	7	8	9	T	E	10	11
3	3	4	5	6	7	8	9	T	E	10	11	12
4	4	5	6	7	8	9	T	E	10	11	12	13
5	5	6	7	8	9	T	E	10	11	12	13	14
6	6	7	8	9	T	E	10	11	12	13	14	15
7	7	8	9	T	E	10	11	12	13	14	15	16
8	8	9	T	E	10	11	12	13	14	15	16	17
9	9	T	E	10	11	12	13	14	15	16	17	18
T	T	E	10	11	12	13	14	15	16	17	18	19
E	E	10	11	12	13	14	15	16	17	18	19	1T

·	0	1	2	3	4	5	6	7	8	9	T	E
0	0	0	0	0	0	0	0	0	0	0	0	0
1	0	1	2	3	4	5	6	7	8	9	T	E
2	0	2	4	6	8	T	10	12	14	16	18	1T
3	0	3	6	9	10	13	16	19	20	23	26	29
4	0	4	8	10	14	18	20	24	28	30	34	38
5	0	5	T	13	18	21	26	2E	34	39	42	47
6	0	6	10	16	20	26	30	36	40	46	50	56
7	0	7	12	19	24	2E	36	41	48	53	5T	65
8	0	8	14	20	28	34	40	48	54	60	68	74
9	0	9	16	23	30	39	46	53	60	69	76	83
T	0	T	18	26	34	42	50	5T	68	76	84	92
E	0	E	1T	29	38	47	56	65	74	83	92	T1

7. $\{56_{(five)}\}$ **9.** $\{10_{(two)}\}$ **11.** $\{1_{(four)}\}$ **13.** $\{12_{(four)}\}$ **15.** $\{10_{(five)}\}$
17. $1100_{(seven)}$ **19.** $1,110,100_{(two)}$ **21.** $215_{(six)}$ **23.** $2312_{(four)}$ **25.** $100,011_{(two)}$
27. $2420_{(six)}$ **29.** $20_{(three)}$ **31.** Base seven **33.** Base twelve **35.** Base two
37. Base two through ten

Exercises 8.3   (page 229)

1. A number is divisible by ten if and only if its last digit is 0
3. A number is divisible by twelve if and only if it is divisible by 3 and by 4
5. A number is divisible by eighteen if and only if it is divisible by 2 and by 9
7. $\{2, 3, 4, 6, 8\}$ **9.** None **11.** $\{2, 4, 8\}$ **13.** $\{1, 4, 7\}$ **15.** $\{2, 8\}$
17. 33,539 **19.** 761 **21.** 3000 **23.** 24,864 **25.** 160
27. Multiplication property **29.** Distributive property
31. Renaming and associative property of addition

Exercises 8.4—Review   (page 231)

1. Four   **3.** Eight   **5.** If and only if the sum of the digits is divisible by 9
7. 6$_{(\text{ten})}$ **9.** 142$_{(\text{ten})}$ **11.** 572$_{(\text{ten})}$ **13.** 27$_{(\text{eight})}$ **15.** 10,110,110$_{(\text{two})}$
17. .5625$_{(\text{ten})}$ **19.** .4$_{(\text{five})}$ **21.** 201$_{(\text{four})}$ **23.** 152$_{(\text{six})}$ **25.** 20,201$_{(\text{five})}$
27. 365$_{(\text{eight})}$ **29.** 3   **31.** 5   **33.** None   **35.** 92,808   **37.** 4911   **39.** 24,540

Exercises 9.1   (page 235)

1. Exact   **3.** Exact   **5.** Approximate   **7.** Approximate   **9.** Approximate, exact
13. 52,994.7 feet and 53,005.3 feet   **15.** Minimum 2520, maximum 3080

Exercises 9.2   (page 238)

1. .1, ±.05   **3.** 100, 3   **5.** .00001, ±.000005   **7.** 10,000,000, 3, ±500,000
9. 4, ±.5   **13.** Same precision   **15.** .002 inch   **17.** Same accuracy
19. Same accuracy   **21.** 93,000,000
23. When they have the same maximum error
25. .21%, 3.84%   **27.** .54%, .25%

Exercises 9.3   (page 243)

1. 3.235   **3.** 12.84   **5.** 2002   **7.** 3.15   **9.** 7002.12   **11.** 8.360   **13.** 78.46
15. 22.36   **17.** 4769.6   **19.** 600.9   **21.** 57.93   **23.** 1938.67   **25.** 99.5
27. 14630   **29.** 2190.86   **31.** 2.0045   **33.** .2849   **35.** 217   **37.** 14.32
39. Maximum: 9506 square feet, minimum: 9484 square feet   **41.** 69
43. (1) 2.64, (2) 3.05, (3) 2.94   **45.** $688

Exercises 9.4   (page 250)

1. 72, 182.88, 1.8288   **3.** Yards, feet, 3.21870   **5.** grams, .2835, pounds
7. Quarts, pints, 11.3556   **9.** 177.80   **11.** 3.105   **13.** 68.04   **15.** 450
17. exact: 9, 10, 11, 12; approximate: 13, 14, 15, 16   **19.** 12 mi 3230 ft
21. 12 gal 1 qt 1.9 pt   **23.** 3 gal 3 qt 0.2 pt   **25.** 1.82 miles
27. $432,000, $157,680,000   **29.** $1216.21

Exercises 9.5 (page 256)

1. 5050 square feet **3.** 7340 square feet **5.** 17,100 square feet
7. 160 square feet **9.** 151.29 square feet **11.** 41.07125 square feet
19. 3240 square feet **23.** 1033.5 grams per square centimeter
25. 11 **27.** 21 **29.** 95 **31.** 1.73 **33.** 2.75 **35.** 9.58 **37.** 8.39 **39.** 14.04
41. Width $\doteq$ 140 feet, length $\doteq$ 280 feet **43.** 4.0 **45.** 10.0 **47.** 8.0
49. $\doteq$ 71 feet 4 inches **51.** $\doteq$ 425 miles **53.** $\doteq$ 333 feet

Exercises 9.6 (page 267)

1. 16 **3.** 55 **5.** 104 **7.** 2.5 **9.** .125 **11.** 1.414 **13.** 2.236 **15.** 28.844
17. 89.453 **19.** 776.006 **21.** 3.162; 3.873 **23.** True **25.** True **27.** True
29. Distributive property

Exercises 9.7 (page 271)

1. $\doteq$ 139.54 cubic feet **3.** 245π cubic inches **5.** 1728 cubic inches
7. 57.75 cubic inches, 28.875 cubic inches **9.** 27,500 cubic feet, $89,375
11. 6250 pounds per square foot **13.** $79.64 **15.** 136.111 cubic feet
17. $\doteq$ 2.27 hours **19.** 3456×10^{11}

Exercises 9.8—Review (page 274)

1. Approximate **3.** Maximum error **5.** Least precise number
7. Square root **9.** 19, 20 **11.** False **13.** True **15.** False **17.** True
19. False **21.** 21 feet $3\frac{13}{32}$ inches and 21 feet $3\frac{11}{32}$ inches
23. Maximum $\doteq$ 113.31 square feet, minimum $\doteq$ 112.92 square feet
25. 88 **27.** 9.297 acres **29.** .0762 **31.** 17 **33.** 7.8 **35.** 70,000 cubic feet

INDEX

311

312